21.95

ELECTRICAL EQUIPMENT TESTING AND MAINTENANCE

ELECTRICAL EQUIPMENT TESTING AND MAINTENANCE

A.S. Gill, M.S.E.E., P.E.

Associate Professor and Lecturer
George Washington University
Washington, D.C.

Consulting Engineer

Reston Publishing Company
A Prentice-Hall Company
Reston, Virginia

Library of Congress Cataloging in Publication Data

Gill, A. S.
    Electrical equipment, testing and maintenance.

    Bibliography: p.
    Includes index.
    1. Electric power systems—Testing. 2. Electric power
systems—Maintenance and repair. I. Title.
TK401.G54   621.37   82–327
ISBN 0–8359–1625-1   AACR2

10 9 8 7 6 5 4 3 2 1

.

Printed in the United States of America

To Patricia, Shaun, Rajan,
Jason, and Rania

CONTENTS

CHAPTER 1

CHAPTER 2

CHAPTER 3

CHAPTER 4

CHAPTER 5

CHAPTER 6

PREFACE

This book is an outgrowth of notes developed while teaching a course on the maintenance and testing of electrical power system equipment over the past six years at George Washington University to groups of practicing engineers and electricians as part of a continuing professional engineering education program. The author has been very fortunate in having a broad group of professionals with whom to interact, comprised of both students and guest lecturers. The author hopes that the participants of this course learned as much as he did from the many interactions and discussions. It was a truly gratifying learning experience to answer or attempt to answer the innumerable penetrating questions from participants in this course.

This book deals with the maintenance and testing of electrical apparatus and equipment found in large industrial and commercial facilities. Chapter 1 covers introductory material on the planning and benefits of maintenance and testing and is, as well, a basic review of electrical power distribution systems. The subject matter covered in this book is very broad, and to carry out the maintenance program successfully, one must acquire knowledge of equipment design, installation, maintenance routines, test procedures, and safety factors. It is also important today for maintenance personnel to be informed and knowledgeable of the latest trends in changing maintenance requirements because of innovative advancements and the use of new materials in the manufacture of electrical power equipment.

The field of electrical maintenance is diverse, and the application of various maintenance practices and test methods varies from facility to facility. New viewpoints are being adopted because of the detailed attention this field is receiving from manufacturers, professional societies, insurance companies, and owners. Since the proper selection, installation, and servicing of electrical equipment play a major role in its reliability, Chapters 2 and 3 have been exclusively devoted to the discussion of this subject. The doctrine of preventive maintenance, rather than necessary maintenance, is now gaining and being adopted by various local codes.

The testing of electrical equipment has been divided into direct current and alternating current for purposes of classification; these are covered in

Chapters 4 and 5, respectively. A particular type of test as it applies to various types of electrical equipment is treated individually in order to provide the maintenance personnel with detailed but generalized procedures for conducting that test. Chapter 6 deals with tests that are difficult to classify as either dc or ac tests. Examples are gas analysis, fault locating, phasing and identification of cables, and so on, which are conducted for locating trouble or assessing the integrity of electrical equipment. The testing and maintenance of protective relays and devices, instrument transformers, and control power are treated in Chapter 7 because of their special requirements. It is hoped that the information provided will allow maintenance personnel with some training to perform the necessary testing and calibration of these devices. An adequate grounding system is necessary for personnel and equipment safety; therefore, periodic testing is essential to maintain its effectiveness. Chapter 8 covers the methods used for measuring grounding electrode resistance, along with the various types of grounding systems used for electrical distribution systems. Chapter 9 covers electrical safety, switching practices, and precautions, which are very necessary for assuring that all work is conducted with complete safety.

The author views this book as introductory to this field and urges the serious reader to pursue the various topics for full treatment in the bibliography offered in this book or in other references available. To make this book useful and interesting, many tables and connection diagrams are given throughout the book. Also, evaluation of field test data is discussed in Chapters 4 and 5 in order to call to the reader's attention the fact that the interpretation of data requires special skills. It is difficult to make judgments on whether the readings taken are good, marginal, or bad in terms of assessing equipment integrity. The knack for interpretation of data can only be gained through experience. The analysis of test data in most cases is always based upon comparison with previous years' data in order to assess whether the equipment has deteriorated since it was last tested. Therefore, before data can be compared, they should be normalized to the same base temperature, humidity, and so on. To facilitate such comparisons, data from year to year must be recorded and maintained.

Appendix A contains information on inspection and test forms for the recording of data and pertinent factors of readings taken during field testing. These forms are mostly available from industrial firms who perform such services or from test-equipment manufacturers. Appendix B lists the ANSI device numbers that are commonly used for protective relay and switchgear applications.

A. S. Gill

ACKNOWLEDGMENTS

The production of a book requires the cooperation and effort of many people and institutions. It is always difficult to provide appropriate acknowledgments to organizations and individuals who helped in the development of a book of this type.

The author would particularly like to thank the major electrical manufacturers, testing service companies, test equipment manufacturers, various private and government organizations, and professional societies for making information available for the development of this book. Where possible, the author has tried to give recognition to the source of the information obtained.

The author wishes to acknowledge explicitly that the section on maintenance of liquid insulation, mineral oils, and askarels is condensed from publication "Power O and M," Bulletin No. 11, September 1974, published by the U.S. Department of the Interior, Bureau of Reclamation, Denver, Colorado. Similarly, the section on the maintenance of transformer liquids Silicon, RTemp, and WECOSOL is condensed from information supplied by General Electric Company, RTE, and Westinghouse, respectively. The section on the maintenance of motors and generators is condensed from a publication of the National Electrical Manufacturers Association (NEMA) entitled "Maintenance of Motor and Generator," publication RP-1968. The chapter on safety, switching practices, and precautions is condensed from the General Electric Company manual, "On Site Electrical Safety and Accident Prevention," and the information on electrical fire emergencies was supplied by the Philadelphia Electric Company.

The late Bill Bee, test engineer, Potomac Electric and Power Company, Ken Ebert of Hipotronics, Inc., and Tom Black of Black and Associates, Inc., helped with much of the teaching and developing of notes over the years. The author is grateful for their help, advice, criticism, and support.

The author wishes to thank all those participants who helped critique the notes and contributed to the development of this book.

Liability

This textbook and the instruction offered in it are designed to acquaint students with accepted good practice for the maintenance, operation, and testing of electrical equipment and/or systems. This book does not purport to be complete nor is it intended to be specific for the products of any manufacturer, testing procedures, or maintenance routines. The publisher, the author, companies, and other organizations referenced in this book will not accept any liability whatsoever for work undertaken on the basis of this text. All work undertaken based on this text is the sole responsibility of the reader and user of this book. The manufacturer's operating, maintenance, and testing procedures are the only reliable guide in any specific instance and, therefore, they should be consulted.

ELECTRICAL EQUIPMENT
TESTING AND MAINTENANCE

CHAPTER 1

INTRODUCTION TO ELECTRICAL EQUIPMENT MAINTENANCE AND TESTING

1-1 INTRODUCTION

The deterioration of electrical equipment is normal, and this process begins as soon as the equipment is installed. If deterioration is not checked, it can cause electrical failures and malfunctions. In addition, load changes or circuit alterations may be made without overall design coordination, which can result in improper settings of protective devices or wrong trip units installed in the circuits. The purpose of an *electrical preventive maintenance and testing program* (EPMT) should be to recognize these factors and provide means for correcting them. With an electrical preventive maintenance and testing program, potential hazards that can cause failure of equipment or interruption of electrical service can be discovered and corrected. Also, the EPMT program will minimize the hazards to life and equipment that can result from failure of equipment when it is not properly maintained. Properly maintained equipment reduces downtime by minimizing catastrophic failures. To carry out the successful operation of electrical equipment and apparatus, it is essential to set up an effective maintenance and testing program. This program can be implemented by setting up a maintenance department or by contracting the work to a private company engaged in this practice.

The EPMT program should consist of conducting routine inspections, tests, repairs, and service of electrical power system apparatus such as transformers, cables, circuit breakers, switchgear assemblies, and the like, along with associated equipment comprised of control wiring, protective devices and relays, supervisory equipment, and indicating and metering instruments.

1-2 WHY MAINTAIN AND TEST

A well-organized and implemented program minimizes accidents, reduces unplanned shutdowns, and lengthens the mean time between failures (MTBF) of electrical equipment. Benefits of EPMT can be categorized as direct and in-

1

direct. Direct benefits are derived from reduced cost of repairs, reduced down-time of equipment, and improved safety of personnel and property. Indirect benefits can be related to improved morale of employees, better workmanship, increased productivity, and the discovery of deficiencies in the system that were either designed into the original system or caused by later changes made in the system.

1-3   PLANNING AN EPMT PROGRAM

There are management, economic, and technical considerations, along with other requirements, that need to be discussed and understood in order to develop a maintenance program. Let us review these items from the viewpoint of developing an effective and comprehensive maintenance program. The main parts of the maintenance program can be classified into maintenance management considerations, technical requirements, and those items that should be included in the EPMT program.

MAINTENANCE MANAGEMENT CONSIDERATIONS

The design of any maintenance program must meet the ultimate goals of plant management. Maintenance is like an insurance policy: it has no direct payback, yet it is a cost that adds to the cost of the final product. However, one must hasten to say that it has inherent paybacks such as those listed in Section 1-2. It is generally observed that management resists the investment in a maintenance program even though they realize the need for good maintenance. In view of this, it is up to electrical personnel to show management how a properly planned electrical maintenance and testing program is justifiable.

The planning of EPMT programs should then include the advantages of a well-planned maintenance along with cost data for lost production due to equipment failure versus cost of budgeted preventive maintenance. Any maintenance program should prove that it is cost effective and minimizes equipment failure. The planning of the program should include considerations for proper test equipment, tools, trained personnel to carry out maintenance tasks, and time required to perform inspections, tests, and maintenance routines. Also, consideration should be given to record-keeping systems, which can range from fully computerized to manual file systems. To set up an electrical preventive maintenance and test program, the following steps may be undertaken.

- Determine the factors that will form the basis of the maintenance program, such as the necessity for continuous production, management policy on budgeting for planned maintenance versus replacement of equipment, and the like.

- Survey and consolidate data on equipment breakdowns and cost of lost production. Make an analysis of the cost data to convince management of the benefits of planned maintenance.

- Establish electrical maintenance priorities. These consist of on-line production sequence, determining the most important to least important equipment, weighing the reliability of the equipment, and other factors.

- Establish the best maintenance techniques. This involves selecting the best maintenance method and personnel for the various types of equipment and systems.

- Schedule and implement the program. Monitor its benefits and costs. Analyze program functions periodically for improvement of the program.

After the program has been set up, it is essential that it consist of five elements that will prove it to be a success: responsibilities; inspection; scheduling; work orders; recordkeeping.

Responsibilities

The responsibilities of the maintenance organization should be clearly defined by organization charts with functional work statements for each unit. The functional work statements must be established by management as a matter of policy. Every other department must be informed of the responsibilities assigned to maintenance organizations. The effectiveness of the maintenance departments will depend upon how well they are organized and how well personnel are utilized.

Inspection

Inspection is the key to the success of any maintenance program. Sufficient time should be allocated for inspection to verify the condition of new and installed equipment. The purpose of inspection is to provide advance warning as to the condition of the equipment under investigation. When inspection is performed on definite cycles by qualified people, impending deterioration can be detected in advance so that repair or replacement can be made before failure of the equipment occurs.

Scheduling

To perform maintenance, a definite schedule of work to be performed must be established. Maintenance schedules must be based upon minimum downtime for the various operating segments. The schedule for inspection, routine maintenance, and other work may vary for different equipment and will depend upon many factors. These factors can be age of equipment, frequency of service, hours of operation, environmental conditions, damage due to abuse, and safety requirements. Frequency of scheduling of all tasks should be adjusted as data on various equipment are recorded and analyzed to provide a balance between cost of maintenance and replacement cost of the equipment.

Work Orders

Work orders are job requests that need action for completion. Work orders can be established for all inspection service and other work on equipment in terms of routines. Any of these routines should include information on when such work is to be performed, where it is to be performed, and exactly what has to be done. These routines can be generated by a computer-based maintenance system. The routines should include all the pertinent information concerning the equipment.

Record Keeping

The success of a planned maintenance program depends upon the impetus given by top management and the interest of the maintenance personnel in the program. To have an effective program, it is imperative that maintenance and test inventory data on all equipment should be complete and readily available throughout the service life of the equipment. To that end, recordkeeping is very important. All forms and reports should be organized to provide ready accessibility to data when needed and to flag down problem areas. Such data may also be used over the years to analyze trends for equipment deterioration. If data are not recorded and maintained properly, the whole purpose of planned maintenance is lost.

TECHNICAL REQUIREMENTS

Technical requirements can be stated as follows:

- Survey of plant equipment.
- Listing of plant equipment in order of critical importance.
- A plan to perform EPMT on a regular frequency.
- Development of instructions and procedures for the EPMT program.

Survey of Plant Equipment

To perform an effective EPMT program, it is necessary to have accurate data about the electrical power system. This may include one-line diagrams, short-circuit coordination study, wiring and control diagrams, and other data that can be used as a reference point for future maintenance and testing. The purpose of these diagrams is to document and serve as an official record of equipment and circuit installation. The National Electrical Manufacturers Association (NEMA) has established standards for diagram symbols, device designations, and electrical symbols. The types of diagrams and drawings in common use are the following:

- *Process or flow diagram:* a conceptual diagram of the functional inter-relationship of subsystems in pictorial form.

- *Block diagram:* a group of interconnected blocks, each of which represents a device or subsystem.

- *One-line (single-line) diagram:* shows, by means of single lines and graphic symbols, the flow of electrical power or the course of electrical circuits and how they are connected. In this diagram, physical relationships are usually disregarded. A typical one-line diagram is shown in Figure 1–1.

- *Schematic (elementary) diagram:* shows all circuits and device elements of the equipment. This diagram emphasizes the device elements and their functions, and it is always drawn with all devices shown in deenergized mode. A typical elementary diagram is shown in Figure 1–2(a).

- *Control sequence (truth-table) diagram:* a description of the contact positions, or connections, that are made for each position of control action or device.

- *Wiring diagram (connection diagram):* locates and identifies electrical devices, terminals, and interconnecting wires in an assembly. This diagram may show interconnecting wiring by lines or terminal designations. A typical wiring diagram is shown in Figure 1–2(b).

- *Interconnection diagram:* shows only the external connections between controllers and associated equipment or between various housing units of an assembly of switchgear apparatus as shown in Figure 1–2(c).

- *Circuit layout and routing diagram:* show the physical layout of the facility and equipment and how the circuit to the various equipment is run.

- *Short-circuit coordination study:* electrical power system data, diagrams, and drawings are needed during maintenance and testing of electrical equipment. This may involve information and data relating to protective devices and relays. Such data are usually found in a short-circuit coordination study and usually encompass all the short-circuit values available in the power system, relays, and trip device settings. Normally, this study is performed during the construction phase of the facility. It would be much more desirable to perform this engineering study as part of the initial facility design, and then validate it during the construction phase to assure that equipment and values specified have

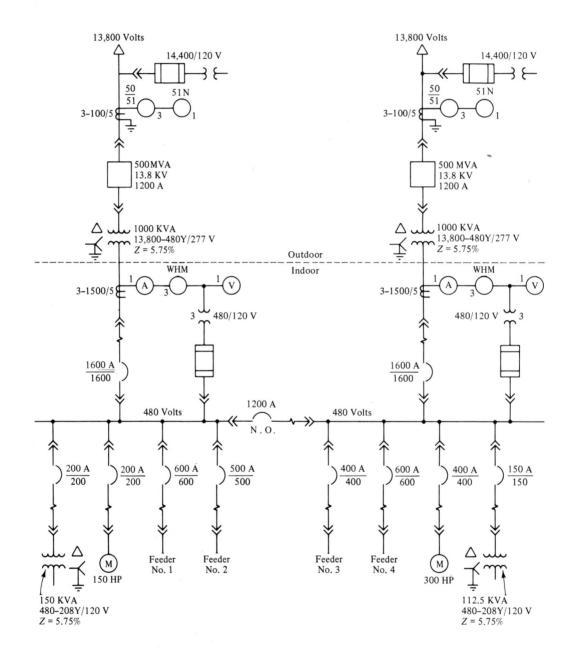

FIGURE 1–1.
Typical one-line diagram of a power distribution system.

been met. When accepting the facility, this study data should be used as a bench mark, and any changes that may have been made during construction in the system should be incorporated to update the study for future references.

- *System diagrams:* In addition to other data assembled, system diagrams will generally be needed for large systems. Such diagrams may consist of the following:

Control and monitoring system.

Lighting system.

Ventilation system.

Heating and air conditioning system.

Emergency system.

Other systems.

All the system diagrams may interface with one another, such as electrical diagrams, fire and security diagrams, emergency power, hydraulic, pneumatic, and/or mechanical systems. Therefore, it is important to know how these interfaces work and how they can be coordinated in the maintenance program.

Listing of Plant Equipment in Order of Critical Importance

Electric power system equipment, like any other plant equipment, is vital to the operation of the plant or facility. Failure of the power system may be considered a serious threat to people and property. The listing may be difficult to accomplish because the criticalness of any piece of equipment will vary for each plant or facility. Therefore, a team to mutually identify and list the critical equipment (electrical and other) vital to the operation of a facility may be necessary. The team should consist of representatives from each area of expertise involved in the operation of the plant. All the critical equipment and/or systems should be identified on the drawings. The maintenance department should understand each of these systems, equipment, and/or their functions and how they may affect or interface with other systems. The more knowledgeable the maintenance members are about their system, the better job they will perform in their duties.

A Plan to Perform EPMT on Regular Frequency

Several factors should be considered in establishing the frequency with which equipment is to be maintained:

- Environmental conditions.
- Load conditions.

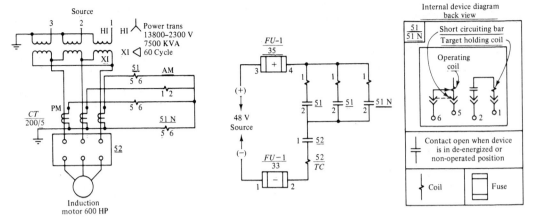

(a) Elementary control diagram

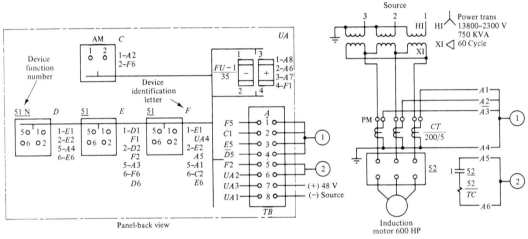

(b) Connection diagram

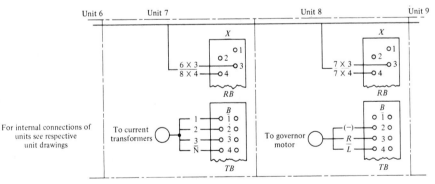

(c) Interconnection diagram

FIGURE 1-2.

Typical electrical elementary, connection, and interconnection diagrams.

- Duty requirements.
- Critical nature of the equipment.

The purpose of the maintenance schedule is to establish the condition of the equipment and determine what work will be required before its next scheduled maintenance. Usually, manufacturers' service manuals specify recommended frequency of maintenance and/or inspection. These time intervals are based upon standard operating conditions and environments. If these standard conditions change for the equipment, then the frequency should be modified accordingly. However, once the frequency of scheduled maintenance is established, this schedule should be adhered to for at least several maintenance cycles. The schedule should be adjusted if the equipment begins to experience unexpected failures. The frequency can be reduced by as much as 50 percent. On the other hand, if the equipment does not require maintenance for more than two inspections, the period of frequency for that equipment can be increased by as much as 50 percent. Adjustment should be continued until the optimum interval is found. Generally, the test frequency can vary from 6 months to 3 years.

Development of Instruction and Procedures for the EPMT Program

The final technical function in developing an EPMT program involves establishment of instructions, procedures, and methods to ensure that the equipment and system components operate without failure. The maintenance department should have fully developed procedures and instructions for thoroughly servicing all equipment and components. In addition, the maintenance department should also develop shutdown procedures, safeguards, interlocking of equipment, alarms, and methods of recording data (forms) and reporting unusual conditions to the proper authority. The maintenance records should be further utilized to evaluate results and as an indicator of possible modifications or changes in the maintenance program. In other words, the recorded information should be used as historical data and for feedback to modify the maintenance program.

WHAT SHOULD BE INCLUDED IN THE EPMT PROGRAM

The electrical preventive maintenance and testing program should encompass the following activities:

- Electrical preventive maintenance and testing.
- Electrical repairs.
- Analysis of failures.

To have an effective and efficient operation, it is essential to carry out these three activities.

Electrical Preventive Maintenance and Testing

This activity involves inspection, cleaning and adjustment, and testing of equipment to ensure troublefree operation until its next scheduled maintenance. Preventive maintenance and testing also allow the prediction of impending failure of a particular piece of equipment so that plans can be made to replace it without catastrophic results. The information on testing can be obtained from several different standards, such as the Insulated Cable Engineering Association (ICEA), National Fire Protection Association (NFPA), Institute of Electrical and Electronic Engineers (IEEE), American National Standard Institute (ANSI), National Electrical Manufacturer's Association (NEMA), Insurance Company Manuals (ICM), and others, depending on the equipment to be tested.

Electrical Repairs

The repair of electrical equipment and related machinery associated with plant production is the fundamental requirement of good maintenance programs. The maintenance should be performed economically and expeditiously. The basic objective of the maintenance program should be to avoid unexpected breakdowns of equipment. Furthermore, when breakdowns occur, spare parts should be on hand to make the necessary repairs. The maintenance personnel should be properly trained to perform the repairs promptly and correctly in order to minimize the downtime of the equipment.

Analysis of Failures

The failure of electrical equipment should be analyzed to assess reasons for its breakdown. Unless the cause is obvious, the equipment quality may be questioned. Reliability can be built into the equipment, but it requires upkeep to retain it. The tendency to ignore regular maintenance and testing generally prevails over regularly scheduled maintenance because regular maintenance may be considered unnecessary and too expensive. Therefore, the best designed and built equipment may break down through lack of attention. Every failure should be analyzed for its cause so that corrective measures can be implemented to prevent similar breakdowns.

1-4   OVERVIEW OF TESTING AND TEST METHODS

The testing of electrical equipment is usually performed in the field after equipment has been installed. The manufacturer conducts electrical tests on equipment before it leaves the factory; these tests, known as *factory tests*, are outside the scope of this text and therefore will not be discussed. Field tests are conducted to see whether newly installed equipment has been damaged, to indicate whether any corrective maintenance or replacement is necessary on existing equipment, to indicate if the equipment can continue to perform its design functions safely and adequately, to chart the gradual deterioration of the equipment over its service life, and to check new equipment before energization. In view of these objectives, the electrical testing of equipment can be divided into the following:

- Types of tests.
- Types of testing methods.

TYPES OF TESTS

The types of tests are acceptance tests, routine maintenance tests, and special maintenance tests that are conducted for specific purposes.

Acceptance Tests

These tests are known as *proof tests* and are performed on new equipment, usually after installation and prior to energization. Tests of this type are made at 80 percent of the final factory test voltage value. They are run to determine the following:

- Whether the equipment is in compliance with the specification.
- To establish a bench mark for future tests.
- To determine that the equipment has been installed without damage.
- To verify whether the equipment meets its design intent and limits.

Routine Maintenance Tests

These tests are performed at regular intervals over the service life of the equipment. They are made concurrently with preventive maintenance and at 60 percent of the final factory test voltage value. In the course of routine maintenance tests, it is very helpful to record the information as it is found on the equipment and to also record the condition in which the equipment is left. Therefore, these tests can be further subdivided into the following:

- *As-found tests:* These tests are performed on equipment on receipt or after it has been taken out of service for maintenance, but before any maintenance work is done.
- *As-left tests:* These tests are performed after maintenance has been performed and just before reenergization. They can indicate the degree

of improvement in the equipment and serve as a bench mark for comparison for future tests.

Special Maintenance Tests

These tests are performed on equipment that is known to be defective or has been subjected to adverse conditions that may affect its operating characteristics. An example might be the fault interruption by a circuit breaker, which requires inspection, maintenance, and tests before it can be put back into service.

TYPES OF TESTING METHODS

The testing of electrical power system equipment involves checking the insulation system, electrical properties, and other factors as they relate to the overall operation of the power system. Therefore, testing of electrical equipment can be divided into the following types:

- Solid insulation testing.
- Protective device testing.
- Insulating liquid testing.
- Circuit breaker time-travel analysis.
- Grounding electrode resistance testing.
- Fault gas analysis testing.
- Infrared inspection testing.

Solid Insulation Testing

Insulation can be either solid, liquid, or gaseous dielectric materials that prevent the flow of electricity between points of different potential. Insulation testing is done to determine the integrity of the insulating medium. This usually consists of applying a high potential voltage to the sample under test and determining the leakage current that may flow under test conditions. Excessive leakage current flows may indicate a deteriorated condition or impending failure of the insulation. Insulation testing can be performed by applying either of the following voltages:

- Direct current (dc) voltage.
- Alternating-current (ac) voltage.

The testing of solid insulation with these voltages can be categorized as nondestructive testing and destructive testing, respectively. The destructive test may cause eqiupment under test to fail or render it unsuitable for further service. Nondestructive tests are performed at low voltage stress, and the equipment under test is rarely damaged. The alternating-current high-potential test is primarily a "go" or "no-go" test. The voltage is raised to a specified level. If the equipment fails or shows excessive leakage current, the equipment under test is unusable. If the equipment does not fail, it has passed the test. This test can only indicate whether the equipment is good or bad. It cannot indicate with what safety margin the test was passed. The direct-current high-potential test can indicate more than a "go" or "no-go" condition. It can indicate that equipment is all right at the present time but may fail in the future. Direct-current testing is done to obtain information for comparative analysis on a periodic basis. With direct-current testing, the leakage current is measured during the progress of the test and compared to leakage current values of previous tests. Some of the advantages and disadvantages of dc high-voltage tests are the following:

ADVANTAGES

- Direct-current test is preferred on equipment whose charging capacitance is very high, such as cables.
- Direct-current voltage stress is considered much less damaging to insulation than ac voltages.
- The time of voltage application is not as critical with dc voltage as with ac voltage.
- The test can be stopped before equipment failure.
- Measurements can be taken concurrently.
- It is not necessary to make a separate insulation resistance test prior to making a dc overpotential test.

DISADVANTAGES

- The stress distribution for transformers, motors, and generator winding is different for dc voltage than for ac voltage.
- The residual charge after a dc voltage test must be carefully discharged.
- The time required to conduct a dc high-potential test is longer than for an ac high-potential test.

DIRECT-CURRENT VOLTAGE TESTING OF SOLID INSULATION

Before we can understand the various tests that are conducted with dc voltage, let's look at the various currents that take place when dc voltage is applied across solid insulation. These currents are the following:

- Capacitance charging current.
- Dielectric absorption current.

- Surface leakage current.
- Partial discharge current (corona).
- Volumetric leakage current.

Capacitance Charging Current

The capacitance charging current is high as the dc high potential is applied and can be calculated by the formula

$$i_g = \frac{E^{e \, - \, t \, /rc}}{R}$$

where

i_g = capacitance charging current

e = voltage in kilovolts

r = resistance in megohms

c = capacitance in microfarads

t = time in seconds

The charging current is a function of time and will decrease as the time of the application of voltage increases. It is the initial charging current when voltage is applied and therefore not of any value for test evaluation. Test readings should not be taken until this current has decreased to a sufficiently low value.

Dielectric Absorption Current

The dielectric absorption current is also high as the test voltage is applied and decreases as the voltage application time increases. This current can be calculated by the formula

$$ia = VCDT^{-n}$$

where

ia = dielectric absorption current

V = test voltage in kilovolts

C = capacitance in microfarads

D = proportionately constant

T = time in seconds

n = constant

Again, time should be allowed before recording test readings so that this current has decreased sufficiently.

Surface Leakage

The surface leakage current is due to the conduction on the surface of the insulation where the conductor emerges and points of ground potential. This current is not desired in the test results and should therefore be eliminated by carefully cleaning the surface of the conductor to eliminate the leakage paths.

Partial Discharge Current

The partial discharge current, also known as corona current, is caused by overstressing of air at sharp corners of the conductor due to high test voltage. This current is not desirable and should be eliminated by the use of stress control shielding at such points during tests.

Volumetric Leakage Current

The volumetric leakage current that flows through the insulation volume itself is of primary importance. This is the current that is used to evaluate the condition of the insulation system under test. Sufficient time should be allowed for the volumetric current to stabilize before test readings are recorded. The total current, consisting of various leakage currents as described, is shown in Figure 1–3.

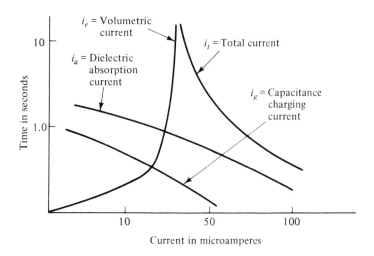

FIGURE 1–3.

Various leakage currents due to the application of dc high voltage to an insulation system.

After seeing how dc voltage affects the insulation, let's now take a look at the various tests that are conducted with this voltage. Two tests can be conducted on solid insulation with the application of dc voltage:

- Insulation resistance testing.
- High-potential voltage testing.

Insulation Resistance Testing

This test is conducted at applied voltages of 100 to 5,000 volts (V). The instrument used is a megohmmeter, either hand cranked, motor driven, or electronic, which indicates the insulation resistance in megohms. An electronic megohmmeter is shown in Figure 1–4. The quality of insulation is evaluated based upon the level of insulation resistance. The insulation is a variable, dependent upon temperature, humidity, and other environmental factors.

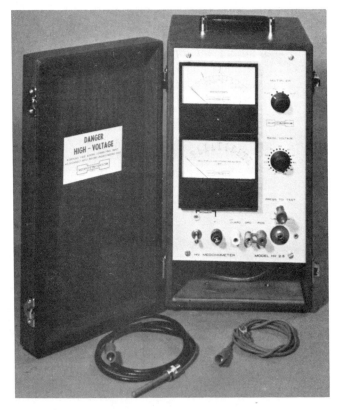

FIGURE 1–4.
Electronic megohmmeter, 2,500 volts. (Courtesy of Hipotronics, Inc., Brewster, N.Y.)

Therefore, all readings must be corrected to the standard temperature and humidity for the class of equipment under test (see Table 3–3 for conversion factors). The megohm value of insulation resistance is inversely proportional to the volume of insulation being tested. As an example, a cable 1,000 feet (ft) long would have one-tenth the insulation resistance of cable 100 ft long, provided other conditions were identical. This test can be useful in giving an indication of deteriorating trends in the insulation system. The insulation resistance values by themselves do not indicate the weakness of the insulation nor its total dielectric strength. However, they can indicate the contamination of the insulation and trouble ahead within the insulation system if a downward trend continues in the insulation resistance values.

Insulation resistance measurement values can be accomplished by five common test methods:

- Short-time readings.
- Time-resistance readings (dielectric absorption ratio test).
- Step-voltage readings.
- Dielectric absorption test.
- Polarization index test.

SHORT-TIME READINGS

This test simply measures the insulation resistance value for a short duration of time, such as 30 or 60 second(s), through a spot reading that lies on the curve of increasing insulation resistance values. The reading only allows a rough check of the insulation condition. However, comparison of this value with previous values is of importance. A continued downward trend is indicative of insulation deterioration ahead. For interpreting the results, the values used for comparison should all be normalized to 20°C with humidity effects considered.

TIME-RESISTANCE READINGS

A good insulation system shows a continued increase in its resistance value over the period of time in which voltage is applied. On the other hand, an insulation system that is contaminated with moisture, dirt, and the like will show a low resistance value. In good insulation, the effect of absorption current decreases as time increases. In bad insulation, the absorption effect is perpetuated by high leakage current. The time-resistance method is independent of temperature and equipment size. It can provide conclusive results as to the condition of insulation. The ratio of time-resistance readings can be used to indicate the condition of the insulation system. The ratio of a 60-s reading to a 30-s reading is called the dielectric absorption ratio (DAR):

$$\mathrm{DAR} = \frac{\text{resistance reading at 60 s}}{\text{resistance reading at 30 s}}$$

A DAR ratio below 1.25 is cause for investigation and possible repair of the electrical apparatus. Usually, the DAR readings are confined to the hand-driven megohmmeter.

STEP-VOLTAGE READINGS

In this method, voltage is applied in steps to the insulation under test through a multivoltage test set. As voltage is increased, the weak insulation will show lower resistance that was not obvious at lower voltage levels. Moisture, dirt, and other contaminants can be detected at lower voltage levels, that is, below operating voltages, whereas aging and physical damage in clean, dry insulation systems can only be revealed at higher voltages. The step-voltage test is very valuable when conducted on a regular periodic basis.

DIELECTRIC ABSORPTION TEST

The dielectric absorption test is conducted at voltages much higher than the usual insulation resistance test values and can exceed 100 kilovolts (kv). Under this test, the voltage is applied for an extended period of time, from 5 to 15 minutes (min). Periodic readings are taken of the insulation resistance or leakage current. The test is evaluated on the basis of insulation resistance. If insulation is in good condition, the apparent insulation resistance will increase as the test progresses. The dielectric absorption tests are independent of the volume and the temperature of the insulation under test.

POLARIZATION INDEX TEST

The polarization index test is a specialized application of the dielectric absorption test. The polarization index is the ratio of the insulation resistance at 10 min to the insulation resistance at 1 min. A polarization index of less than 1 indicates equipment deterioration and the need for immediate maintenance. This test is used for cables, transformers, and rotating machines.

High-Potential Voltage Test

A dc high-potential voltage test is a voltage applied across the insulation at or above the dc equivalent of the 60-hertz (Hz) operating crest voltage (i.e., dc value = 1.41 times rms value). This test can be applied as a step-voltage test. When the high-potential voltage is applied as a dielectric absorption test, the maximum voltage is applied gradually over a period of from 60 to 90 s. The maximum voltage is then held for 5 min with leakage current readings taken each minute. When this test is applied as a step-voltage test, the maximum voltage is applied in a number of equal increments, usually not less than eight, with each voltage step being held for an equal interval of time. The time interval between each step should be 1 to 4 min. At the end of each interval, a leakage current or insulation resistance reading is taken before proceeding to the next step. A plot of test voltage versus leakage current or insulation resistance can then be drawn to indicate the condition of the insulation system. Routine maintenance tests are conducted with a maximum voltage at or below 75 percent of the maximum test voltage permitted for acceptance tests.

ALTERNATING-CURRENT VOLTAGE TESTING OF SOLID INSULATION

Several tests can be performed on solid insulation with the application of ac voltage to evaluate the condition of the insulation system. They include the following:

- High-potential testing.
- Insulation power factor testing.

High-Potential Testing

The high-potential test, commonly known as ac hi-pot test, is usually made at voltage above normal system operating voltage for a short duration, such as 1 min. Since many different voltages are involved in the operation of an electrical power system, it is recommended that manufacturer's instructions or applicable standard values be followed in conducting these tests. Later chapters of this text will list the various ac values recommended for conducting this test on particular types of equipment. A typical ac hi-pot test set is shown in Figure 1–5.

FIGURE 1–5.
Alternating-current hi-pot test set, 5 and 2 kilovolts. (Courtesy of Hipo-tronics, Brewster, N.Y.)

Insulation Power Factor Testing

When the insulation system is energized with an ac voltage, the power factor is equal to the cosine of the angle between the charging current and the applied voltage. The evaluation is based upon the fact that for low values of power factor the dissipation factor can be assumed to be the same as the power factor. The dissipation factor is equal to the tangent of angle δ, where δ is equal to $(90 - \theta)$ as shown in Figure 1–6.

The insulation power factor is an important tool in determining the quality of the insulation for transformer, circuit breakers, rotating machines, cables, regulators, and insulating liquid. Several precautions should be followed when making the power factor test:

- The equipment under test should be isolated from the rest of the system.
- The test should be conducted above 32°F and with relative humidity below 70 percent.
- The test equipment should be able to produce a sine wave of 60 Hz at a voltage of at least 2,500 V. The minimum test voltage should be not less than 500 V in all cases.
- The evaluation of test data should be based on comparative industry standards, with values of other similar equipment, or with previous test results on similar equipment.

Protective Device Testing

Protective device testing involves the testing and maintenance of low-voltage molded-case breakers, low-voltage drawout power circuit breakers, protective relays, and associated equipment such as instrument transformers and wiring. The function of protective maintenance and testing is to assure that a particular breaker or protective relay is able to perform its basic protective function under

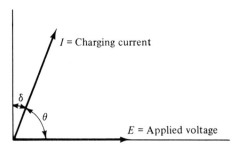

FIGURE 1–6.
Relationship of charging current and applied voltage.

TABLE 1–1.
ASTM METHOD OF TEST FOR INSULATING LIQUIDS

Test	ASTM Test Method
Acidity	D1534 or D1902
Color	D1500
Dielectric breakdown	D877, silicone, askarel, RTemp, oil
voltage	D1816, oil
Visual examination	D1524, oils
	D1702, askarels
Intrafacial tension	D971
(oil only)	D2285
Neutralization number	D974
	D664
Power factor	D924

actual operating conditions. The tests on protective devices and circuit breakers can be classified as routine testing and verification testing. These tests will be discussed in more detail in the later chapters on protective devices, relays, circuit breakers, and switchgear.

Insulating Liquid Testing

The insulating liquid used in transformers or other electrical apparatus is subject to deterioration and contamination over a period of time. These contaminants have a detrimental effect on the insulating properties of the liquid, as well as on the solid insulation system of the windings. Basically, the elements that cause the deterioration of the insulating liquid are moisture, heat, oxygen, and other catalysts that result in a chemical reaction that produces acid and sludge, which in turn attack the insulating liquids. The insulating liquids that are in use today are oil, askarel, silicone, and RTemp, although the further use of askarel has been banned by federal regulations owing to its high toxicity.

Regular tests are recommended to monitor the condition of the insulating liquid. Samples should be taken from the equipment on a periodic basis to perform the various tests in accordance with ASTM methods, which are listed Table 1–1.

A detailed discussion of the various test methods and the test limits for maintenance of new and existing liquids is covered in the following chapters. Because of the ban on askarel, many new liquids are in the developmental stage. In addition, new cooling systems are being considered for transformers. Therefore, the reader is advised to keep abreast of this continuing change in technology.

Circuit Breaker Time-Travel Analysis

The circuit breaker time-travel analysis test is performed to determine if the operating mechanism of the circuit breaker is operating properly. This test is usually performed on medium- and high-voltage circuit breakers and depicts the position of breaker contacts with relation to time. This relationship can then be used to determine the operating speed of the circuit breaker for opening and closing and contact bounce, and the interval time for closing and tripping. The breaker operating time data can be used to evaluate the condition of mechanical parts of breakers, such as closing mechanism, springs, and shock absorbers.

Grounding Electrode Resistance Testing

The integrity of the grounding system is very important in an electrical power system for the following reasons:

- To maintain a reference point of potential (ground) for equipment and personnel safety.
- To provide a discharge point for traveling waves due to lightning.
- To prevent excessive high voltage due to induced voltages on the power system.

Therefore, to maintain ground potential effectiveness, periodic testing of grounding electrodes and the grounding system is required. An ordinary ground resistance test set can be used to provide a direct reading of the ground resistance with the scale calibrated in ohms.

Fault Gas Analysis Testing

The fault gas analysis test can provide information on incipient faults in oil-filled transformers by measuring combustible gases present in the nitrogen cap of the transformer. Because of arcing or excessive heat, some oil in the transformer decomposes and generates combustible gases, which then mix with the nitrogen above the top oil. A small sample of nitrogen gas is removed from the transformer and analyzed by a test set built for this purpose. The test set is calibrated in a direct reading scale in percentage of combustible gas.

Infrared Inspection Testing

There are many different devices available using infrared guns to check hot spots in switchgear and other energized parts of the power system. They are very useful in routine maintenance and inspection for finding bad connections and joints and overloaded terminals or lines. Since the cost of these devices varies over a very wide range, it may be economical to rent such a device for routine inspection of the electrical power system equipment. Some of these devices have a calibrated scale in degrees; others have a cathode-ray tube display with hot spots being shown as very bright spots on the screen. Such a device is very useful in finding hot spots in 480-V switchgear and apparatus.

1-5 REVIEW OF ELECTRICAL POWER DISTRIBUTION SYSTEM

Because of the trend toward higher voltages for electric distribution within plants and commercial facilities, it has become important for maintenance personnel to know more about the various types of systems for proper maintenance. The plant distribution voltages within buildings may range from 120/208-V system to 15,000 V or above. In any plant design, the selection of power system voltage is an important consideration due to many factors such as cost, expansion, utility service availability, and others. Generally, the various voltages levels may be classified as low, medium, and high.

LOW VOLTAGE

This is usually 600 V and less and confined to supplying utilization voltage directly to the equipment. Common system voltages found in this category are 120/240, 120/208, and 227/480 volts.

MEDIUM VOLTAGE

This system includes voltages from 601 up to 15,000 V. These voltage levels are mainly used for distribution purposes and supplying utilization voltage to large motors. Common system voltages found in this classification are 2,400, 4,160, 6,900, and 13,800 volts.

HIGH VOLTAGE

Voltages in this class are usually above 15,000 V and may be found in large plants or facilities to distribute power over a scattered load area.

The American National Standard Institute (ANSI) standard C92.2 provides a list of the various nominal system and utilization voltages, as shown in Table 1–2 for some of the commonly used voltages up to 34,500 V.

ELECTRICAL POWER DISTRIBUTION SYSTEMS AND CIRCUIT ARRANGEMENTS

The following is a brief review of electric power distribution systems and circuit arrangements commonly used for plants and commercial facilities.

TABLE 1–2.
STANDARD SYSTEM VOLTAGES

Insulation System	Nominal System Voltage		Voltage Range A			Voltage Range B		
	3-wire	4-wire	Minimum Utilization Voltage	Service Voltage	Maximum Utilization Voltage	Minimum Utilization Voltage	Service Voltage	Maximum Utilization Voltage
SINGLE-PHASE SYSTEMS								
Up to 600 volts	120/240		110/220	114/228	126/252	106/212	110/220	127/254
THREE-PHASE SYSTEMS								
Up to 600 volts		120/208Y	110/191Y	114/197Y	126/218Y	106/184Y	110/191Y	127/220
		120/240	110/220	114/228	126/252	106/212	110/220	127/254
	240		220	228	252	212	220	254
		277/480Y	245/440Y	263/456Y	291/504Y	245/424Y	254/440Y	293/508Y
	480		440	456	504	424	440	508
	2,400		2160	2340	2520	2,080	2,280	2,540
5 kV		2,400/4,160Y	2160/3740Y	2,340/4,050Y	2,520/4,370Y	2,080/3,600Y	2,280/3,950Y	2,540/4,400Y
	4,160		3740	4050	4,370	3,600	3,950	4,400
	4,800		4320	4680	5,040	4,160	4,560	5,080
	6,900		6210	6730	7,240	5,940	6,560	7,260
15 kV		7,200/1,2470Y		7,020/12,160Y	7,560/13,090Y		6840/11,850Y	7620/13,200Y
		7,620/13,200Y		7,430/12,870Y	8,000/13,860Y		7,240/12,540Y	8,070/13,970Y
	13,800		12,420	13,460	14,490	11880	13,110	14,520
Above 15 kV	2,300	14,400/24,900Y		14,040/24,328Y	15,120/26,190Y		13,680/23,690Y	15,240/26,400Y
	34,500	19,920/34,500Y		19,420/33,640Y	20,920/36,230Y		18,930/32,780Y	21,080/36,510Y

Radial

A radial system can be divided into the two subcategories of simple radial and modern radial. The simple radial system receives power at utility supply voltage at a single substation and steps the voltage down to utilization level. These types of systems were commonly used in older designs. Normally, the power would be distributed at the utilization voltage. This system is shown in Figure 1–7.

The modern radial system uses a medium voltage to distribute power to one or more substations within a facility. The system uses the load-center concept in which medium voltage is carried to the load areas and then stepped down to utilization voltage. The system is safe, cost effective, and very simple. In the event of step-down transformer (or other equipment) failure, only the area served would be affected. This is a distinct advantage compared to the total power outage that would occur in the case of the simple radial system. The modern radial system is shown in Figure 1–8.

To perform maintenance on any type of radial system, the substation and the area it serves must be shut down. This is a drawback for routine maintenance. Normally, maintenance of this type of system would have to be scheduled during off-hours to provide uninterrupted service during working hours.

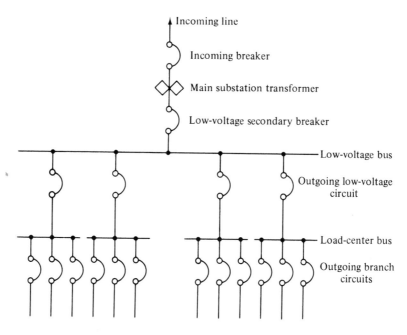

FIGURE 1–7.
Simple radial system.

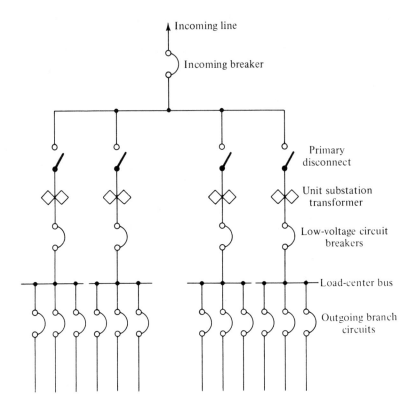

FIGURE 1–8.
Modern radial system.

The major benefit from a maintenance viewpoint is system simplicity, which avoids the difficulties encountered in other systems.

Secondary–Selective

The secondary selective system, also known as the double-ended substation, is an extension of the radial system using two primary feeders and two load centers instead of one. Each load center is individually supplied from its own primary feeder and transformer under normal conditions. But when the primary feeder or transformer of one side is taken out of service, the load side of both load centers can be supplied from one primary feeder and one transformer by closing the bus tie of two single-ended substations. The secondary system can be either manual transfer or automatic transfer; that is, the bus tie can be manually or automatically closed. Generally, interlocks are provided between the two incoming secondary breakers and the normally open bus tie, so that the tie cannot be closed without first opening one secondary breaker. But in special cases where critical load is served, provision can be made to momentarily close the bus tie to parallel the two radial systems before one secondary breaker is opened. This type of operation has to be concurred upon by the utility supplying the service and understood by operating and maintenance personnel. This system is in reality a radial system with duplicate feeds to each load center. The transformers have to be sized carefully so that one transformer can carry the required load in case one primary feeder or transformer is taken out of service.

The secondary selective system does not have the same handicap as the radial system from the point of view of maintenance. Since it offers redundancy, one transformer or primary feeder can be taken out of service for maintenance. The secondary selective system is shown in Figure 1–9.

Primary Selective

The primary selective system uses two primary feeder circuits to each load center. Each primary feeder is sized to handle twice the total load connected on it, so if one feeder is out of service, the remaining primary feeder can carry all the load. The load from the dead feeder to the second primary feeder can be transferred by manual or automatic load switches or circuit breakers. Even

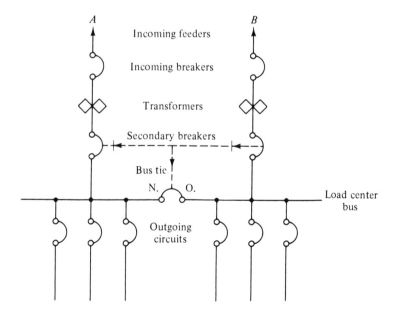

FIGURE 1–9.
Secondary selective system.

though this system offers the advantages of having two primary feeders, a transformer fault can interrupt the service to the load center. Service cannot be restored until the transformer is repaired and put back into service. This system is shown in Figure 1–10.

Looped Primary System

The looped primary system is similar to the modern radial system with the addition of a built-in restorability feature. It provides quick restoration of service when a primary feeder or transformer fault occurs. The primary feeder is sectionalized between each transformer load center in the form of a controlled loop fed by a primary breaker. In case of fault on the feeder, all transformers will be out of service because of feeder outage; but service can be restored quickly by sectionalizing the faulted portion of the feeder. Maintenance personnel should not restore service until the trouble on the faulted section has been definitely established and isolated. Manually operated load break switches are generally installed to provide sectionalizing, with two of these switches being installed where the feeder branches from a loop. This system is shown in Figure 1–11.

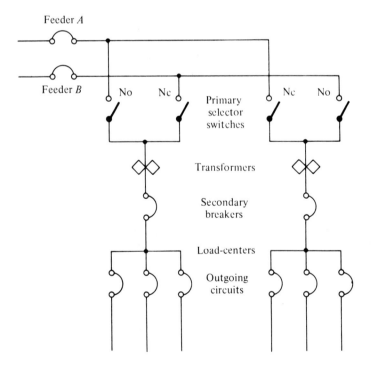

FIGURE 1–10.
Primary selective system.

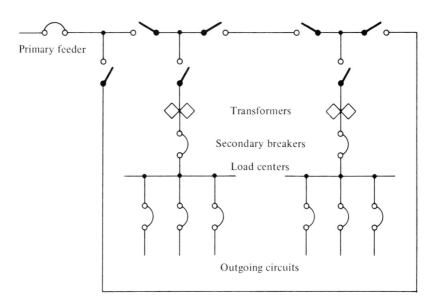

FIGURE 1–11.
Looped primary system.

Secondary Network System

The secondary network system is essentially a secondary selective system except that the bus-tie breaker is normally closed instead of open. Another major difference between the network system and secondary selective system is that a network protector is used instead of the usual secondary breakers. The network protector has built-in features to provide reserve power protection and automatic closing of the network protector, provided voltage conditions will permit the flow of power to the load. The biggest benefit of the network system is service continuity. This is accomplished by tieing all transformer secondaries together by a ring bus to feed the load. Upon loss of one primary feeder circuit, the remaining primary feeders have sufficient capacity to carry the entire load. No single fault on the system will interrupt service to more than a small portion of the system load. Another advantage is the flexibility offered for maintenance purposes. Any primary feeder circuit and transformer can be taken out of service for maintenance without affecting the continuity of service to the load. On the other hand, maintenance personnel must be familiar with the in-built capability and flexibility of the system. Generally, secondary networks are provided for high-density load areas. The voltage level for this type of system is confined to 120/208-V and 277/480-V systems, and, in isolated cases, network systems can be found in 2,400-V distribution systems. The secondary network is shown in Figure 1–12.

Another form of secondary network, usually found in suburban areas, is the spot-network. It is used to provide highly reliable service to shopping malls or office complexes. The simple spot-network is most economical where more than two or three primary feeders are needed to serve the load.

1-6   MAINTENANCE CONSIDERATIONS AND REQUIREMENTS

Electrical equipment and apparatus are more susceptible than other production equipment to damage by operating and environmental conditions. Many maintenance and plant operating personnel are not aware of this condition and expect electrical equipment to last a long time without care. Therefore, properly installed equipment is essential. Equipment should be installed to facilitate maintenance and extend its operating life.

Another consideration is properly trained personnel who understand the equipment's operation and maintenance requirements and who are able to make repairs. It may also become necessary to engage manufacturer's trained specialists and engineers to perform maintenance and repairs on complex equipment.

A further area of concern is scheduling outages for maintenance purposes. Outages are frequently hard to obtain because few people in management understand the need for periodic maintenance. Many plant and facility

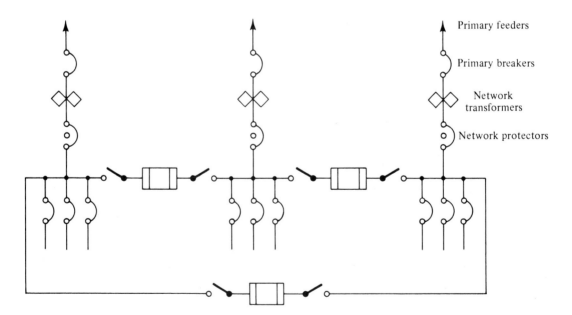

Primary feeders

Primary breakers

Network transformers

Network protectors

FIGURE 1–12.
Secondary network system.

managers now recognize this need and are adopting scheduled outages for maintenance purposes.

Environmental conditions, such as water, dust, corrosive gases, and vibrations, can impair the operation and life of the equipment. Equipment that is neglected and not maintained, particularly under adverse conditions, can fail prematurely and, in some cases, be completely destroyed. It is good practice the follow manufacturer's recommendations for operation and maintenance in order to minimize potential failures. The general precautions, as stated in most manufacturer's instructions for electrical equipment, are *keep it tight, keep it clean, and keep it dry.*

Loose connections can cause air pockets between two or more connection points, leading to arcing and pitting. Certain types of equipment operate at high speed, thereby causing wear and tear of moving parts. Continual attention should be provided to detect this loosening of connections in order to prevent unnecessary failures.

The greatest cause of electrical failure is dirt and grime. Unchecked dirt will contaminate electrical equipment and cause breakdowns. If dirt is left uncontrolled, it can reduce the creepage distances, as well as obstruct air movement, thus causing increased operating temperatures, which are detrimental to equipment life.

Electrical equipment requires dry atmospheres, because in wet atmospheres the electrical metal parts oxidize, which increases the resistance of electrical connections and contacts. Increased resistance causes increased temperatures, which, in turn, affect equipment insulation life.

Periodic inspection, maintenance, and testing is a valuable asset to successful operation of electrical equipment. The average cost is usually a very small percent (less than 1 percent) of the dollar value of the equipment that may be lost because of electric system failure or the loss in plant production. Insurance companies report many millions of dollars lost annually through damage caused by electrical failure. Many electrical protective devices such as circuit breakers, relays, and trip units are found to be inoperative after they have been installed or have been in service for some years. The equipment originally installed may be underrated and in serious jeopardy if plant load and service capacity has been increased manyfold.

Equipment test and evaluation during periodic maintenance is the most effective means of preventing unexpected equipment failures. The various electrical tests for the maintenance of power system equipment are listed in Table 1–3. These tests may be used as a recommended guide for establishing a maintenance test program.

TABLE 1-3.
ELECTRICAL APPARATUS: TEST PROGRAM GUIDE

Test	Power Transformer Oil	Power Transformer Dry	Instrument Transformer PT	Instrument Transformer CT	Circuit Breaker Oil	Circuit Breaker ACB	Motor/ Generator	Switchgear	Arrestor	Capacitor	Cable
Insulation resistance	X	X	X	X	X	X	X and P/I	X	X	X	X
High potential	X (ac)	X (ac)	X (ac)	X (ac)	X (ac)	X (ac)	X (dc)	X (ac)	X (ac)	X (dc)	X (dc)
Power factor	X	X	X	X	X	—	X	—	X	—	—
Transformer turns ratio (TTR)	X	X	X	X	—	—	—	—	—	—	—
Polarity	X	X	X	X	—	—	—	—	—	—	—
Winding resistance	X	—	—	—	—	—	X	—	—	—	—
Insulating liquid	X	—	X	X	X	—	—	—	—	—	—
Gas analysis	X	—	—	—	X	—	—	—	—	—	—
Contact resistance	—	—	—	—	X	X	—	—	—	—	—
Travel analysis	—	—	—	—	X	—	—	—	—	—	—
Protective relays	X	X	—	—	X	X	X	X	—	—	—
RTDS	—	—	—	—	—	—	X	—	—	—	—

X, denotes desired test; ac, alternating voltage; dc, direct voltage.

CHAPTER 2

SELECTION AND APPLICATION OF ELECTRICAL EQUIPMENT

2-1   INTRODUCTION

The design of an electrical power distribution system involves many considerations in order to obtain a suitable, reliable, flexible, maintainable, economical, and safe power system. One important consideration is the selection and application of electrical equipment such as transformers, circuit breakers, cables, motors, protective devices, and so on. This equipment has to be applied properly so it can provide a safe and reliable service throughout its life. To do so, the design of the distribution system of a plant should consider the basic loads and plant functions in order to select the proper equipment to be applied at selected voltage and frequency. To ensure troublefree service over the life of the equipment, it has to be maintained regularly. The purpose of this chapter is to provide information on the basic design, construction, and application of electrical equipment, which will help toward better maintenance.

2-2   TRANSFORMERS

A transformer is an energy transformation device that transforms alternating current or voltage at one level to alternating current and voltage at another level. A transformer can economically convert voltage or current from low to high levels. The transformer usually consists of two or more insulated windings on a common iron core. In industrial and commercial applications, transformers are used to step down voltages from utility service voltage to lower distribution voltage levels or lower utilization voltages that may be required for a facility or a plant. Transformers are very reliable devices and can provide service for a long time if maintained and serviced regularly. Transformer failures, when they occur, are usually of a very serious nature, which may require costly repairs and long downtime. The best insurance against transformer failure is to ensure that they are properly installed and maintained.

33

TRANSFORMER CATEGORIES AND TYPE

For consideration of maintenance requirements, transformers can be divided into the following categories:

- Insulating medium
- Construction
- Application and use

Insulating Medium

The transformer insulating medium can be subdivided into two types: dry and liquid filled.

DRY TYPE
Dry-type transformers are usually air cooled with winding insulation of class A, B, C, or H. The dry-type transformer can be either self-cooled or forced air cooled.

- *Self-cooled:* A self-cooled transformer of the dry type is cooled by natural circulation of air through the transformer case. The cooling class designation for this transformer is AA.
- *Forced air cooled:* A forced-air-cooled transformer of dry type is cooled by means of forced circulation of air through the case. Transformers of this type have air-blast equipment such as fans with louvered or screened openings. These transformers are rated at 133 percent of the rating of the self-cooled dry-type transformer. The cooling class designation for this transformer is FA. Dry-type transformers can be obtained with both self-cooled and forced-air-cooled rating. The designation for such a transformer is AA/FA. Dry-type transformers can also be cooled by gas instead of air. For such transformers, a sealed tank is required.

LIQUID-FILLED TRANSFORMER
In this type of transformer, the windings and core are totally immersed in a liquid contained in the transformer tank. The tank is equipped with cooling fins for circulation of the transformer liquid. The transformer liquid provides an insulating medium for the coils as well as for dissipation of heat. Two liquids have been used extensively in the past for transformers: mineral oils and polychlorinated biphenyls (PCB), commonly known as askarel. Askarel has been extensively used in transformers for indoor applications because it is a nonflammable synthetic insulating fluid. Askarel is a nonbiodegradable fluid and highly toxic. Its use in transformers and other electrical equipment has been severely restricted, and its availability for reuse or for new applications is

almost nonexistent. Newer fluids have been introduced in the last few years, such as silicone and RTemp. Others are still in developmental stages. Regardless of what new fluids come on the market for transformer applications, they would still have to be maintained and tested for transformer integrity.

Several cooling methods are used for liquid-filled transformers.

- *Self-cooled:* A self-cooled transformer uses the natural circulation of the insulating liquid. Heat in the transformer tank is dissipated by convection currents set up in the liquid, which circulates through the tank and cooling fins. The cooling class designation for this transformer is OA.

- *Forced air cooled:* In this type of transformer, air is forced over the cooling surface of the tank to supplement the self-cooled rating. The supplemental air is provided by fans mounted on the transformer tank, which can be manually or automatically controlled. The cooling class designation for this type of transformer is OA/FA.

- *Forced air cooled and forced oil cooled:* This transformer uses a pump to circulate oil through a heat exchanger to increase heat dissipation, which supplements the self-cooling and forced air cooling. The cooling class designation for this transformer is OA/FA/FOA.

- *Water cooled:* This transformer uses water instead of air to provide the cooling. The cooling system consists of a heat exchange by means of water pumped through a pipe coil installed inside or outside the transformer tank. The cooling class designation for this transformer is FOW.

Construction

Transformers can be classified by tank construction and core construction.

TANK CONSTRUCTION
Several types of transformer tank construction are used to prevent exposing liquid to the atmosphere. These types are as follows:

- *Free breathing:* This type is open to the atmosphere (i.e., the air space above the liquid is at atmospheric pressure). The transformer breathes as the air pressure and temperature change outside the tank. Some of these transformers can be equipped with dehydrating compounds in the breather.

- *Conservator or expansion-tank type:* These transformers are equipped with small expansion tanks above the transformer tank. The transformer tank is completely filled with oil, and the transformer breathes by means of this small tank, usually through a dehydrating compound. The purpose of the small tank is to seal the transformer fluid from the atmosphere and to reduce oxidization and formation of sludge.

- *Sealed tank:* These transformers are equipped with an inert gas that is under pressure above the liquid in the transformer tank. Generally, the pressure range for this type of transformer is −8 to +8 pounds per square inch.

- *Gas-oil sealed:* These transformers have an auxiliary tank to completely seal the interior tank, containing transformer liquid, from the atmosphere.

- *Inert gas:* These transformers have an inert gas, such as nitrogen, under positive pressure above the liquid in the tank.

- *Vaporization:* This type of transformer uses a special nonflammable insulating fluid, such as halocarbon (General Electric R-113), which is nonflammable, and a special condenser assembly welded on top of the transformer tank. The cooling tube ends are swaged and welded to tube headers. This transformer uses the technique of sprayed liquid on core and coil assembly (i.e., vaporization cooling known as pool boiling). The purpose of the condenser is to cool the boiling vapor into liquid for continued circulation of the fluid.

CORE CONSTRUCTION
Transformers employ basically two types of core-construction techniques.

- *Core type:* In core-type construction, the transformer winding surrounds the laminated core. The coils can be cylindrical, flat, or disc shaped. They can be arranged to fit around the rectangle or square cross section of the core, as shown in Figure 2–1. Core-type construction provides a single-path magnetic circuit through the magnetic core. Most small distribution transformers are of this construction.

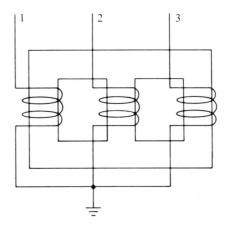

FIGURE 2–1.
Three-phase core construction.

- *Shell type:* In shell-type construction, the magnetic core surrounds the windings, as shown in Figure 2–2. The primary and secondary windings may be interspaced side by side or circularly stacked one above the other. Most large-type power transformers have this form of construction. One advantage of the shell type is that it offers a separate path for the zero-sequence currents through the core, as compared to the core type in which the zero-sequence path exists only through the transformer tank and end connections.

Application and Use

Transformers used for converting energy can be classified into five categories according to their application and use.

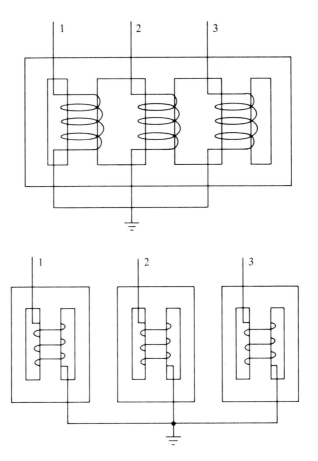

FIGURE 2–2.
Three-phase and three-single phase shell type of construction.

- *Distribution transformers:* A distribution transformer has a rating from 3 to 500 kilovolt-amperes (kVA). There are various types of distribution transformers, depending upon the cooling and insulating medium, service application, and mounting method. Voltage ratings as high as 15,000 volts (V) are available. Virtually all distribution transformers are self-cooled.

- *Network transformer:* This is considered a distribution transformer per NEMA standards and has characteristics similar to the distribution transformer. However, its application is different. It has special and severe requirements for network service, such as ventilation, vault size, submersibility, and short-circuit requirements. Network transformers can have kVA ratings in excess of 500 kVA and primary voltage up to 23 kV.

- *Arc-furnace transformer:* The arc-furnace transformer is a special-purpose transformer used in process industries. It is a low-voltage and high-amperage transformer and is specially braced to withstand mechanical stresses caused by fluctuating current requirements. Due to distorted waveform because of arcs, it has extra insulation and impedance in its winding circuit.

- *Rectifier transformer:* The rectifier transformer is also a special-purpose transformer used in the rectification of alternating current to direct-current applications in the process industry. These transformers are specially braced to withstand mechanical stresses produced by high currents.

- *Power transformer:* The power transformer has a rating in excess of 500 kVA and is primarily used in transforming energy from generating stations to transmission lines, from transmission lines to distribution substations, or from utility service lines to plant distribution substations.

TRANSFORMER FUNDAMENTALS

The transformer was invented in 1886 by William Stanley and is a very useful device. A power transformer can be divided into three parts: primary winding, secondary winding, and core. The primary and secondary windings are linked by common flux produced in the iron core, as shown in Figure 2–3. The following symbols are used for transformer voltages, currents, and impedances.

Primary side:

$$Vp = \text{primary voltage}$$
$$Np = \text{primary turns}$$

Z_{ps} = leakage impedance in ohms (Ω)

I_p = primary current

Secondary side:

V_s = secondary voltage

N_s = secondary turns

Z_{sp} = leakage impedance in ohms (Ω)

I_s = secondary current

Let's assume that the primary winding is energized by connecting it to an ac supply voltage, V_p. This sets up the primary current, which produces an alternating magnetic field in the iron core that is continually building up and collapsing in both positive and negative directions. The instantaneous induced voltage-e_p in the primary winding can be expressed by Faraday's law as

$$e_p = - N_p \frac{d\phi}{dt} 10^{-8} \text{ V}$$

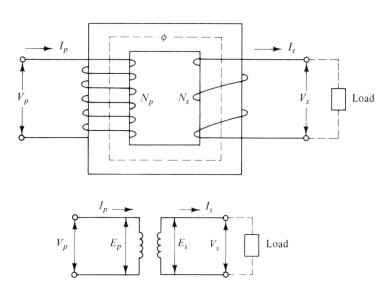

FIGURE 2-3.
Connection and circuit diagram of a simple transformer.

where $\phi = \phi_{max}$ Sin ωt and ϕ_{max} = maximum instantaneous flux in the core. The rms value of this voltage can be expressed as

$$E_p = 4.44 f N_p A B_{max} 10^{-8} \text{ V}$$

where
f = frequency
N_p = number of turns in primary winding
A = area of the core
B_{max} = maximum flux density

The alternating flux produced by the primary winding in the core links the secondary winding and thus induces an alternating voltage in the secondary winding, which can also be expressed as

$$E_s = 4.44 f N_2 A B_{max} 10^{-8} \text{ V}$$

where N_2 = number of secondary turns.

Assuming that the secondary winding is open (no-load condition, $I_s = 0$) and the transformer is energized from the primary side, a small current, I_n, will flow in the primary winding. This current is called exciting current and sets up the alternating flux consisting of the following:

- Mutual flux whose path is through the core.
- Leakage flux whose path is through the air.

In commercial power transformers, the leakage flux is very small and is often neglected. The alternating flux in the iron core induces voltage in the primary and secondary windings. The induced voltage in the secondary produces a back electromotive force (emf) due to self-inductance. According to Lenz's law, the back emf is equal to applied voltage to the primary winding under no-load conditions. The applied voltage can be expressed as follows:

Applied voltage = total induced voltage − resistance drop in the primary winding

Neglecting the resistance drop in the primary winding, we can write

Applied voltage = induced voltage

$$V_p = E_p$$

When load is applied to the secondary winding, a proportional primary current will flow corresponding to the secondary current. As the load is applied to the transformer, the voltage transformation ratio will deviate from the true transformer winding turns ratio. These small errors can generally be neglected in power transformers. In addition to the voltage drop in primary and secondary windings, losses due to the exciting current and load current have to be considered. Power transformer losses can be divided in two types:

- *Copper loss (I²R):* This is power loss in the resistance of the primary and secondary winding due to load and magnetizing current of transformer.

- *Core loss:* This is power loss in the transformer core and is due to the exciting current. The core loss can be subdivided into eddy current and hysteresis losses. Eddy current losses are due to eddy and small circulating currents in the core, whereas hysteresis losses are caused by the energy required to align the domains in the magnetic core material. Core loss is continuous as long as the transformer is energized.

A two-winding power transformer can be represented by an equivalent circuit diagram as shown in Figure 2–4. The exciting current of the transformer represented by I_n is shown as flowing to the magnetizing branch of shunt conductance and susceptance. The exciting current for power transformers usually ranges from 3 to 6 percent. To simplify the equivalent circuit, the exciting current may be neglected. Furthermore, the equivalent circuit diagram can be based upon the primary or secondary voltage. Figure 2–5a shows the equivalent circuit diagram of a transformer based on the secondary side. Sometimes it is desirable to represent a transformer by vector diagrams (the relationship of the primary and secondary currents and voltages). The vector diagram shown in the Figure 2–5b is based upon the equivalent circuit diagram shown in Figure 2–5a.

It is important to know the relationship between transformer voltage and current as energy is transformed from one voltage level to another. Consider the transformer shown in Figure 2–6. The voltage, current, and impedance are expressed as follows:

Voltage Relationship

According to Faraday's law,

$$V_p = e_p = N_p \frac{d\phi}{dt}$$

$$V_s = e_s = N_s \frac{d\phi}{dt}$$

$$\frac{V_p}{V_s} = \frac{N_p(d\phi/dt)}{N_s(d\phi/dt)} = \frac{N_p}{N_s} = N$$

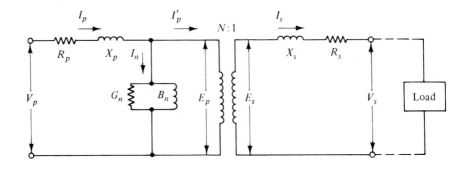

V_p = primary applied voltage
E_p = primary induced voltage
I_p = primary current
I_p' = $(I_p - I_n)$ current
R_p = primary resistance
X_p = primary reactance
I_n = exciting current
G_n = magnetic conductance
B_n = magnetic susceptance

V_s = secondary load voltage
E_s = secondary induced voltage
R_s = secondary resistance
X_s = secondary reactance
I_s = secondary current
N = transformer turns ratio

FIGURE 2–4.
Transformer equivalent diagram.

Current Relationship

$$\text{Power in} = \text{power out (ideal transformer)}$$

$$V_p I_p = V_s I_s$$

$$N_p I_p = N_s I_s$$

$$\frac{V_s}{V_p} = \frac{I_p}{I_s} = \frac{N_s}{N_p} = \frac{1}{N}$$

Impedance Relationship

Z_{ps} is defined as the leakage impedance between primary and secondary winding measured in ohms on the primary winding with the secondary winding short circuited. The value of Z_{ps} is given by the following:

$$Z_{ps} = \frac{V_p}{I_p}$$

Zsp is defined as the leakage impedance between secondary and primary winding measured in ohms on the secondary winding with the primary winding short circuited. The value of Zsp is given by the following:

$$Z_{sp} = \frac{V_s}{I_s}$$

Summary

The voltage, current, and impedance equations for the transformer can be rewritten as follows:

$$\frac{V_p}{V_s} = \frac{I_s}{I_p} = \frac{N_p}{N_s} = N$$

or $\quad V_p = \dfrac{N_p}{N_s} V_s = N V_s \quad$ and $\quad I_p = \dfrac{N_s}{N_p} I_s = \dfrac{1}{N} I_s$

$$Z_{ps} = \frac{N V_s}{(1/N) I_s} = N^2 \frac{V_s}{I_s} = N^2 Z_{sp}$$

Conversely,

$$Z_{sp} = \frac{1}{N^2} Z_{ps}$$

Generally, for power transformers the impedance is specified in a percentage rather than actual ohms. The percentage of impedance of a transformer can be expressed as

$$Z_{ps} \% = \frac{I \text{ rated} \times Z_{ps}}{V_p \text{ rated}} \times 100$$

$$= \frac{\text{voltage drop at rated load}}{\text{rated voltage}} \times 100$$

The percentage of impedance can be expressed independently of the terminal voltages and is based on the kVA rating of the transformer. The equivalent circuit diagram of a transformer on a percentage basis is shown in Figure 2–7.

TRANSFORMER POLARITY, TERMINAL MARKINGS, AND CONNECTIONS

Single-Phase Transformers

Primary and secondary terminals of a single-phase transformer have the same polarity when the current enters the primary terminal and at the same time

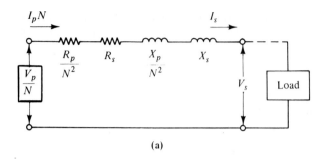

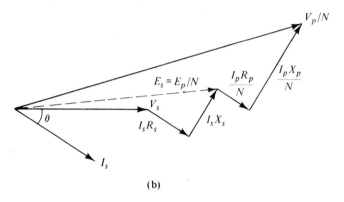

FIGURE 2–5.
(a) Simplified equivalent diagram of transformer; (b) simplified vector diagram of transformer.

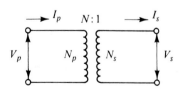

FIGURE 2–6.
Graphical representation of a power transformer.

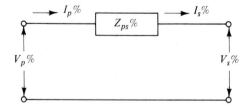

FIGURE 2–7.
Percentage equivalent circuit of transformer.

leaves the secondary terminal. Transformers are constructed with subtractive and additive polarities.

SUBTRACTIVE POLARITY

When the high-side lead, H_1, and low-side lead, X_1, are brought out the same side of the transformer, the polarity is said to be subtractive, as shown in Figure 2–8a. If leads H_1 and X_1 are connected and the high side is energized with a given voltage, the resulting voltage, which appears across the H_2 and X_2 leads, will be less than the applied voltage (see Figure 2–8b). This is due to the fact that in this series connection the low-voltage winding opposes the high-voltage winding, and thus the low voltage is subtracted from the high voltage (see Figure 2–8c).

ADDITIVE POLARITY

When the high-side lead, H_1, and low-side lead, X_2, are brought out on the same side of the transformer, the polarity is said to be additive. If the leads H_1 and X_2 are connected and a given voltage is applied to the high side, the resultant voltage across the H_2 and X_1 leads is the sum of the high- and low-voltage windings. Additive polarity is shown in Figure 2–9.

In general, polarity is not indicative of a higher or lower arrangement of potential stresses within a transformer or arrangement of windings. Both subtractive and additive polarities are found in transformers. Additive polarity is more prevalent in distribution-type transformers and subtractive polarity in power transformers.

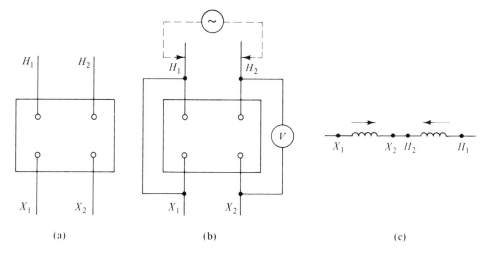

(a)   (b)   (c)

FIGURE 2–8.
Subtractive polarity of single-phase transformer.

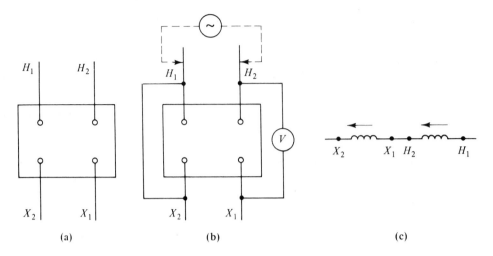

FIGURE 2–9.
Additive polarity of single-phase transformer.

The connections of single-phase distribution transformers usually have their windings divided into two or more sections. When the two secondary windings are connected in parallel, their currents add, and if the two windings are connected in series, their voltages add. The connection output is the same in both cases; for example, for series connection for each secondary winding rated at 115 V and 100 amperes (A), the output is equal to $230 \times 100 = 23,000$ VA or 23 kVA, and for parallel connection it is equal to $115 \times 200 = 23,000$ VA or 23 kVA. These connections are shown in Figure 2–10.

Three-Phase Transformers

The polarity of three-phase transformers is fixed by the connections between phases, as well as by the relative locations of leads, and can be designated by a sketch showing lead markings and a vector diagram showing the electrical angular shift between terminals. The basic three-phase transformer configurations are as follows:

- Delta-delta
- Wye-wye (star-star)
- Delta-wye (star)
- Wye (star)—delta

These are shown in Figure 2–11.

The standard angular displacement between reference phases of a delta-delta bank or a star-star bank is 0°. The standard angular displacement between reference phases of a star-delta or a delta-star bank is 30°. The ANSI standard C57.12 for such three-phase banks is that the high-voltage reference phase angle is 30° ahead of the reference low voltage, regardless of whether the bank connections are star-delta or delta-star.

The lead marking of three-phase transformers has been standardized by ANSI and NEMA for the purpose of paralleling operation. The high-voltage lead, H_1, is brought out on the right side when facing the high-voltage side of the transformer case. The remaining high size leads H_2 and H_3 are brought out and numbered in sequence from right to left. The low side lead, X_1, is brought out on the left side facing the low side of the transformer case. The remaining low side leads, X_2 and X_3, are numbered in sequence from left to right. This is shown in Figure 2–12.

The four basic three-phase transformer configurations can be accomplished by connecting three single-phase transformers or by connecting three phase windings within one tank. All the configurations provide symmetrical connections. The relationship between each phase for high and low side voltage is 120°, as shown in the vector diagrams of Figure 2–13a and b.

There are many other connections that give different phase displacement, and the reader is urged to review a text on transformer connections.

For parallel operation of single- or three-phase transformers, it is essential that certain conditions be maintained. For example, when placing single-phase transformers in parallel, it is important to have the same voltage ratios and impedances. Similarly, the like polarities of each transformer must be connected together when placing single-phase transformers in parallel. One

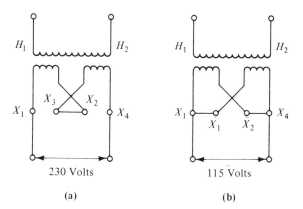

FIGURE 2–10.

Single-phase transformer connections: (a) series connections; (b) parallel connections.

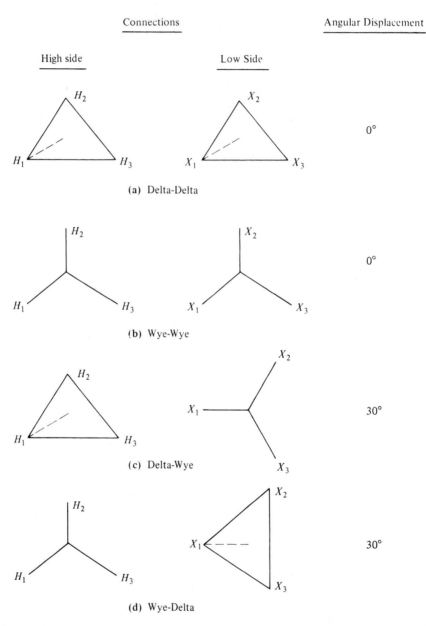

FIGURE 2–11.
Three-phase connection and angular displacement.

should be very careful in paralleling transformers, because many problems can arise if proper consideration is not given to the transformer connections and characteristics. Some of the problems in paralleling transformers that require careful analysis are the following:

- Paralleling transformers having different winding connections.
- Transformers with different impedances or turns ratio or different primary voltages.
- Transformers of different polarity and phase displacement.

The reader is urged to consult a transformer text before paralleling transformers.

TRANSFORMER CHARACTERISTICS

Most transformers used in industrial and commercial facilities range from 500 through 2,500 kVA and are three-phase, liquid-filled or dry type located indoors. These transformers are part of secondary unit substations supplying service to load centers. Transformers used for the distribution of power in plants and buildings have similar characteristics, which have been standardized as follows:

- *kVA rating:* The rating must be adequate to carry the connected load.
- *Voltage ratings:* The voltage rating provides the primary and secondary voltage to transform electrical energy from primary voltage to secondary voltage. This rating is associated with the winding turns ratios of the primary and secondary windings. Some examples of standard voltage ratings for power transformers are shown in Table 2–1.

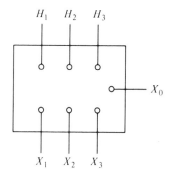

FIGURE 2–12.
Three-phase transformer terminal marking.

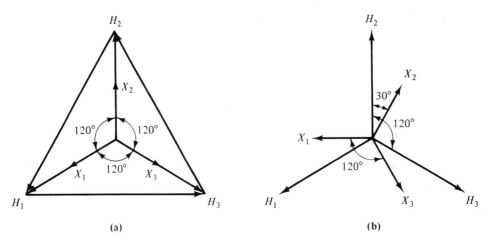

FIGURE 2–13.
*Phasor relationship of high and low side voltages: (a) delta-delta or
wye-wye connection; (b) delta-wye or wye-delta connection.*

- *Cooling:* The type of cooling determines the method of meaium used
  to dissipate heat generated in the transformer. Transformer kVA rating
  is specified based upon the temperature rise allowed for a given transformer.

- *Insulation class:* The insulation class of a transformer is based upon
  the nominal voltage levels at which the system voltages and currents
  are transformed. For example, the American National Standards Institute (ANSI) standard C57.12 secondary and primary substation voltage ratings are listed in Table 2–1 for the various insulation-class levels.

- *Impedance level:* The impedance of a transformer can be expressed as
  an impedance drop expressed in percent. This is equal to impedance-
  drop voltage expressed as a percentage of rated terminal voltage. For
  most power transformers, the impedance can be considered equal to
  the reactance since the resistance component is very small. The National Electrical Manufacturers Association (NEMA) has standardized the impedance values for transformers, which are shown in Table
  2–2.

- *Short-circuit conditions:* The ANSI standard C57.12 defines the short-
  circuit withstand capability of a transformer as the ability to withstand
  without injury short-circuits on any external terminals, with rated line
  voltages maintained on all terminals intended for connection to sources

of power. The duration and values of the short-circuit are limited by ANSI as follows:

Symmetrical Current	Time in Seconds
25 rated current	2
20 rated current	3
16.6 rated current	4
14.3 or less rated current	5

- *Voltage taps:* Many power transformers for industrial applications are equipped with voltage ratio tap changers. The tap-changer is used to maintain a constant secondary voltage with variable primary voltage or to control the secondary voltage with a fixed primary voltage. Usually, most transformers will have two 5 percent taps or four 2½ percent taps on the high-voltage side for adjustment to maintain constant secondary voltage.

- *Sound level:* All transformers hum and create noise when they are energized. This noise is generated by vibrations in the laminated core, and the noise frequency is double the fundamental frequency. The noise level of transformers should be considered during installation in order not to exceed Occupational Safety and Health Administration (OSHA) regulations. Typical ratings for distribution transformers are listed as follows:

OIL-IMMERSED DISTRIBUTION TRANSFER CLASS OA, OW, AND FOW (FROM NEMA TRI)

kVA (15k and below)	Average Sound Level (dB)
0–9	40
10–50	48
51–100	51
101–300	55
301–500	56

- *Basic impulse level (BIL):* A basic impulse insulation level (BIL) is the crest value of the impulse voltage that the transformer is required to withstand without failure. The transformer BIL impluse duration is 1.2×50 microseconds (μs). That is, the impulse reaches its peak value in 1.2 μs and then decays to 50 percent of its peak value in 50 μs. In addition to full BIL value, transformers are tested for chopped-wave withstand (115% of BIL) and front-of-the-wave withstand (160% of

BIL). These tests are intended to simulate conditions that can occur when transformers are subjected to lightning surges.

2-3 CABLES

The generation, transmission, and distribution of power involves electrical facilities, apparatus, and components to carry the electrical energy from its generating site to where it is utilized. An important part of this power system is the medium-voltage cable system that is used exclusively to carry power from

TABLE 2−1.
TRANSFORMER THREE-PHASE STANDARD VOLTAGE
RATINGS

Secondary Substation	
High-Side Voltage	Low-Side Voltage
15-kV-class insulation	600-V-class insulation
13,800	600
13,200	480
12,000	480Y/277
7,200	240
6,900	208Y/120
5-kV-class insulation	
4,800	
4,160	
2,400	

Primary Substations		
69-kV-class insulation	15-kV-class insulation	5-kV-class insulation
67,000	14,400	4,800
	13,800	4,360
46-kV-class insulation	13,200	4,160
43,800	13,090	2,520
	12,600	2,400
	12,470	
34.5-kV-class insulation	12,000	
34,400	8,720	
26,400	8,320	
	7,560	
	7,200	
25-kV-class insulation	6,900	
22,900	5,040	

the main substation to secondary substations at load centers. Low-voltage cable is used to distribute power from the load centers in conduits and ducts, even though other methods such as cable trays, direct burial for outdoor applications, and aerial cable are used. Electrical, mechanical, and environmental considerations are the main factors in selecting and applying cable systems for distribution and utilization of electrical power. The splices and terminations of medium-voltage cables or connections of different type of cables (such as aluminum and copper) require careful consideration and evaluation during installation, as well as throughout their service life. Proper installation and preventive maintenance of cable systems will assure continued electrical power service.

CABLE CONSTRUCTION AND CLASSIFICATION

It is difficult to select and apply cables to power systems without some knowledge of the cable insulation system and of cable components. Therefore, it is important to review some basic considerations and fundamentals of cables for their application to power systems. The following materials are presently used for cables.

COPPER CONDUCTOR
The copper material used in the manufacture of cable is pure electrolytic copper, which has 100 percent conductivity. This means that a wire 1 foot (ft) long and 1 circular mil (1/1,000 of inch) in cross sectional area has a resistance of 10.371 ohms (Ω) at 20°C. Tinning of copper is also required for many rubber and rubberlike insulation compounds to prevent corrosion of copper due to the sulfur that is used in the vulcanizing process.

TABLE 2–2.
NEMA STANDARD IMPEDANCE VALUES FOR TRANSFORMERS

| High-Voltage Ratings (kV) | Transformers 500 kV and Above | |
	Low Voltage Rated at 2,400 V or Higher (%)	Low Voltage Rated at 480 or 208 V (%)
2.4 to 22.9	5.5	5.75
Up to 34.4	6.0	6.25
Up to 69	7.0	6.75
Transformers below 500 kVA		
112.5 kVA through 225 kVA: not less than 2%		
300 kVA through 500 kVA: not less than 4.5%		

ALUMINUM CONDUCTOR

Aluminum conductors are made from 99.9 percent pure aluminum which has a conductivity of 61 percent. Normally, three-fourths aluminum is used for construction of aluminum conductors. Three-fourths hard drawn aluminum has a strength of 17,000 to 22,000 psi. Some of the disadvantages of aluminum are low conductivity, high resistance of aluminum oxide, which forms very rapidly when aluminum is exposed to air, cold flow characteristics, and galvanic action when connected to dissimilar materials.

Types of Conductors

The following types of conductors are in use in power distribution systems.

- *Solid conductors:* Normally, solid conductors are available up to size 6 American wire gauge (AWG). However, they can be made available up to size 4/0 AWG.
- *Stranded conductor:* Most systems use concentric stranding for the applications discussed here.

OVERHEAD CABLE

The strandings available for this application are type AA and A confined to bare conductors.

INDUSTRIAL-TYPE CABLE

The following types of strandings are used in this application.

- *Class B:* This class of stranding is used exclusively for industrial cables for 600-V, 5-kV, and 15-kV power systems. The cable usually consists of 19 or 26 strands.
- *Classes C and D:* These classes are used where a more flexible cable is required. Class C uses 37 strands and class D uses 61 strands for cable construction.
- *Classes G and H:* These classes are used to provide more flexible cable than class D. Classes G and H are also known by rope or bunch stranding. Class G uses 133 strands and class H uses 259 strands for cable construction. Examples of cables in these classes are welding and portable wire for special apparatus or large cables.

UTILITY-TYPE CABLE

Cables used for utility systems are of somewhat specialized construction. Some of these are as follows:

- *Compact strand (compact round):* This type of construction allows for smaller diameter and less weight than solid conductor.

- *Annular:* This construction uses a hollow space or rope core in the center of the cable.
- *Segmental:* Consists of four segments stranded together and operated in parallel.
- *Concentric cable:* Consists of an inner and outer conductor with equivalent cross sections, which are separated by insulation.
- *Sector.* A multiconductor cable in which the conductor is shaped like a sector in a circle.

Conductor Arrangement

Conductors may be arranged in various ways to form a cable. The common arrangements used in power system applications are the following:

- *Single-conductor cable:* A single conductor of either shielded or nonshielded construction.
- *Three-conductor cable:* Three single conductors bound together with a nonmetalic tape. Three-conductor cables may also be bound together by interlocking galvanized steel, aluminum, or bronze tape. This type of cable is known as interlocked armor cable. Three-conductor cables may come with ground wires, which are used for system ground or equipment ground. Ground wires are usually located in the interstices of the three-conductor cable. Three-conductor cable can be either shielded or nonshielded.

Cable Types

Power cables are classified with respect to insulation as follows:

- *Laminated type:* This type of cable uses paper, varnished cambric, or other types of tape insulation material.
- *Extruded type:* This type of cable uses rubber and rubberlike compounds for the insulation system.

Insulations

Cables are classified according to their insulation system as follows:

- Paper
- Varnished cambric
- Asbestos
- Rubber and rubberlike compounds
- Mineral-insulated cables

Each of these materials has unique characteristics that renders it suitable for a given application.

PAPER INSULATION

Paper can be wound onto a conductor in successive layers to achieve a required dielectric strength, and this insulation is generally used for cables operating at 10,000 V and higher. Paper can be impregnated in different ways, and, accordingly, cables so insulated can be subdivided into solid and oil-filled types.

- *Solid paper:* Insulated cables are built up of layers of paper tape wound onto the conductor and impregnated with viscous oil over which is applied a tight-fitting, extended lead sheath. The three-conductor cables are of either belted or shielded construction.

  Belted construction: Consists of three separately insulated conductor cables wrapped together with another layer of impregnated paper or belt, before the sheath is applied.

  Shielded construction: Each conductor is individually insulated and covered with a thin metallic nonmagnetic shielding tape; the three conductors are then cabled together, wrapped with metallic binder tape, and sheathed with lead. The purpose of the metallic shielding tape around each conductor is to control electrostatic stress, reduce corona formation, decrease thermal resistance, minimize circulating currents, and limit power loss under normal operating conditions. Shielding tape of only 3 mils thickness is used in cable construction.

- *Oil-filled cables:* Oil-filled paper-insulated cables are available in single- or three-conductor cables. Single-conductor oil-filled cable consists of a concentric stranded conductor built around an open helical spring core, which serves as a channel for the flow of low-viscosity oil. This cable is insulated and sheathed in the same manner as the solid cable. Three-conductor oil-filled cables are all of shielded design and have three oil channels composed of helical springs that extend through the cable in the space normally occupied by filler material.

VARNISHED CAMBRIC

A thin plain cotton or linen fabric of fine, close weave that is applied as tape; it has a high dielectric strength, low dielectric losses, excellent resistance, good flexibility, good mechanical strength, and fair resistance to moisture. It can be used outdoors aboveground and is always covered with an impervious jacket, such as flamenol. Underground installations using this type of cable require a lead sheath. it has a maximum operating temperature of 85°C at 5 kV and below 77°C at 15 kV. The maximum short-circuit temperature is 200°C for this cable.

ASBESTOS
Asbestos-insulated wire and cable have their principal usefulness in locations where the ambient temperature is high (over 50° or 60°C). Their use is imperative in ambients over 85°C since this is the maximum safe operating temperature of most commonly used insulating materials, except silicone insulation.

RUBBER AND RUBBERLIKE COMPOUNDS
This type of cable can be classified as follows:

- National Electrical Code (NEC) compounds
- Thermoplastics
- Thermosettings

The rubber and rubberlike insulated cables enjoy their popularity owing to moisture resistance, ease of handling, ease of splicing, and extreme flexibility. The thermoplastics soften when they are reheated, whereas thermosetting-type cables have very little tendency to soften upon reheating after vulcanization. The earlier oil-based natural rubber insulating compounds had many serious disadvantages. The natural rubber compounds have been replaced by synthetic materials, which have better electrical and mechanical characteristics. The following synthetic rubber compounds are in use today:

- *Polyvinyl chloride (PVC), a thermoplastic compound:* It is flexible, has good electrical properties and requires no external jacket. Cables using this insulation are rated up to 600 V; maximum operating temperature is 60°C for power applications; maximum short-circuit rating temperature is 150°C. NEC designation is T, TW. It is available in several colors and is mainly used as low-voltage cable systems.

- *Polyethylene, a thermoplastic compound:* It melts at very low temperatures (i.e., 110°C). It is also severely affected by corona. It has a high coefficient of thermal expansion. However, it has excellent electrical and moisture-resistance properties. It has a low cost. Its maximum operating temperature is 75°C and maximum short-circuit temperature is 150°C. It is used in low- and medium-voltage applications.

- *Buna, a thermosetting compound:* It combines the most desirable properties of low-voltage insulation. It has the advantages of heat and moisture resistance, excellent aging qualities, and good electrical characteristics. However, it lacks resistance to ozone. NEC designation is RHW. Its maximum operating temperature is 75°C and short-circuit temperature is 200°C.

- *Butyl, a thermosetting compound:* It has high resistance to moisture, heat, and ozone. NEC designation is RHH. It has a maximum operating temperature of 90°C and short-circuit temperature of 200°C.

- *Silicone rubber, a thermosetting compound:* It is extremely resistant to flame, ozone, and corona. It has a maximum operating temperature of 125°C and a maximum short-circuit temperature of 250°C. It has poor mechanical strength.

- *Crossed-linked polyethylene, a thermosetting compound:* It has excellent electrical properties and high resistance to moisture and chemical contaminants. It is severely affected by corona and has a low melting temperature of 90°C. Its short-circuit temperature is 250°C. It can be applied on up to 35 kV distribution systems.

MINERAL-INSULATED CABLES (MI)

The design of mineral-insulated cable differs very widely from conventional types of cable. Basically, it consists of a single- or multiple-conductor insulated cable with magnesium oxide and sheathed with copper tubing. National Electrical Code operating temperture designation for this cable is 85°C. However, it can be used up to 250°C operating temperature.

SHIELDING AND SEMICONDUCTING TAPE

Power cables at voltages above 600 V usually have shielding and semiconducting tape.

Shielding

Shielding is accomplished by wrapping a thin (0.005 inch) copper tape spirally around the insulation to form a continuous shield along the entire length of the cable. This tape may or may not be perforated to reduce losses and is held to ground potential by suitable grounding.

Shielding is necessary on medium- and high-voltage cables to:

- Prevent damage from corona.
- Confine dielectric field to the inside of cables or conductor insulation.
- Give symmetrical stress.
- Reduce induced voltages.
- Provide increased safety to human life.

The shield must be grounded at one end and preferably at more than one point. The usual practice is to ground the shield at each termination and splice. Shielding is discussed in more detail under "Cable Selection and Application."

Semiconducting Tape

Except on 600-V rubber and varnished cambric cables, semiconducting tape is used to separate the conductor from the rubber insulation to prevent possible damage of the insulation from corona and ionization. The solid line in Figure 2–14 shows how voltage stress may develop in the air spaces between conductor strands and insulation, thereby causing the ionization of air and breakdown of cable insulation. The application of semiconducting tape smoothes the voltage stress, as shown by the dashed lines, and keeps such voltage stress constant and to a minimum.

FINISHES

A wide variety of finishes are used; they are referred to as *jackets, sheaths, armors,* and *braids.* These coverings are required primarily because of the physical or chemical characteristics of the particular insulation involved and the required mechanical protection. Finishes can be divided into two categories, (1) metallic finishes, and (2) nonmetallic finishes.

Metallic Finishes

Metallic armor should be applied where a high degree of mechanical protection is required along with protection from rodents, termites, and the like. All metallic sheaths are subject to electrolytic damage. Metallic finishes are subdivided into the following:

- *Lead sheaths:* One of the earliest types of metallic sheaths still in use.
- *Flat-band armor:* Consists of jute bedding, two helical tape wraps, and a protective jute covering over the tapes. The tape may be either galvanized or plain steel.

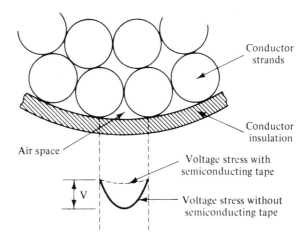

FIGURE 2–14.
Distribution of voltage stress within a cable.

- *Interlocked armor:* Consists of galvanized steel, aluminum, or bronze strip (0.750 in. wide and 0.020 to 0.030 in. thick) over the cable in such a way as to provide excellent protection.

- *Aluminum-sheathed cable:* A recently introduced cable that offers advantages such as light weight, resistance to fatigue, good corrosion resistance, and positive moisture barrier.

- *Wire armor:* Available in two types, round and basket-weave or braided wire.

  Round wire armor offers extremely strong cable and has high tensile strength for vertical applications.

  Braided or basket-weave wire armor consists of a braid of metal wire woven directly over the cable as an outer covering where additional mechanical strength is required.

Nonmetallic Finishes

- *PVC:* Usually used where non-metallic finishes are required. This covering (i.e., finish) offers excellent moisture-resistance characteristics, but does not provide mechanical protection.

- *Braids:* Generally, present-day trends are away from the use of non-metallic braid coverings. Braids may be of the following types:

  Heat- and moisture-resistant cotton braid.

  Flame-resistant cotton braid.

  Asbestos braid.

CABLE CHARACTERISTICS

The electrical characteristics of cables are concerned with the electrical constants most commonly required for power system calculations. These electrical constants, such as positive sequence impedance (Z_1), negative sequence impedance (Z_2), and zero sequence (Z_0), are used in the application of symmetrical components for calculations of short-circuit currents, unbalanced voltages, and their phase relationships among sheaths and conductors, which are important in the calculation of reactance, capacitance, insulation resistance, and dielectric loss. The cable geometry for single- and three-conductor cable is shown in Figure 2–15. The cable ratings provide the basic information regarding its application and use. A basic knowledge of cable ratings is essential for proper selection and application of cables. Exceeding cable ratings or their misapplication can be hazardous to property and personnel, as well as to successful operation of the plant or facility.

Cable Properties

The two properties of cables, as mentioned, are geometry of cables and electrical constants. A general rule is that regardless of the complexity of mutual inductive relations between component parts of individual phases, the method of symmetrical components can be applied rigorously whenever there is symmetry among phases. All three conductor cables satisfy this condition by the nature of their construction; single conductor cable may or may not. However, the error is very small when they are treated similarly as three-conductor cables. The space relationship among sheaths and conductors in a cable circuit is a major factor in determining reactance, capacitance, charging current, insulation resistance, dielectric loss, and thermal resistance. The physical characteristics of cables can be determined from the geometry of cables, which is described next.

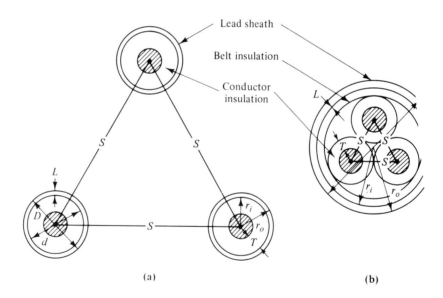

D = cable diameter d = conductor diameter
L = sheath thickness T = conductor insulation thickness
r_i = sheath inside radius r_o = sheath outside radius
S = distance between cables

FIGURE 2–15.
Cable geometry: (a) single-conductor cable; (b) three-conductor cable.

GEOMETRIC MEAN RADIUS (GMR)

This factor is a property usually applied to the conductor alone, and depends on the material and stranding used in its construction. One component of conductor reactance is normally calculated by evaluating the integrated flux linkages both inside and outside the conductor within an overall 12-in. radius. Consider a solid conductor that has some of the flux lines lying within the conductor and contributing to the total flux linkages, even though they link only a portion of the total conductor current. Now consider a tubular conductor having an infinitely thin wall substituted for the solid conductor; it has flux that would necessarily lie external to the tube. Therefore, a theoretical tubular conductor, to be inductively equivalent to a solid conductor, must have a smaller radius so that the flux linkages present inside the solid conductor, but absent within the tube, will be replaced by additional linkages between the tube surface and the limiting cylinder of 12-in. radius. A solid copper conductor of radius $d/2$ is equivalent to a tubular conductor of radius $0.779\, d/2$. This equivalent radius is called the geometric mean radius (GMR) of the actual conductor. This quantity can be used in reactance calculations without further reference to the shape or makeup of the conductor. The factor by which actual radius must be multiplied to obtain GMR varies with stranding and hollow-core construction.

GEOMETRIC MEAN DISTANCE (GMD)

Spacing among conductors or between conductors and sheaths is important in determining total circuit reactance. The total flux linkage surrounding a conductor can be divided into two components, one extending inward from the cylinder of 12-in. radius and the other extending outward from this cylinder to the current return path beyond which there are no net flux linkages.

The flux linkages per unit conductor current between the 12-in. cylinder and the return path are functions of the separation of the conductor and its return path. Geometric mean distance is therefore a term that can be used in the expression for the external flux-linkages, not only in the simple case of two adjacent conductors, where it is equal to the distance between conductor centers, but also in the more complex case where two circuits, each composed of several conductors, are separated by an equivalent GMD.

The positive or negative sequence reactance of a three-phase circuit depends on separation among phase conductors. If the conductors are equilaterally spaced, the distance from one conductor center to another is equal to the GMD among conductors for that circuit. The GMD for three-conductor cable is $GMD_{3c} = S$ for an equilateral circuit where S is the distance between each conductor. If the conductors are arranged other than equilaterally as shown in Figure 2–16, but transposed along their length to produce a balanced circuit, the equivalent separation may be calculated by deriving the geometric mean distance from the cube root of three distance products. This is expressed as follows:

$$GMD_{3c} = 3\sqrt{S_{ab}S_{bc}S_{ca}}$$

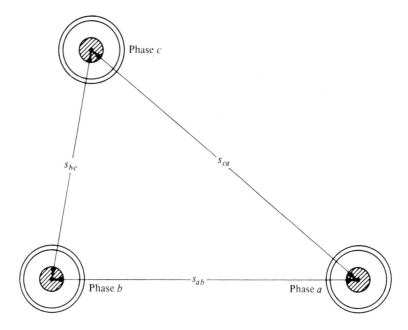

FIGURE 2–16.
Single-conductor cable unsymmetrically spaced but perfectly transposed.

The component of circuit reactance caused by flux outside a 12-in. radius
is widely identified as the *reactance spacing factor* (X_d) and can be calculated
directly from GMD.

$$X_d = 0.2794 \, \frac{f}{60} \, \log_{10} \frac{\text{GMD}_{3c}}{12} \; \Omega/\text{phase mile}$$

When equivalent separation is less than 12 in., as can occur in cable circuits, the
reactance spacing factor is negative so as to subtract from the component of
conductor reactance due to flux out to a 12-in. radius.

The zero-sequence reactance of a three-phase circuit may depend on
spacing among conductors and sheath.

GEOMETRIC FACTOR

The relation in space between the cylinders formed by the sheath internal
surface and conductor external surface in a single-conductor lead-sheath cable
can be expressed as a geometric factor. The factor is applicable to the calculation of cable characteristics such as capacitance, charging current, dielectric

loss, leakage current, and heat transfer. The mathematical expression for geometric factor G in a single-conductor cable is

$$G = 2.303 \log_{10} \frac{2r_i}{d}$$

where r_i = inside radius of sheath
d = outside diameter of conductor

ELECTRICAL CONSTANTS

The following electrical constants are used in the application of power cables.

Positive- and Negative-Sequence Resistance

The resistance of a conductor to positive- and negative-sequence currents is affected by the following factors.

- *Skin effect:* This effect is due to unequal distribution of alternating current flowing in a conductor because of the tendency of the current to flow more on the outside than inside strands of the conductor. This results in a higher resistance to alternating current than direct current. Usually this effect can be neglected in smaller conductors.
- *Proximity effect:* This effect is due to alternating magnetic flux produced by circulating current in a conductor caused by the current flowing in a neighboring conductor. This effect increases the resistance of a conductor. It can become pronounced where cables are installed parallel to metal beams, plates, walls, and the like.
- *Sheath currents:* The alternating current flowing in a sheathed single conductor induces voltage in the sheath. Since the sheath is bonded and grounded at both ends, currents flow longitudinally causing I^2R losses. One way to account for these losses is to increase the resistance of the conductor.

Positive- and Negative-Sequence Reactance

The reactance of a single lead-sheath conductor to positive- and negative-sequence current can be calculated by taking into account the effect of sheath currents. It can be expressed mathematically by the following:

$$X_1 = X_2 = X_a + X_d - X_s \ \Omega/\text{mile/phase}$$

where X_1 = positive-sequence reactance
X_2 = negative-sequence reactance
X_a = self-reactance of conductor at 1-ft radius

X_d = reactance of conductor beyond 1-ft radius
X_s = equivalent reactance value due to sheath currents

For three-phase conductors, X_s can be neglected and the positive and negative reactances are $X_1 = X_2 = X_a + X_d$ Ω/mile/phase.

Zero-Sequence Resistance and Reactance

When zero-sequence currents flow in the three-phase system, the return path is usually either through the earth ground, sheath, ground wire, or a combination of these paths. In actual installation, the following combination of paths should be considered.

- All currents in the ground, none in sheath.
- All currents in the sheath, none in ground.
- All currents in sheath and ground.

When low-voltage cables are installed in magnetic ducts, the zero-sequence resistance and reactance are influenced by the magnetic material surrounding the conductor. No methods have been developed yet to accurately calculate the zero-sequence impedance. However, test data are available to give the required zero-sequence impedance data in standard reference handbooks on transmission and distribution of electrical power for various sizes of cables.

Shunt Capacitance Reactance

The positive-, negative-, and zero-sequence shunt capacitive reactances of cable are the same and can be expressed mathematically as follows:

$$C_1 = C_2 = C_0 = \frac{0.0892K}{G} \text{ microfarads } (\mu F)/\text{phase/mile}$$

or

$$X_1' = X_2' = X_0' = \frac{1.79G}{f \times K} \text{ megohms } (M\Omega)/\text{phase/mile}$$

where K = dielectric constant
X_1', X_2', X_0' = positive-, negative-, and zero-sequence reactances.
C_1, C_2, C_0 = positive-, negative-, and zero-sequence capacitive reactances
G = conductance of the cable
f = frequency of the power system

The charging current can be calculated by the following fomula:

$$I_1' = I_2' = \frac{0.97 f \cdot K \cdot kV}{1000 G} \text{ A/phase/mile}$$

$$I_0 = \frac{0.323 f \cdot K \cdot kV}{1{,}000 G_0} \text{ A/phase/mile}$$

where I_1', I_2', I_0' are positive-, negative-, and zero-sequence charging currents.

Insulation Resistance

The insulation resistance of the cable is very difficult to calculate because of varying insulation properties. However, a generalized formula can be expressed in terms of the power factor of the insulation system. For single-conductor cable,

$$r_1' = r_2' = r_0' = \frac{1.79 G' 10^6}{f \cdot K \cdot \cos \theta} \text{ } \Omega/\text{phase/mile}$$

and for three-conductor belted cable,

$$r_1' = r_2' = \frac{0.597 G' 10^6}{f \cdot K \cdot \cos \theta} \text{ } \Omega/\text{phase/mile}$$

where r_1', r_2', r_0' = positive-, negative-, and zero-sequence shunt
                          resistances
       G' = geometric factor
       K = dielectric constant
       $\cos \theta$ = insulation power factor per unit

CABLE RATINGS

A basic knowledge of cable ratings is very important in order to select and apply cables for distribution and utilization of power. The following brief description of cable ratings will provide the basis for selecting and applying cables.

Continuous Current-Carrying Rating

The current-carrying capacity of cable is affected by several factors:

- Maximum allowable temperature.
- Total watt loss ($I^2 R_c$) of the cable.
- Ability to dissipate heat.
- Ambient temperature.

The maximum conductor temperature is determined by the maximum temperature the insulation system can stand for extended periods of time without damage. The maximum temperature in turn can be affected by the ability to dissipate heat and the ambient temperature of the medium in which the cable is installed to operate. The sum of ambient temperature and temperature rise in the insulation system should not exceed the total allowable temperature of the conductor for safe operation. Aluminum conductors can be expressed in terms of copper conductors for purposes of current-carrying capacity. The conversion factors to convert the current capacity of the same size aluminum conductor as copper can be expressed in terms of the resistance ratio of copper to aluminum, that is, $\sqrt{R_{\mathrm{Cu}}/R_{\mathrm{Al}}}$, where R_{Cu} and R_{Al} are, respectively, the resistance of copper and aluminum conductors at rated temperature. The effect of temperature on current rating is shown in Figure 2–17. As the temperature of the conductor goes up, so does its resistance. The total loss of the cable is a function of the effective resistance of the conductor at maximum allowable temperature.

Emergency Current-Carrying Rating

The service life of cable is based upon its normal loading limits and normal operating temperature. The normal life expectancy of a cable insulation system

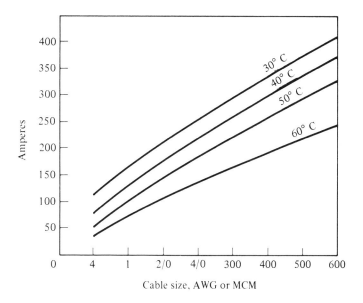

FIGURE 2–17.

Effect of ambient temperature on current rating. (G.E. Cable Data Book)

is approximately 30 years. However, if the cable system is operated at 5° to 10° above its temperature rating, it is to be expected that the cable life expectancy will be halved and its average rate of failure doubled. Another disadvantage in operating cables over their temperature rating is that copper loss is directly proportional to the square of current and resistance. Furthermore, because of increased resistance and current, the voltage drop may be excessive and may jeopardize equipment and service continuity. Any program to operate the cables beyond the limit of their current and temperature ratings must be judiciously undertaken. To calculate the emergency rating of cables, the following formula may be used:

$$j_o = j_c \sqrt{\frac{(t_o - t_a)}{(t_c - t_a)} \times \frac{R_c}{R_o}}$$

where j_o = emergency overload current
j_c = continuous current
t_o = emergency overload temperature
t_a = ambient temperature
t_c = maximum operating temperature
R_c = conductor resistance at maximum operating temperature
R_o = conductor resistance at emergency overload temperature

Overloading should be less than 100 hours/year. Rubber-insulated cables may be operated at overloading temperature in accordance with Table 2–3.

Voltage Rating

The voltage ratings of cables are specified as the line-to-line voltage that they can withstand. However, the insulation thickness is based upon line-to-ground

TABLE 2–3.
EMERGENCY OVERLOAD TEMPERATURE OF RUBBER-INSULATED CABLES

Voltage Rating	Type of Cable	Maximum Operating Temperature (°C)	Emergency Overloading Temperature (°C)
600 V	PVC	60	75
	Butyl	90	125
	Silicone	125	150
1-5 kV	Polyethylene	75	85
	PVC	75	85
	Butyl	90	125
	Silicone	125	150
15 kV	Butyl	85	105
	Silicone	125	150

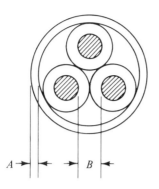

In this type of construction each conductor insulation is based on one-half line-to-line voltage. The belt insulation is based upon the difference of line-to-ground voltage minus one-half the line-to-line voltage. The overall thickness of insulation is the sum of the belt and conductor thickness. Insulation required at A and B is:

$$A = \frac{13.8 \text{ kV}}{1.73} - \frac{13.8 \text{ kV}}{2} = 2.0 \text{ kV}$$

$$B = \frac{13.8}{2} = 6.7 \text{ kV}$$

The insulation thickness required for the 13.8 kV grounded system is $A + B = (2.0 + 6.7) \text{ kV} = 8.7 \text{ kV}$

FIGURE 2–18.
Insulation thickness for three-phase belted cable.

voltage. To specify the system voltage for procurement and installation of cables is not sufficient. It is necessary to specify also the type of system that the cable will use. Assume a cable application on a grounded 15-kV system, for which the insulation will be based upon line-to-ground voltage, that is, 15/1.73 = 8.66 kV. Whereas on a 15-kV ungrounded system, the insulation thickness will be based on 15 kV since that is the voltage imposed on unfaulted conductors. The basis for voltage thickness for 15-kV belted cable operating at 13.8-kV grounded system is illustrated in Figure 2–18.

Short-Circuit Rating

All cable systems have thermal limitations, which are specified in terms of short-circuit withstand temperatures and current ratings. Under a short-circuit condition, the temperature of the conductor rises very rapidly. If the conductor is not sized to withstand the available short-circuit current, it will melt, resulting in cable failure. Because of the insulation sheath surrounding the conductor and its characteristics, it will cool off very slowly after the fault has been removed. The temperatures shown in Table 2–3 should not be exceeded per standards of the Insulated Cable Engineering Association (ICEA) for more than 10 second (s). Cable manufacturers publish current-withstand ratings for all sizes of conductors. The National Electrical Code (NEC) requires that systems should be designed to have full withstand capability. Every cable installation should be checked for the short-circuit withstand rating; otherwise, severe damage or complete failure may result. Failure may be accompanied by fire and smoke, thus resulting in danger to personnel and property. Also, because of thermal expansion due to intense heat under short-circuit conditions, the cable may be permanently damaged if not properly selected for this purpose.

CABLE SELECTION AND APPLICATION

It is essential to know cable construction, characteristics, and ratings to understand problems related to cable systems. However, to properly select a cable system and assure its satisfactory operation, additional knowledge is required. This knowledge may consist of service conditions, type of load served, mode of operation and maintenance, and the like. The key to the successful operation of a cable system is to select the most suitable cable for the application, make a proper installation, and perform the required maintenance. In this section, discussion is based on the proper selection and application of a cable system for power distribution and utilization. Cable selection can be based upon the following five factors:

- Type of cable installation.
- Type of cable construction.
- Type of cable operation.
- Cable size.
- Shielding requirements.

Cable Installation

Cables can be used for outdoor or indoor installations depending upon the distribution system and the load served. Installation of a cable system is more fully discussed in Chapter 3, Section 3–4.

Cable Construction

Selection and application of cable involves the type of cable construction needed for a particular installation. Cable construction involves conductors, cable arrangement, and insulation and finish covering.

CONDUCTORS
Conductor materials such as copper and aluminum should be given consideration with regard to workmanship, environmental conditions, and maintenance. The requirements for aluminum conductors with regard to these factors are more critical than for copper conductors. Cable conductors should be selected based upon the class of stranding required for a particular installation.

CABLE ARRANGEMENT
Conductors can be arranged to form single-conductor or three-conductor cable.

There are certain advantages and disadvantages to both types of arrangements. Single conductors are easier to install, easier to splice, and allow the formation of multiple-cable circuits. On the other hand, they have higher reactance than three-conductor cable. Shielded single conductors carry high shield currents, and consideration must be given to preventing overheating of the cable. Single-conductor cables are subject to considerable movement owing to the mechanical stresses produced by the short-circuit currents or high inrush currents. Three-conductor cable with an overall jacket has the lowest reactance, and voltage stress distribution is balanced owing to equivalent spacing between conductors.

The availability of ground wire in three-conductor cable or a separate ground wire with single-conductor cable is an important consideration. Since the ground conductor in three-conductor cable construction provides the lowest impedance path, it offers a good system ground. Similarly, a separate ground in the same conduit as the power conductors provides a better ground return path than a ground path via the equipment or building steel. The selection and application of a cable system should be based on proper selection of the type of cable arrangement required for the purpose.

INSULATION AND FINISH COVERING
The selection of cable insulation and finish covering is normally based on the type of installation, ambient operating temperature, service conditions, type of load served, and other criteria as applicable. In many installations unusual conditions may be prevalent, such as corrosive atmosphere, high ambient temperature, insect and rodent hazard, presence of oil and solvents, presence of ozone, and extreme cold. In certain applications, two or more of these unusual conditions may be present, in which case the selection of suitable cables becomes much more difficult.

Cable Operation

The current capacity that the cable needs to carry is determined by the load it serves. The National Electrical Code is very specific in terms of sizing conductors for systems operating below 600 V. The current-carrying ability of cable is based upon an operating ambient temperature. When cables are installed in multiple duct banks, it is essential to derate the cable current capacity in order not to exceed its thermal rating. In cases where cables may be load cycled, the current-carrying capacity may be calculated by the following formula:

$$I_{eq} = \frac{EI^2t}{T}$$

where I_{eq} = equivalent current-carrying capacity
I = constant current for a particular time period
t = time period of constant current
T = total time of duty cycle

The equivalent current-carrying capacity should be used for selecting the conductor size for thermal withstand.

Cable Size

The selection of cable size is based upon the following factors:

- Current-carrying capacity.
- Voltage regulation.
- Short-circuit rating.

These factors should be evaluated before selecting a cable size. In many instances voltage regulation and short-circuit rating factors are overlooked. This oversight can result in danger to property and personnel, as well as destruction of the cable itself.

CURRENT-CARRYING CAPACITY

The current-carrying capacity of a cable is based upon its thermal heating. The National Electrical Code (NEC) publishes tables listing the current capacity for various-sized cables. The Insulated Cable Engineering Association (ICEA), publishes current ratings for various types of insulations and installation conditions. If it is required to carry current capacity larger than 500 MCM, it is normal practice to parallel two smaller conductors. The current rating of cable is based upon certain spacing to permit thermal dissipation. If this spacing is smaller where the cable is to be installed, then derating of cable is required.

VOLTAGE REGULATION

In properly designed electrical power systems, voltage regulation is usually not a problem. Voltage drops for excessively long runs at low voltage should be checked to ensure proper load voltage. In rotating loads, checks should be made both on steady-state voltage regulation and during starting. The NEC specifies a 5 percent limit of voltage drop for electrical power distribution systems.

SHORT-CIRCUIT RATING

The cable size selected should be checked for short-circuit withstand capability, which should be based upon the circuit opening time for short-circuit condition. In other words, the cable should hold without any thermal damage to it until such time as the fault can be removed by the switching device, such as a circuit breaker or fuse.

Shielding

In selecting and applying cables at medium voltage, a major consideration involves whether the cable should be shielded or nonshielded. Shielding was briefly discussed previously as to why it is necessary at medium voltages. The conditions under which shielded cable is to be selected and applied need further discussion. The application of shielded cable involves the following considerations:

- Type of insulation system.
- Whether the system neutral is grounded or ungrounded.
- Safety and reliability requirements of the system.

In power systems where there is no shield or metallic covering, the electric field is partly in the air and partly in the insulation system. If the electric field is intense, such as in the case of high and medium voltage, surface discharges will take place and cause ionization of the air particles. The ionization of air causes ozone generation, which can deteriorate certain insulations and finish coverings. In the application of nonshielded cable on ungrounded systems, damage to insulation or jackets can be caused by leakage current if the surface of the cable is moist or covered with soot, grease, dirt, or other conducting film.

In duct-type installations where nonshielded, nonmetallic cable is used, the external electric field may be high enough to pose a safety hazard to personnel working on single cable in multicircuit installations. In cases where portable cables, cable assemblies, or exposed overhead cable installations are used and may be handled by personnel, serious safety hazards may exist if nonshielded cable is used.

Shielding should be considered for nonmetallic cable operating in excess of 2 kV where any of the following conditions exist:

- Damp conduits.
- Connection to aerial wires.
- Transition from a conducting to a nonconducting environment, such as from moist to dry earth.
- Dry soil.
- Dirty environment containing soot, salt, and other contaminants.
- Where safety to personnel is required.
- Where radio interference is expected.

The Insulated Cable Engineers Association has set up voltage limits above which insulation shielding is required for rubber and thermoplastic insulated cables. These values are shown in Table 2–4. The insulation shield must be grounded at least at one end and preferably at two or more points. The cable shield must be grounded also at all terminations, splices, and taps with stress cones. The shield should be operated at ground potential. Multiple grounding will ensure safety and reliability of the cable circuits. The ground

TABLE 2–4.
INSULATION SHIELDING REQUIREMENTS FOR RUBBER AND
THERMOPLASTIC INSULATED CABLES

No.	Cable Type	Single Conductor		Three Conductor	
		Grounded (kV)	Ungrounded (kV)	Grounded (kV)	Ungrounded (kV)
1	Sheathed cable	5	5	5	5
2	Interlocked cable	5	5	5	5
3	Fibrous covered cable	2	2	2	2
4	Non-ozone resistant	2	2	2	2
5	Ozone resistant				
	a) In metallic conduits	5	3	5	5
	b) Ungrounded conduits	3	3	5	5
	c) Aerially on ties	3	3	5	5
	d) Aerially with metal-lic binder	5	5	5	5
	e) Direct buried	3	3	5	5

path from the shield should be of low resistance to keep the shield near ground potential.

2-4   SWITCHGEAR AND CIRCUIT BREAKERS

Switchgear is a commonly used name for metal-enclosed distribution apparatus of modular, cubicle-type construction. Despite this commonly used name, there are technical and physical distinctions between various classes of switchgear assemblies. The American National Standards Institute (ANSI) and National Electrical Manufacturers Association (NEMA) have published standards for electrical equipment. These standards are followed by most manufacturers of electrical switchgear. The ANSI lists switchgear assemblies under three main categories, which are further classified into subcategories as shown in Table 2–5.

MEDIUM-VOLTAGE SWITCHGEAR

Medium-voltage metal-enclosed power switchgear is defined as a switchgear assembly completely enclosed on all sides and top with sheet metal (except for ventilating and inspection openings) containing primary power circuit switching and/or interrupting devices with buses and connections, and may include control and auxiliary devices. The rated voltage and insulation levels for medium-voltage-class metal-enclosed switchgear assemblies are shown in Table 2–6.

Construction Features

Switchgear is a general term used to define switching (and/or interrupting), protective, regulating, and metering devices, including all associated controls, and interconnections, and accessories used for generation, transmission, and distribution of electrical power. As shown in Table 2–5, switchgear equipment

TABLE 2–5.
ANSI CLASSIFICATION OF SWITCHGEAR ASSEMBLIES

Metal-Enclosed Power Switchgear	Metal-Enclosed Bus	Switchboards	
		Control	Power
Metal clad	Nonsegregated	Enclosed and dual duplex	Enclosed
Metal-enclosed interrupter	Segregated	Vertical Panel	Dead front
Station-type cubicle	Isolated phase	Benchboard	Live front
Low-voltage power circuit breaker		Control desk	
		Dual benchboard Duplex benchboard	

TABLE 2–6.
METAL-ENCLOSED SWITCHGEAR ASSEMBLIES VOLTAGE AND INSULATION RATINGS

Switchgear Assembly	Voltage (rms, kV)		Insulation (rms kV)	
	Nominal Rated	Maximum Rated	60-Hz, 1-min Withstand	Basic Impulse Level
Metal-clad switchgear	4.16	4.76	19	60
	7.2	8.25	36	95
	13.8	15.0	36	95
	34.5	38.0	80	150
Metal-enclosed interrupter	4.16	4.76	19	60
	7.2	8.25	26	75
	13.8	15.0	36	95
	14.4	15.5	50	110
	23.0	25.8	60	125
	34.5	38.0	80	150
Station-type cubicle	14.4	15.5	50	110
	34.5	38.0	80	150
	69.0	72.5	160	350

comes in various forms and ratings that can be used to perform particular functions. There are some fundamental differences among the various types of equipment available in the medium-voltage class. These differences are important from a maintenance and operation point of view and are discussed next.

METAL-CLAD SWITCHGEAR

Metal-clad switchgear consists of indoor and outdoor types with power circuit breakers rated from 4.16 to 13.8 kV, 1,200 to 3,000 A, 75 to 1,000 MVA interrupting capacity. Metal-clad switchgear has the following additional features:

- The interrupting and switching device is removable and can be physically moved into disconnect, test, or operating position.
- The primary bus conductors and connections are insulated.
- All live parts are enclosed within grounded metal compartments.
- Automatic shutters close off and prevent exposure of the primary circuit elements when the circuit breaker is removed from operating position.
- The primary and secondary contacts are self-aligning and self-coupling.
- Mechanical interlocks are provided to ensure a proper and safe operation.
- The circuit breaker housing cell door may be used to mount relays, instruments, and wiring. The relays, control devices, and associated wiring are isolated by grounded metal barriers from primary conductors.
- The elements of primary circuits such as circuit-breakers, buses, and potential transformers are completely enclosed and grounded by metal barriers.

METAL-ENCLOSED INTERRUPTER SWITCHGEAR

Metal-enclosed interrupter switchgear consists of indoor and outdoor types with or without power fuses rated from 4.16 to 34.5 kV, to 1,200 A. This switchgear is characterized by the following features:

- The primary buses and connections are uninsulated.
- The disconnecting device is an interrupter switch that may be removable or stationary.
- The interrupter switch is equipped with power fuses that may be removable or stationary.
- This switchgear has instrument transformers, control wiring, and accessory devices.

STATION-TYPE CUBICLE

The station-type cubicle switchgear consists of indoor and outdoor types with power circuit breakers rated from 14.4 to 34.5 kV, 1,200 to 5,000 A, 1,500 to 2,500 MVA interrupting capacity. This switchgear has the following features:

- Power-operated stationary circuit breaker.
- Bare buses having continuous carrying capacity equal to the service required.
- Bare connections having current-carrying capacity equal to that of the power circuit breaker.
- Each phase of primary is segregated and enclosed by metal.
- Three-pole, single-throw, group-operated disconnect switches that are interlocked between power circuit breaker and front door giving access to primary compartment.
- A set of instrument transformers.
- Control wiring, terminal blocks, ground bus, and accessory devices.

Short-Circuit Considerations and Power Circuit Breaker Ratings

To understand the rating basis of power circuit breakers, it is important to understand how the circuit breaker will perform under conditions where the short-circuit current varies with time. The rating structure of a power circuit breaker is complicated because of the opening time of the circuit breaker during a short-circuit condition. The total operating time of the circuit breaker is based on the following:

- Protective relay operation time.
- Circuit breaker operation time.

The protective relay operation time is a function of relay type and its setting. The types of relays and their operating characteristics will be discussed in Chapter 7. The breaker operation time (i.e., mechanical time) consists of the following:

- Circuit breaker trip coil to energize its operating mechanism.
- Circuit breaker contact parting time.
- Circuit breaker to quench the arc in the arc chamber (or in the vacuum bottle in case of vacuum interrupters).

High mechanical stresses are produced instantaneously in the circuit during the interruption of a short circuit. These stresses vary as the square of the current and are greatest at maximum current. The fault current magnitude varies from short-circuit inception to the time when it reaches a steady-state condition. This variation is due to the closing angle of the fault changing motor impedance and the delay in the dc component of the fault current. Consequently, the circuit breaker interrupts the fault current at some time (usually a few cycles) after the short circuit occurred. Therefore, power circuit breaker ratings are established on two bases:

- Momentary rating, that is, circuit breaker ability to close and latch on the maximum short-circuit current available without mechanical damage.
- Interrupting rating, that is, circuit breaker ability to interrupt the flow of fault current without mechanical damage.

The fault current is highly asymmetrical from the time of fault inception to several cycles later. It becomes symmetrical after it reaches steady-state conditions. To understand fully the varying phenomena of short-circuit current, let us briefly review short-circuit definitions and the kinds of current available in a fault.

ROOT-MEAN-SQUARE (EFFECTIVE) VALUE
This is an effective value of alternating current and is usually expressed as $0.707Im$, where Im is the ac peak value. This rms current value is shown in Figure 2–19.

PEAK VALUE (CREST)
This is the maximum value of the ac wave peak.

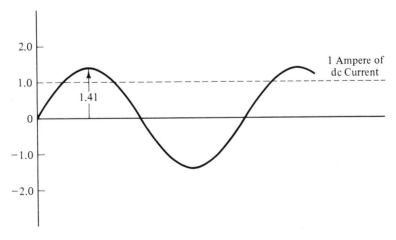

FIGURE 2–19.
Alternating-current and direct-current effective values.

AVERAGE VALUE

The average value of an ac wave is zero because the positive and negative loops have the same area. However, the average value of the positive loop of a symmetrical wave can be expressed in terms of peak value. For sine wave the average value is expressed as $0.636Im$, where Im is the peak value.

INSTANTANEOUS (MOMENTARY) VALUE

It is difficult to manipulate analytically the instantaneous value of alternating wave forms. In general, for short-circuit considerations the instantaneous value (or momentary value) is the peak value of the sine wave occurring at first half-cycle.

SYMMETRICAL CURRENT

A symmetrical current wave is symmetrical about the zero axis of the wave. This is shown in Figure 2–20.

ASYMMETRICAL CURRENT

An asymmetrical current wave is not symmetrical about the zero axis. The axis of symmetry is displaced or offset from the zero axis. This is shown in Figure 2–21. An asymmetrical wave can be partially offset or fully offset. Offset waves are sometimes called displaced waves.

DC COMPONENT

The axis of symmetry of an offset wave resembles a dc current, and symmetrical currents can be readily handled if considered to have an ac and a dc component. Both of these components are theoretical. The dc component is generated within the ac system and has no external source.

Figure 2–22 shows a fully offset asymmetrical current with a steady dc component as its axis of symmetry. The symmetrical component has the zero axis as its axis of symmetry. If the rms or effective value of the symmetrical current is 1, the peak of the symmetrical current is 1.41. This is also the effective

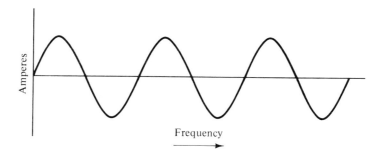

FIGURE 2–20.
Symmetrical current wave.

value of the dc component. We can add these two effective currents together by the square root of the sum of the squares and get the effective or rms value of asymmetrical current.

$$I_{asy} = \sqrt{I^2 dc + I^2 \text{ sym}} = \sqrt{(1.41)^2 + 1^2} = \sqrt{3} = 1.73$$

The rms value of a fully offset asymmetrical current is 1.73 times the symmetrical rms current. It is readily apparent that the peak asymmetrical current is twice the peak symmetrical current: $2 \times 1.41 = 2.82$.

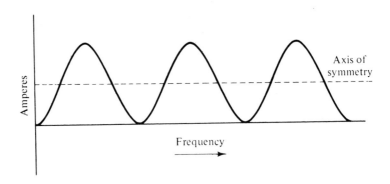

FIGURE 2–21.
Asymmetrical current wave, fully offset.

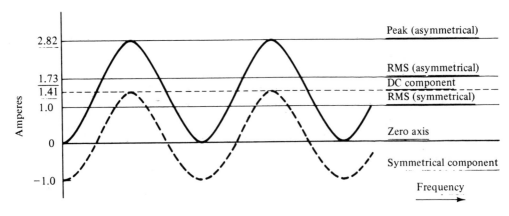

FIGURE 2–22.
Fully offset asymmetrical wave with dc component.

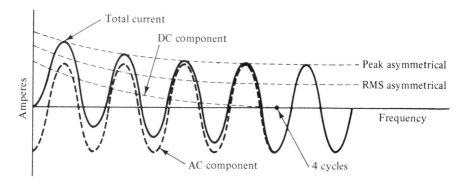

FIGURE 2–23.
DC component and ac component currents.

TOTAL CURRENT

The term total current is used to express the total or sum of the ac and dc components of an asymmetrical current. Total current and total asymmetrical current have the same meaning and may be expressed in peak or rms amperes.

DECAY

Unfortunately, fault currents are neither symmetrical nor fully asymmetrical but somewhere in between. The dc component is usually short-lived and decays after several cycles.

In Figure 2–23 the dc component decays to zero in about four cycles. The rate of decay is called decrement and depends upon the circuit constants. The dc component would never decay in a circuit having reactance but zero resistance and would remain constant forever. In a circuit having resistance but zero reactance, the dc component would decay instantly. These are theoretical conditions; all practical circuits have some resistance and reactance, and the dc component disappears in a few cycles.

CLOSING ANGLE

A short-circuit fault can occur at any point on the voltage wave. So far we have avoided discussing voltage characteristics, but the voltage wave resembles the current wave. The two waves may be in phase or out of phase, and the magnitude and symmetry of the current wave of a short circuit depends on the point on the voltage wave at which the fault occurs. This is known as the closing angle of the fault.

RANDOM CLOSING

In real life, faults occur at any and every point on the voltage wave. In a laboratory, this can be duplicated by closing the circuit at random. This is known as random closing. The following is true of a short circuit having negligible resistance:

- If the fault occurs at zero voltage, the current wave is fully asymmetrical, as shown in Figure 2–24.
- If the fault occurs at maximum voltage, the current wave is completely symmmetrical, as shown in Figure 2–25.

Most natural faults occur somewhere in between these two extremes.

AVAILABLE SHORT-CIRCUIT CURRENT (FIRST HALF-CYCLE CURRENT)
What is the available short-circuit current value of a wave that is neither symmetrical nor asymmetrical? Referring to Figure 2–26, the current wave is symmetrical about four cycles after the dc component becomes zero. We can also determine the total rms asymmetrical current at one, two, or three cycles or at any other time after the short circuit started.

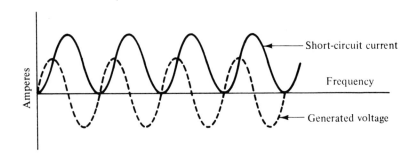

FIGURE 2–24.
Asymmetrical current wave when fault occurs at zero voltage.

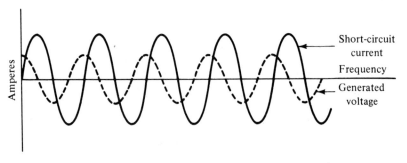

FIGURE 2–25.
Symmetrical current wave when fault occurs at maximum voltage.

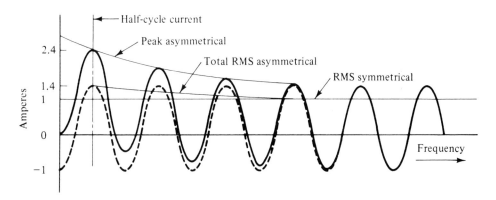

FIGURE 2–26.
First half-cycle current.

The accepted practice is to use the current that is available one half-cycle after the short circuit starts. For a fully offset wave the maximum current does occur at the end of the first half-cycle of time. Because this is the worst case, we should determine the peak and rms currents at this point.

As already mentioned, the rate of decay depends upon the circuit constants. A study of actual circuits of 600 V or less indicates that the proper half-cycle value for rms asymmetrical current is 1.4 times the rms symmetrical current, and the peak instantaneous current is 1.7 times the rms asymmetrical current. Half-cycle available current is $1.7 \times 1.4 \approx 2.4$ rms symmetrical current.

CURRENT LIMITATION

Current-limiting fuses and circuit breakers do not allow the short-circuit current to reach the full available value. They interrupt the circuit in less than one half-cycle before the current builds up to the maximum value. The various times associated with fuses are the following:

- *Melting time:* The time required to melt the fusible link.
- *Arcing time:* The time required for the arc to burn back the fusible link and reduce the current to zero.
- *Total clearing time:* The sum of the melting and arcing times, or the time from fault initiation to extinction.

Figure 2–27 shows the current-limiting action of the fuse.

LET-THROUGH CURRENT

The maximum instantaneous or peak current that passes through the fuse is called the let-through current. This can be expressed in rms amperes, also.

TRIANGULAR WAVE

The rise and fall of the current through a current-limiting fuse resembles an isosceles triangle, and can be assumed to be a triangle without introducing appreciable error. Since this is not a sine wave, the rms value of the let-through current can't be determined by taking 0.707 of the peak value as is done for a sine wave. The effective or rms value of a triangular wave is equal to the peak value divided by $\sqrt{3}$.

$$I_{rms} = \frac{I\ peak}{\sqrt{3}} = \frac{I\ peak}{1.73}$$

The let-through current of a current-limiting fuse varies with the design, ampere rating, and available short-circuit current. Fuse manufacturers furnish let-through curves for the various types of current-limiting fuses.

THREE-PHASE SHORT CIRCUIT

Three-phase short-circuit currents can be determined in exactly the same way as single-phase currents if we assume the three phases are symmetrical. The three phases have different current values at any instant. Only one can be fully asymmetrical at a given time. This is called the maximum or worst phase, and its rms current value can be found by multiplying the symmetrical rms current by the proper factor. The currents in three phases can be averaged, and the average three-phase rms amperes can be determined by multiplying the symmetrical rms current by the proper factor, which is determined by the X_R ratio of the power system.

X/R RATIO

Every practical circuit contains resistance (R) and inductive reactance (X). These are electrically in series. Their combined effect is called impedance (Z).

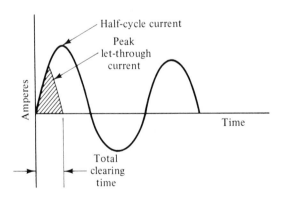

FIGURE 2–27.
Current-limiting fuse action.

When current flows through an inductance (coil), the voltage leads the current by 90°, and when current flows through a resistance, the voltage and current are in phase. This means that X and R must be combined vectorially to obtain impedance. The impedance triangle relating X, R, and Z is shown in Figure 2–28.

$$Z = \sqrt{R^2 + X^2}$$

$$\frac{X}{R} = \tan \Theta$$

The resultant angle Θ is the angle between the voltage and current waves and is called the phase angle. The voltage leads the current or the current lags the voltage by an amount equal to the phase angle. The asymmetrical current may be obtained from known symmetrical current by multiplying with the known X/R ratio. The X/R ratios for commercial and industrial systems vary between 1.0 and 1.6.

POWER FACTOR
Power factor is defined as the ratio of real power (kW) to apparent power (kVA).

$$\text{PF} = \frac{\text{kW}}{\text{kVA}} = \frac{\text{real power}}{\text{apparent power}}$$

Kilowatts are measured with a wattmeter. Kilovolt-amperes are determined with a voltmeter and an ammeter, and the voltage and current waves may be in phase or out of phase. The relationship of kilowatts, kilovars, and kilovolt-amperes is shown in Figure 2–29.

Power Circuit Breaker Rating

The ANSI ratings for power circuit breakers are expressed by two rating structures. The older standard ANSI C37.6 expresses the interrupting rating of ac

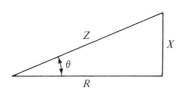

FIGURE 2–28.
Impedance triangle.

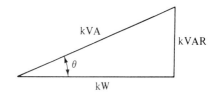

FIGURE 2–29.
Power triangle.

high-voltage breakers megavolt-amperes (MVA) based on total or asymmetrical current at the time of contact parting. The newer standard ANSI C37.06, which was introduced in 1964, expresses the interrupting of ac high-voltage breakers based on total rms symmetrical currents at the time of contact parting. The rating and characteristics of the ANSI C37.06 and ANSI C37.6 are shown in Tables 2–7 and 2–8, respectively.

The standards define that a circuit breaker shall be capable of performing the following in succession:

- Close and immediately latch at normal frequency current, which does not exceed its momentary capability.
- Carry its maximum rated symmetrical current at specified operating voltage for duration of its rated permissible tripping delay.
- Interrupt all currents not greater than its rated symmetrical interrupting current at a specified operating voltage and its related asymmetrical current based on its rated contact parting time. The typical short-circuit current consists of the following:

Symmetrical ac wave shape.

DC component.

Total current.

Let us now compare the rating structure of the two standards by making calculations for a 13.8 kV, 1,200-A 500-MVA rated breaker. The calculations for short-circuit interrupting MVA capability using ANSI C37.06 and C37.6 are made for power circuit breakers operating at minimum, nominal, and maximum voltages. These values are shown in Table 2–9.

It is interesting to note from Table 2–9 that the maximum interrupting MVA calculated based on ANSI C37.06 is less than the MVA rating based on ANSI C37.6. The MVA based on ANSI C37.06 also varies for different operating voltages as compared to ANSI C37.6 MVA values. The reduction in capability of these breakers is a result of an arbitrary decision of the standards committee developing new standards as stated in ANSI C37.06, 1971. The emphasis under the ANSI C37.06 is to rate the circuit breakers in rms amperes rather than MVA, as is the case in the ANSI C37.6. The rms symmetrical rating system is based on the symmetrical component of the short-circuit current at the time of contact opening. Since the short-circuit current is varying from fault inception until it reaches steady-state conditions, some fixed relationship must be defined (or calculated) between symmetrical and asymmetrical currents based on breaker opening time. This fixed relationship is defined in ANSI C37.04-4.5.2.2 by the S curve, which is shown in Figure 2–30.

In summary, the ANSI C37.06 standard requires that the proper breaker should be selected by calculating the total symmetrical rms current at contact parting time. The reason for selecting the contact parting time as the basis of fault interrupting rating is that the breaker should be able to withstand the high mechanical stresses imposed upon it by the first half-cycle fault current, if the breaker is closed in on a fault. The contact parting time of a circuit breaker is the sum of one half-cycle tripping delay plus the operating time of the circuit breaker. For breakers rated at eight, five, three, and two cycles of interrupting time, the related standard contact parting times are four, three, two, and one and a half cycles, respectively.

Selection and Application of Power Circuit Breakers

The application of power switchgear is relatively a simple procedure in most cases whether the switchgear is metal clad or fused interrupter switches. The following steps are usually considered in applying this equipment:

- Selection of switching scheme.
- Calculation of available fault current for breaker or fused interrupter selection.
- Main bus continuous current rating selection.
- Current and potential transformer selection.
- Protective relay selection.
- Circuit breaker control power selection.
- Other special considerations.

Many different switching schemes are available in power switchgear to meet the desired reliability or operational flexibility. A choice should be made based on system requirements, maintenance considerations, reliability, and future expansion.

The selection of the power circuit breaker or fused interrupter switch involves the calculation of available fault current for interrupting duty purposes. Insofar as the interrupting duty of the circuit breaker is concerned, the following limits should not be exceeded.

- Interrupting rms symmetrical amperes between the operating voltage limits.
- Total fault current that is available at contact parting time in terms of symmetrical rms amperes.
- Momentary current that is available during the first half-cycle. The standards allow the momentary rating of circuit breakers to be 1.6 times the rms interrupting rating at an X/R ratio of 10. In general industrial systems, where X/R ratios exceed 15, the interrupting duty will be greater than in systems where the X/R ratio is 10 or less.
- The continuous current that the breaker is rated to carry.

TABLE 2-7.
POWER CIRCUIT BREAKER RATINGS AND CHARACTERISTICS, ANSI C37.06

ANSI Line Number	Nominal Voltage Class kV, rms	Nominal 3-phase mVA Class	Rated Maximum Voltage (1)* kV, rms	Rated Voltage Range Factor, K (2)	Low Frequency kV, rms	Impulse kV Crest	Rated Continuous Current at 60 Hz amp, rms	Rated Short-circuit Current (at Rated Max kV) (3) (4) kA, rms	Rated Interrupting Time Cycles	Rated Permissible Tripping Delay, Y Sec	Rated Maximum Voltage Divided by K kV, rms	Maximum Symmetrical Interrupting Capability (5) K Times Rated Short-circuit Current kA, rms	3 Sec Short-time Current Carrying Capability K Times Rated Short-circuit Current kA, rms	Closing and Latching Capability 1.6 K Times Rated Short-circuit Current kA, rms
1	4.16	75	4.76	1.36	19	60	1200	8.8	5	2	3.5	12	12	19
3	4.16	250	4.76	1.24	19	60	1200	29	5	2	3.85	36	36	58
4	4.16	250	4.76	1.24	19	60	2000	29	5	2	3.85	36	36	58
5	4.16	350	4.76	1.19	19	60	1200	41	5	2	4.0	49	49	78
6	4.16	350	4.76	1.19	19	60	3000	41	5	2	4.0	49	49	78
8	7.2	500	8.25	1.25	36	95	1200	33	5	2	6.6	41	41	66
9	7.2	500	8.25	1.25	36	95	2000	33	5	2	6.6	41	41	66
11	13.8	500	15	1.30	36	95	1200	18	5	2	11.5	23	23	37
12	13.8	500	15	1.30	36	95	2000	18	5	2	11.5	23	23	37
13	13.8	750	15	1.30	36	95	1200	28	5	2	11.5	36	36	58
14	13.8	750	15	1.30	36	95	2000	28	5	2	11.5	36	36	58
15	13.8	1000	15	1.30	36	95	1200	37	5	2	11.5	48	48	77
16	13.8	1000	15	1.30	36	95	3000	37	5	2	11.5	48	48	77

(1) Maximum voltage for which the breaker is designed and the upper limit for operation.

(2) K is the ratio of rated maximum voltage to the lower limit of the range of operating voltage in which the required symmetrical and asymmetrical interrupting capabilities vary in inverse proportion to the operating voltage.

(3) To obtain the required symmetrical interrupting capability of a circuit breaker at an operating voltage between 1/K times rated maximum voltage and rated maximum voltage, the following formula shall be used:

$$\text{Required Symmetrical Interrupting Capability} = \text{Rated Short-circuit Current} \times \frac{(\text{Rated Max. Voltage})}{(\text{Operating Voltage})}$$

For operating voltages below 1/K times rated maximum voltage, the required symmetrical interrupting capability of the circuit breaker shall be equal to K times rated short-circuit current.

(4) With the limitation stated in 04-4.5 of ANSI C37.04, all values apply for polyphase and line-to-line faults. For single phase-to-ground faults, the specific conditions stated in 04-4.5.2.3 of ANSI C37.04 apply.

(5) Current values in this column are not to be exceeded even for operating voltages below 1/K times rated maximum voltage. For voltages between rated maximum voltage and 1/K times rated maximum voltage, follow (3) above.

ANSI-C37.06 symmetrical rating basis is supplementary to ANSI-C37.6 (total current rating basis) and does not replace it. When a changeover from the total current basis of rating to the symmetrical basis of rating is effected, the older standards will be withdrawn.

In accordance with ANSI-C37.06, users should confer with the manufacturer on the status of the various circuit breaker ratings.

TABLE 2-8.
POWER CIRCUIT BREAKER RATING AND CHARACTERISTICS, ANSI C37.6

1	2	3	4	5	6	7	8	9	10	11	12	13
				Insulation Level Withstand Test			Current Ratings in Amperes		Interrupting Ratings			
Nominal 3 Phase MVA Class	Rated kV	Max. Design kV	Minimum Operating kV at Rated Mvs	Low Frequency RMS kV	Impulse Crest kV	Cont. at 60 Cycles	Short-time Momentary	Short-time 4-second	3-phase Rated Mvs	In Rms Total Amperes At Rated Voltage	Maximum Rating	Rated Interrupting Time Cycles (60-Cycles Basis)
50	4.16	4.76	2.3	19	60	(600) (1,200)	20,000	12,500	50	7,000	12,500	8
100/150	2.4/4.16	4.76	2.3/3.5	19	60	(600) (1,200) (2,000)	40,000	25,000	100/150	21,000	25,000	8
150/250	2.4/4.16	4.76	2.3/3.85	19	60	(1,200) (2,000)	60,000	37,500	150/250	35,000	37,500	8
250	7.2	8.25	4.6	36	95	(1,200) (2,000)	51,000	32,000	250	20,000	32,000	8
300	7.2	8.25	6.6	36	95	(600) (1,200) (2,000)	70,000	44,000	500	40,000	44,000	8
150	13.8	15.0	6.6	36	95	(600) (1,200)	20,000	13,000	150	6,300	13,000	8
250	13.8	15.0	6.6	36	95	(1,200) (2,000)	35,000	22,000	250	10,600	22,000	8
500	13.8	15.0	11.5	36	95	(1,200) (2,000)	40,000	25,000	500	21,000	25,000	8

TABLE 2—9.

COMPARISON OF CALCULATED MVA VALUES BASED ON ANSI C37.06 AND C37.6

Voltage (kV)	Breaker	ANSI C37.06	ANSI C37.6
11.5	1200 A 13.8-500	23,000 × 1.73 × 11.5 = 460 MVA	25,000 × 1.73 × 11.5 = 500 MVA
13.8	Same	$18{,}000 \times \dfrac{15}{13.8} \times$ 1.73 × 13.8 = 468 MVA	21,000 × 1.73 × 13.8 = 500 MVA
15	Same	18,000 × 1.73 × 15 = 468 MVA	19,000 × 1.73 × 15 = 500 MVA

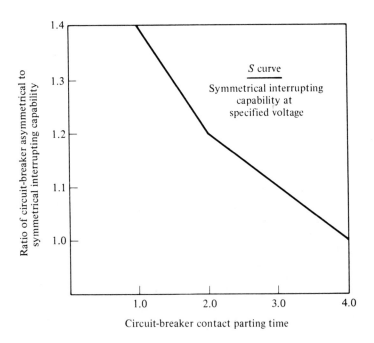

FIGURE 2—30.
S *curve per ANSI C37.04-4.*

- The operating voltage limits, that is, the minimum and maximum design voltages of the circuit breaker.
- The breakers used for reclosing or repetitive duty should be derated in accordance with NEMA SG4 standards in order to be applied properly.

LOW-VOLTAGE SWITCHGEAR

The low-voltage switchgear covered in this section is metal-enclosed, low-voltage power circuit breaker switchgear rated for 600 V ac and below. This switchgear assembly is completely enclosed on all sides and top with sheet metal (except for ventilating openings and inspection windows) and contains primary power circuit switching or interrupting devices, or both, with buses and connections. The circuit breakers may be stationary or removable types and are contained in individual grounded metal compartments. The service conditions for the design and performance of low-voltage switchgear are based upon ambient temperature of from $-30°C$ to $+40°C$, altitude not to exceed 6,000 ft, and switchgear installed in nonexplosive atmosphere.

Construction Features of Low-Voltage Switchgear

There are two basic types of low-voltage switchgear structures, that is, indoor and outdoor types. Indoor switchgear consists of a front section containing circuit breakers, meters, relays and controls, bus section, and cable entrance section. The outdoor section is similar to the indoor switchgear except a structure is provided around it for weatherproofing. Heaters are provided to prevent condensation. Bus bars are available either in copper or aluminum. When aluminum bus is specified, bolted joints should be made with Belleville washers to minimize cold flow characteristics and maintain tight connections. Generally, bare bus bars are used. However, insulation can be specified on special orders. The normal clearance between phase to phase and phase to ground is 2 in. to minimize creepage for 600-V rated equipment. The standard high-voltage withstand is 2,200 V for phase to phase and phase to ground for a period of 1 minute.

Low-Voltage Circuit Breakers

Low-voltage circuit breakers are of three types.

MOLDED-CASE CIRCUIT BREAKERS
Molded-case circuit breakers are available in wide range of ratings and are generally used for low-current, low-energy power circuits. The breakers have self-contained overcurrent trip elements. Conventional thermal magnetic circuit breakers employ a thermal bimetallic element that has inverse time-current characteristics for overload protection and a magnetic trip element for short-circuit protection. Many manufacturers are now switching over from bimetallic

elements to power sensor (solid-state) type trip elements. Magnetic-trip-only breakers have no thermal element. Such breakers are principally used only for short-circuit protection. Nonautomatic circuit breakers have no overload or short-circuit protection. They are primarily used for manual switching and insulation.

INSULATED-CASE CIRCUIT BREAKERS
Insulated case circuit breakers are molded-case breakers using glass-reinforced insulating material for increased dielectric strength. In addition, they have push-to-open button, rotary-operated low-torque handles with independent spring-charged mechanism providing quick-make, quick-break protection. A choice of various automatic trip units is available in the insulated-class breakers. Continuous current ratings range up to 4,000 A with interrupting capacities through 200,000 A.

HEAVY-DUTY POWER CIRCUIT BREAKERS
Heavy-duty power circuit breakers employ spring-operated, stored-energy mechanisms for quick-make, quick-break manual or electric operation. Generally, these breakers have draw-out features whereby individual breakers can be deenergized for maintenance purposes. The manual stored-energy breakers are charged and closed by the operation of the operating handle. The electrically operated breakers are operated by a motor or solenoid. The continuous ampere ratings range from 400 through 4,000 A with interrupting capacities of up to 85,000 A for the 4,000-A size.

Overcurrent Protective Devices

The low-voltage protective devices are direct-acting trip, and static trip.

DIRECT-ACTING TRIP
This device utilizes the force created by the short-circuit current flowing through it to trip its circuit breaker by direct mechanical action. These devices are operated by (1) an electromagnetic force created by the short-circuit current flowing through the trip device coil (the trip coil is usually connected in series with the electrical circuit or in some instance to the secondary of current transformers) or (2) a bimetallic strip actuated by the heat generated by the fault current. The bimetallic strip is usually connected in series with the circuit.

A combination of thermal (bimetallic strip or equivalent) and instantaneous magnetic trip is commonly used on molded-case breakers to provide time delay operation for moderate overcurrents (overloads) and instantaneous operation for high-magnitude of short-circuit current. The thermal trip is usually nonadjustable in the field, whereas the instantaneous trip is available as adjustable or nonadjustable. The adjustable-trip range varies from low to high with several intermediate steps. The number of steps available may vary for different breaker designs and sizes.

Direct-acting trips on insulated-case and heavy-duty power circuit breakers are of the electromagnetic type. Three trip devices are available: (1) long time delay (LTD), (2) short time delay (STD), and (3) instantaneous (INST). Any combination of the three types is available to provide protection for overcurrents. A trip device is installed in each phase of the electrical circuit. The LTD, STD, and INST trip devices are available in minimum, intermediate, and maximum time bands to facilitate the coordination of various trip devices in series. All these units have adjustable settings.

STATIC TRIPS

Static-trip devices are completely static; that is, there are no moving parts. These devices use semiconductor integrated circuits, capacitors, transformers, and other electronic components. Static-trip devices operate to open the circuit breaker when the current–time relationship exceeds a preselected value. The energy required to trip the breaker is obtained from the circuit being protected. No external power, such as dc batteries, is required. The complete static-trip system is comprised of (1) primary circuit current transformers, (2) the static logic box, and (3) the tripping actuator (a magnetically held latch device).

The current transformer sensors are a toroidal type mounted one per phase on the primary studs of the circuit breaker. These transformers provide a signal to the static-trip device proportional to the primary current. The static logic box receives the signal from the primary current transformer. It monitors the signal, senses overloads or faults, and executes the required action in accordance with preselected settings. The tripping actuator receives the output signal from the static logic box and in turn causes the circuit breaker contacts to open.

The power supply for the static logic boxes and the tripping actuator is supplied from a separate set of sensors mounted in the breaker studs. In addition to the phase overcurrent logic boxes, a ground-fault sensing feature may be provided. The ground-fault feature employs three or four toroidal sensors depending upon whether it is a three- or four-wire system. The ground sensors are connected in a delta connection and the output signal is fed into the ground logic box. The ground sensing works on the principle that the instantaneous value of currents flowing in a closed delta must add up to zero unless there is a ground current flowing. Therefore, it is apparent that if the grounding wire is used it should not be included in this connection. The connection of a static device for a five-wire system is shown in Figure 2–31.

New design advances are continually being made in the development of static trip devices. One such new static trip device is the General Electric Micro-VersaTrip programmer (MVT). Micro-VersaTrip uses advanced solid-state circuiting to provide monitoring, signaling, and tripping functions for circuit protection. The Micro-VersaTrip system consists of the following parts.

Three current sensors are mounted on the breaker and provide the self-powered input to the protection programmer. Where four-wire ground fault is specified, a fourth current sensor is mounted near the neutral bar in the cable compartment. Sensors are constructed of molded epoxy for added protection against damage and moisture. Optional current sensors with four taps are available to increase the flexibility and range of the system.

A flux-shift trip device is automatically powered and controlled by the protection programmer and causes the breaker to trip on command. This low energy positive action tripping device is located near the trip bar on the breaker.

The protection programmer has a programmable micro-electric processor with laser trimmed custom integrated chips that form the basis of the flexible, precise Micro-Versa Trip protection system. Micro-Versa Trip protection programmers may be furnished with:

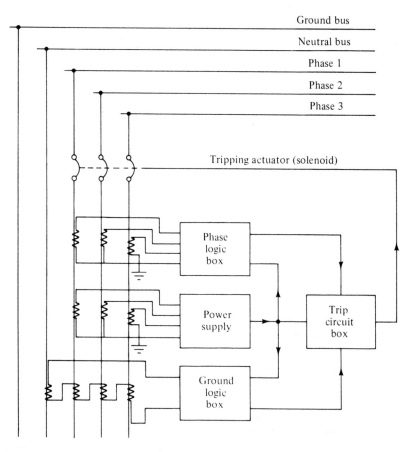

FIGURE 2–31.
Functional diagram of static-trip device.

- Up to nine adjustable time-current functions;
- Three local and remote mechanical fault indicators;
- A local and remote long-time pickup LED indicator;
- Zone selective interlocking; and
- Integral ground-fault trip.

All adjustable programmer functions are automatic and self-contained and require no external relaying, power supply or accessories.

FUSES

The two basic families of fuses are current limiting and non-current limiting. The current-limiting fuse melts and extinguishes the arc in a half-cycle or less. The non-current-limiting type may melt in less than a half-cycle when subjected to very high values of short-circuit current, but is unable to extinguish the arc in a half-cycle. Since the arc is a flexible conductor, the non-current-limiting-type fuse will allow the short-circuit current to reach its maximum peak value. The current-limiting type of fuses are constructed with mechanisms to extinguish the arc, thereby preventing the short-circuit current from reaching its maximum peak value. The fuses are used in conjunction with circuit breakers, motor starters, disconnect switches, and the like to provide protection similar to the circuit breaker overcurrent trip devices. However, fuses have fixed time–current relationships and therefore do not provide the same flexibility as the overcurrent trip devices. Fuses cannot open and close a circuit by themselves. They must be combined with some supplementary device, such as a disconnect switch, a circuit breaker or a contactor. Fuses can be divided into medium- and low-voltage fuses.

Medium-Voltage Fuses

Medium-voltage-fuse types are distribution cutouts, fuse links, expulsion, current limiting, and others, which are governed by ANSI standards C37.40, .41, .44, .47 and .48. Medium-voltage fuses do not provide overload protection. If required, supplementary overload protection should be applied, such as thermal overload relays.

Low-Voltage Fuses

Low-voltage fuses are divided into four broad categories:

- Cartridge fuses, designed for the protection of circuits.
- Plug fuses, designed for the protection of circuits.
- Supplementary fuses, designed for the protection of small appliances, electronic equipment, and the like.

■ Special fuses, designed for the protection of electrical equipment such as capacitors, welders, and rectifiers.

The standards applicable to these fuses are ANSI C97.1 dated 1972, NEMA FU-1 dated 1972, and UL 198.1 through 198.6 and 198F. Furthermore, Underwriters Laboratory has classified fuses as current and non-current limiting, as shown in Table 2–10.

Because fuses are single-phase interrupters, they provide good protection for single-phase circuits. However, for multiphase circuits, these single-phase interrupters can cause problems such as single phasing, backfeeding, and ferroresonance.

Single-phasing can be detrimental to motors owing to the flow of negative-sequence currents, which can cause excessive heating of the motor rotor,

TABLE 2–10.

CURRENT AND NON-CURRENT-LIMITING FUSES

Non-Current Limiting	
Plug fuses (Class S)	Class H
Voltage rating, 125 V ac	Voltage rating, 250 V and 600 V ac
Current rating, 0–30 A	Current rating, 0–600 A
Interrupting rating, not over 10,000 A	Interrupting rating, not over 10,000 A

Current Limiting	
Class J	Class L
Voltage rating, 600 V ac	Voltage rating, 600 V ac
Current rating, 0–600 A	Current rating, 601–6,000 A
Interrupting rating, 200,000 A sym	Interrupting rating, 200,000 A sym
Class K (K-1, K-5 and K-9)	Class R
Voltage rating, 250–600 V ac	Voltage rating, 250 and 600 V ac
Current rating, 0–600 A	Current rating, 0–600 A
Interrupting rating, 50,000 to 200,000 A sym	Interrupting rating, 200,000 A sym
Class T	Class G
Voltage rating, 300 and 600 V ac	Voltage rating, 300 V ac
Current rating, 0–600 A	Current rating, 0–60 A
Interrupting rating, 200,000 A sym	Interrupting rating, 100,000 A sym
Class RK1	Class RK5
Voltage rating, 250–600 V ac	Voltage rating, 250–600 V ac
Current rating, 0–600 A	Current rating, 0–600 A
Interrupting rating, 200,000 A sym	Interrupting rating, 200,000 A sym
Class CC	
Voltage rating, 600 V ac	
Current rating, 0–20 A	
Interrupting rating, 200,000 A sym	

causing motor failure or reducing its normal life. The degree of motor life reduction is a function of motor temperature and elapsed time between single-phase occurrence and motor deenergization.

The term back feeding is used to describe the condition when fault current continues to flow from the remaining energized phases, most probably at a reduced value owing to the additional impedance that has been inserted in the current path. The degree of fault current reduction will determine the time of response of the fuses in the remaining phases. As fuse interrupting time increases, the degree of damage also increases.

DISCONNECT SWITCHES

Disconnect switches are commonly used in low- and medium-voltage systems. The application of disconnect switches can be divided into low-voltage (600 V and below) and medium-voltage (601 V through 15 kV) classes.

Medium-Voltage Switches

The three broad classifications of medium-voltage switches are (1) high-voltage disconnect switches, (2) load break switches, and (3) interrupter switches. The high-voltage disconnect switch has no capability to carry load currents. Its main function is to isolate equipment after the circuit has been deenergized. The load break switch has the capability of switching load currents but not interrupting short-circuit currents. The interrupter switch has the capability of interrupting short-circuit currents up to 10 to 12 times its ratings. However, the short-circuit capability of the interrupter switch can be increased by using current-limiting fuses.

Low-Voltage Switches

Low-voltage switches can be classified into three borad categories: (1) isolating switches, (2) safety switches, and (3) interrupter switches. The isolating switch has no interrupting or load-carrying capability. It serves only to provide isolation of the circuit or load by manual means after the power flow is cut off by the circuit protective device.

The safety switch is a load-break switch having a quick-make and quick-break contact mechanism. Safety switches are used in small power systems with limited short-circuit capacity. The safety switch may be fused or unfused.

The interrupter switch is of quick-make, quick-break type and is capable of interrupting at least 12 times its continuous current rating. They are assigned horsepower rating. These switches are available in continuous rating from 30 to 600 A and can be installed in switchboards, panelboards, and grouped motor control centers. The interrupter switch may be utilized with or without fuses depending upon the application.

SELECTION AND APPLICATION OF LOW-VOLTAGE EQUIPMENT

The modern distribution system has high short-circuit current available and therefore requires special consideration so that equipment may be applied within its rating. Furthermore, the switchgear should be protected against all types of faults, from low-level arcing faults to bolted faults. The protection system should be selective; that is, the fault at a remote location in the system should be localized without necessary tripping of either the main breaker system or any intermediate breakers. The distribution should be planned to provide continuity and reliability of service. This can be achieved by using two or more separate distribution systems instead of one large system. The continuous current rating of the main protective device should be adequate for the load to be served. Protective devices should not be paralleled to obtain a higher rating. As a general rule, the bus bars are rated on the basis of not more than 800 A/in.^{2} of aluminum or 1,000 A/in.^{2} of copper. The operation of protective devices is based upon an ambient temperature of 40°C, and if these devices are to be applied at higher temperature, the manufacturer should be consulted. The short-circuit rating of a bus is limited to the interrupting rating of the lowest rated protective device, and the available short-cirucit current should not exceed this value.

The application of circuit breakers and fuses must be considered to determine which offers the most appropriate protection. Consideration should be given to anti-single-phase devices or three-pole interrupter switches where fuses are used, because fuses are single-pole interrupters. An arcing fault may not be stopped by a single-pole interruption. It can be back fed from the other energized phases. Because of this condition, severe equipment burn-downs may occur. Also ferroresonance is the result of reactance from a saturable magnetic device, such as a transformer interacting with system capacitance, and can occur due to single-phasing conditions. This phenomena occurs mostly in high- and medium-voltage systems and results in a very high voltage on the order of three to five times normal system voltage which is imposed on the circuit involved and thus cause equipment failure.

Always keep in mind that fuses should be applied in systems where the system voltage is compatible with the fuse voltage rating. The reason for this is that the arc voltage generated by a fuse when interrupting is several times its voltage rating and, if misapplied, could subject the system to overvoltage conditions causing equipment failure.

The current-limiting features of current-limiting fuses are definite strong pluses for many applications; however, use the fact wisely, for they do not limit current for all values of fault current. If the fault current magnitude is equal to or greater than the fuse threshold current, they will always be current limiting. However, if the fault current magnitude is less than the fuse threshold current, but greater than the current magnitude indicated at the intersection of the maximum peak current curve and fuse curve, the fuse may or may not be current limiting. For fault current magnitude indicated by the above curve intersection, the fuse is never current limiting.

For this reason and arc-voltage considerations, when applying current-limiting fuses to increase the interrupting rating of other protectors, the fusing recommendations of the product manufacturers, not the fuse manufacturer, should be followed.

Fused equipment can be opened and closed manually or electrically to provide circuit protection. However, the fuse and equipment should be coordinated and tested as a combination. The fuse's adequate performance as a circuit protector and switching device should be certified by one manufacturer.

When fused switches are electrically controlled, caution is required not to let the switch open due to fault conditions. The fault current, if not sufficient to cause interruption before the switch contacts or blades open, could be greater than the contacts' or blades' interrupting capability. This would result in a serious hazardous condition. Fused switches basically require the same application considerations as previously outlined in this section.

Fused motor starters applied in medium- and low-voltage systems avoid the ferroresonance problem owing to their location in the system. Auxiliary devices can be supplied with motor starters to provide a complete overload protection and anti-single-phasing protection.

Low-voltage breakers, when equipped with fuses, extend the short-circuit interrupting capability of the breakers up to 200 kA rms symmetrical. Due to the system voltage, ferroresonance is rarely a problem. Consideration should be given to trip the breaker whenever a fuse blows in order to prevent single-phase conditions.

The selection and application of switchgear should be approached on an engineering basis. To provide reliability, ease of maintenance, and continuity of service, properly rated equipment and adequate circuit protection are necessary throughout the entire system, from the place where the power system enters the facility down to the smallest load.

2-5 MOTORS AND GENERATORS

Motors and generators (except gas turbine or steam) must be installed, operated, and maintained properly. This equipment ranges from very small to very large machines. The attention and care provided in the selection, installation, operation, and maintenance would, therefore, vary for different units. Many precautions must be taken, especially for large rotating apparatus, to avoid damage, because most of this equipment is expensive and hard to replace. The scheduled maintenance, overhauls, or repair of large rotating apparatus may require partial or extensive disassembly. Therefore, maintenance personnel assigned to perform the work should be familiar and knowledgeable with all aspects of the apparatus. This section discusses the selection, application, and rotating apparatus mechanics in order to better understand the maintenance of motors and generators.

The rotating apparatus is an energy-conversion device. That is, it converts mechanical energy into electrical energy, or vice versa. It can be designed precisely to perform the service expected. But to perform best, it must be properly installed, protected, ventilated, and maintained. The objective in applying a motor or generator is to select rating and features so that it can carry the load without exceeding its temperature limits. Since many motor and generator applications will have a bearing on other equipment, it is important to review the engineering information on it. The National Electrical Manufacturers Association (NEMA) has published standards titled MG1-1978, Motors and Generators, that list all the pertinent details of this equipment.

NEMA CLASSIFICATION OF MOTORS AND GENERATORS

Under NEMA MG1 standards, all machines are classified according to size, application, electrical type, environmental protection and method of cooling, and variability of speed.

According to Size

- *Fractional-horsepower motor:* A motor built with frame size having two-digit numbers or a motor built in a frame smaller than that of an integral-horsepower motor.

- *Integral-horsepower motor:* An ac integral-horsepower motor is built in a frame size that has a three-digit number or built in a frame having an open continuous rating of 1 horsepower (hp) at 1,700 to 1,800 rpm or 500 hp at 1,800 rpm. A dc integral-horsepower motor is built with a frame that has a three-digit frame number or built in a frame having an open continuous rating of 1 hp at 1,700 to 1,800 rpm or in a frame larger than required for 800 hp at 1,250 rpm.

- *Large motor:* A motor built in a frame larger than that required for integral-horsepower motors.

According to Application

- *General-purpose ac motor:* An induction motor, rated at 200 hp or less, and of open construction; it is continuously rated, has a service factor of 1.15 for integral-horsepower motors, and has class B insulation system.

- *Industrial dc motor:* An integral-horsepower motor of mechanical construction suitable for industrial applications under usual service conditions.

- *Industrial dc generator:* A generator of mechanical construction suitable for industrial application under usual conditions.

- *Definite-purpose motor:* A motor designed and constructed in standard ratings for service conditions other than usual or for use on a particular type of application.

- *Part-winding-start motor:* A motor arranged to start with part of the winding, subsequently energizing the remainder of the winding in one or more steps.

- *Special-purpose motor:* A motor with special characteristics and/or mechanical construction and not falling under the definition of a general-purpose and definite-purpose motor.

- *General dc industrial motor:* Motors designed for all general industrial service with speed operation (when specified) above base speed by field weakening

- *Metal rolling mill motor:* Motors designed for metal rolling mill service and known as class N or S types.

- *Reversing hot mill motor:* Motors designed for application to reversing hot mills.

According to Electrical Type

ALTERNATING-CURRENT MOTORS
Alternating-current motors are of three types, induction motors, synchronous motors, and series motors. They can be defined as follows:

- *Induction motor:* An ac motor in which the primary winding (the stator) is connected to the electric power source and the secondary winding (the rotor) carries induced current. Induction motors are of two types, squirrel-cage induction motors and wound-rotor motors. In the squirrel-cage induction motor, the secondary circuit consists of a squirrel-cage winding suitably disposed in slots in the secondary core. In the wound-rotor induction motor, the secondary circuit consists of polyphase windings or coils whose terminals are either short circuited or closed through suitable circuits.

- *Synchronous motor:* An induction motor that is equipped with field windings in the secondary circuit and excited with dc voltage. The synchronous motor is started as an induction motor; however, it is operated at synchronous speed (i.e., at the speed of the revolving magnetic field).

- *Series-wound motor:* A motor in which the field circuit and armature circuit are connected in series.

The induction and synchronous motor are built as polyphase or single-phase motors.

POLYPHASE MOTOR

Polyphase motors are constructed with multiphase stator windings and rotor. The rotor is constructed in two types, the cage rotor and the form-wound rotor. Both types of rotor have a laminated cylindrical core with parallel slots in the outside circumference to hold the windings in place. The cage rotor has an uninsulated bar winding, whereas the form-wound rotor has a two-layer distributed winding with preformed coils. In the polyphase motor, the rotor currents are supplied by electromagnetic induction. The stator windings contain two or more out-of-time-phase currents, which produce corresponding magnetomotive forces (mmf). These mmf's establish a rotating magnetic field across the air gap. This magnetic field rotates continuously at constant speed regardless of the load on the motors. The revolving magnetic field produced by the stator cuts across the rotor conductors, inducing a voltage in the conductors. This induced voltage causes rotor currents to flow. This action is known as mutual induction (similar to transformer action), which takes place between the stator and the rotor under operating conditions.

Polyphase motors range in horsepower rating from fractional- to integral-horsepower to large-apparatus motors. The fractional- and integral-horsepower motors are generally cage-rotor type. Large-apparatus induction motors are of cage- and wound-rotor types, where the synchronous motors are of the salient-pole and cylindrical rotor type.

In accordance with NEMA standards, polyphase squirrel-cage integral-horsepower induction motors are designated by design letters:

- *Design A:* A squirrel-cage motor designed to withstand full-voltage starting and develop a starting torque of 110 to 120 percent, starting lock rotor of six to ten times, and having a slip at rated load of less than 5 percent.
- *Design B:* Similar to design A motor with the same starting torque; however, the lock rotor current is limited to five times.
- *Design C:* A squirrel-cage motor designed to withstand full-voltage starting, developing a high starting torque of 200 percent and lock rotor current less than the standard type of motor, and having a slip at rated load of less than 5 percent.
- *Design D:* A squirrel-cage motor designed to withstand full-voltage starting, developing a very high lock rotor torque of 300 percent, low lock rotor current, and having a slip at rated load of 5 percent or more.
- *Design F:* A squirrel-cage motor built to withstand full-voltage starting, developing a low starting torque, very low lock rotor current, and a slip at rated load of less than 5 percent.

SINGLE-PHASE MOTOR

Single-phase motors are not self-starting because they have only one primary (stator) winding and cage rotor. The single primary winding when excited from a single source produces a pulsating magnetic field in the motor air gap, and with the rotor at standstill no breakaway torque is produced. However, if the rotor is brought up to speed by external means, the induced currents in the rotor will combine with the stator currents to produce a revolving field. The revolving field in turn causes the rotor to continue to run in the direction in which it was started. Several methods are used to provide the single-phase induction motor with starting torque. These methods identify the motor as a particular type of single-phase motor. Some of the important single-phase motors are split-phase, capacitor start and run, repulsion, and shaded pole. Single-phase motors are constructed as induction, wound-rotor, and synchronous motor types.

Alternating single-phase motors are designated by design letters similar to polyphase motors. These design letters are the following:

- *Design N:* A single-phase fractional-horsepower motor designed to withstand full-voltage starting and with a lock rotor current not to exceed the values shown in NEMA standard MG1-12.32.

- *Design O:* A single-phase fractional-horsepower motor designed to withstand full-voltage starting and with a lock rotor current not to exceed the values shown in MG1-12.32.

- *Design L:* A single-phase integral-horsepower motor designed to withstand full-voltage starting and to develop a breakdown torque as shown in NEMA standards MG1-10.33 and lock rotor current not to exceed values shown in MG1-12.33.

- *Design M:* A single-phase integral-horsepower motor designed to withstand full voltage starting and to develop a breakdown torque as shown in NEMA standards MG1-10.33 and lock rotor current not to exceed values shown in MG1-12.33.

UNIVERSAL MOTOR

A universal motor is a series-wound motor designed to operate at approximately the same speed and output on either direct current or single-phase alternating current of frequency not to exceed 60 hertz (Hz). There are two types of universal motors:

- *Series-wound motor:* A commutator motor in which the field circuit and armature circuit are connected in series.

- *Compensated series motor:* A motor with compensating field winding.

DIRECT-CURRENT MOTORS

Direct-current motors are of three types:

- *Shunt-wound motor:* A shunt-wound motor is either a straight shunt-wound motor or a stabilized shunt-wound motor. The difference between the two shunt fields is that the stabilized shunt-wound motor has a light series winding to prevent a rise in speed or to obtain a slight reduction in speed.
- *Series-wound motor:* A series-wound motor has the field circuit and armature circuit in series.
- *Compound-wound motor:* A compound-wound motor has two separate field windings, one connected in the shunt field and the other connected in series in the armature.

DIRECT-CURRENT GENERATORS
Direct-current generators are of two general types:

- *Shunt-wound generators:* A generator in which the field is connected in parallel with the armature or to a separate source of excitation.
- *Compound-wound generator:* A generator that has two separate field windings, one, usually the predominating field, connected in parallel with the armature and the other connected in series with the armature.

According to Environmental Protection and Methods of Cooling

The machine is provided with an enclosure to give physical protection from external sources of motor damage. The following standard enclosures have been adopted by NEMA:

- *Open enclosure:* An enclosure with ventilating openings that permit passage of external cooling air over and around the windings of the machine.
- *Dripproof enclosure:* An open enclosure in which ventilating openings are so constructed that successful operation is not interfered with when drops of liquid or solid particles strike or enter the enclosure at any angle from 0° to 15° downward from the vertical.
- *Splashproof enclosure:* An open enclosure in which ventilating openings are constructed so that successful operation is not interfered with when drops of liquid or solid particles strike or enter the enclosure at any angle not greater than 100° downward from the vertical.
- *Guarded enclosure:* An open enclosure in which all openings giving direct access to live metal or rotating parts are limited in size by structural parts or by screens, baffles, grilles, or other means to prevent accidental contact with hazardous parts.
- *Externally ventilated enclosure:* An open enclosure that is ventilated by a separate motor-driven blower mounted on the enclosure.

- *Pipe-ventilated enclosure:* An open enclosure with provision for connecting inlet ducts or pipes. It is called force-ventilated when the air through the enclosure is driven by an external blower.

- *Weather-protected type 1 enclosure:* An open enclosure with ventilating passages constructed and arranged to minimize the entrance of rain, snow, and airborne particles to the live and rotating parts.

- *Weather-protected type 2 enclosure:* An open enclosure with ventilating passages at both intake and discharge constructed and arranged to permit high-velocity air and airborne particles to be discharged without entering the internal ventilating passages of the enclosure.

- *Totally enclosed enclosure:* This enclosure prevents free exchange of air between the inside and outside of the enclosure. The enclosure is not airtight.

- *Totally enclosed nonventilated enclosure:* An enclosure that is not equipped for cooling by means external to the enclosing parts.

- *Totally enclosed fan-cooled enclosure:* An enclosure that is equipped for exterior cooling by means of a fan or fans integral with the enclosure but external to the enclosing parts.

- *Explosionproof enclosure:* A totally enclosed enclosure designed and constructed to withstand an explosion of a specified gas or vapor that may occur within it and to prevent the ignition of gas or vapor surrounding the machine by sparks.

- *Dust-ignition-proof enclosure:* A totally enclosed enclosure constructed in a manner to exclude ignitable amounts of dust or amounts that might affect the performance or rating, and which will not permit heat, arcs, or sparks liberated inside the enclosure to cause ignition of exterior accumulations or atmospheric suspensions of a specific dust on or in the vicinity of the enclosure.

- *Waterproof enclosure:* A totally enclosed enclosure so constructed that it will exclude water coming externally from a hose. Leakage around the shaft is allowed provided it does not enter the oil reservoir. A check valve or drain is provided at the lowest part of the enclosure for drainage.

- *Totally enclosed pipe-ventilated enclosure:* A totally enclosed enclosure except for openings arranged for inlet and out-ducts or pipes for connection to the enclosed for admission and discharge of ventilating air.

- *Totally enclosed water-cooled enclosure:* A totally enclosed enclosure cooled by circulating water or water pipes coming in direct contact with the motor parts.

- *Totally enclosed water-air-cooled enclosure:* A totally enclosed enclosure cooled by circulating air, which in turn is cooled by circulating water.

- *Totally enclosed air-air-cooled enclosure:* A totally enclosed enclosure cooled by circulating internal air through heat exchangers, which, in turn, are cooled by circulating external air.

According to Variability of Speed

- *Constant-speed motor:* A motor that operates at constant or near constant speed.
- *Varing-speed motor:* A motor whose speed varies with the load, ordinarily decreasing as the load increases.
- *Adjustable-speed motor:* A motor whose speed is adjustable over a considerable range and is not affected by load.
- *Adjustable varying-speed motor:* An adjustable-speed motor as described previously, but whose speed will vary as a function of load.
- *Multispeed motor:* A motor that can operate at one or two or more definite speeds, each speed being practically independent of the load.

Terminal Marking of Machines

The terminal markings of machines are made in accordance with NEMA standards. Terminal markings use a combination of capital letters and arabic numerals. The letters and symbols shown in Table 2–11 are used for ac motors and generators in accordance with NEMA standards. (Refer to NEMA MG1-1980 for A.C. Machines Terminal Markings.)

TABLE 2–11.
TERMINAL MARKING FOR AC MOTORS AND GENERATORS

Line: L1, L2, L3, etc.
Stator: T1, T2, T3, etc.
Rotor windings: M1, M2, M3, etc.
Resistors: R1, R2, R3, etc.
Field: F1, F2, F3, etc.

Notes: The numerals 1, 2, 3, etc., indicate the order in which the voltages of a synchronous motor at the terminals reach their maximum positive value with clockwise shaft rotation when facing the connection end of the coil windings.

The terminal markings of polyphase induction machines are not related to the direction of rotation.

The standard direction of rotation for all ac single-phase motors, all synchronous motors, and all universal motors is counterclockwise when facing the end of the machine opposite the drive.

The standard direction of rotation for alternating generators is clockwise when facing the end of the machine opposite the drive.

The terminal markings and connection procedure for *single-phase* motors is based upon three general principles:

- *Principle 1:* The main winding of a single-phase motor is designated by T1, T2, T3, and T4. The auxiliary winding is designated by T5, T6, T7, and T8. This is done to distinguish it from a quarter-phase motor, which uses odd numbers for one phase and even numbers for the other phase.

- *Principle 2:* When odd-numbered terminals of each winding are connected together, they will provide a lower voltage, that is a parallel connection. When odd-to-even-numbered terminals of each winding are connected to odd-numbered, they will provide a higher voltage, that is, a series connection.

- *Principle 3:* The rotor of a single-phase motor is represented as a circle, even though there are no external connections to it. It also serves to distinguish it from a quarter-phase motor in which the rotor is never represented.

Based upon these three principles, the single- and dual-voltage single-phase motors can be represented as in the following:

SINGLE-VOLTAGE MOTORS
T1 and T4 are assigned to the main winding and T5 and T8 to the auxiliary winding. The standard direction is obtained when T4 and T5 are joined to one line and T1 and T8 to the second line. This is shown in Figure 2–32.

DUAL-VOLTAGE MOTORS
For the purposes of terminal markings, the main winding is considered to be divided in two halves. One half is asigned T1 and T2 and the other half is assigned T3 and T4. Similarly, the auxiliary winding is divided into two halves with one half assigned terminal markings T5 and T6 and the other half T7 and

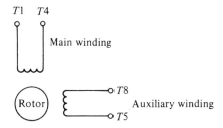

FIGURE 2–32.
Single-phase motor, single-voltage terminal marking.

T8. The standard direction of rotation is obtained when the main winding terminal T4 and auxiliary winding terminal T5 are connected or when an equivalent circuit connection is made between the main and the auxiliary windings. The terminal marking is shown in Figure 2–33. The marking of *polyphase* motors is based on the principle that they show the electrical relationship between the various circuits inside the motor. Therefore, the NEMA standards employ a system that uses a clockwise rotating spiral with T1 at the outer end and finishes with the highest number at its inner end as a means of determining the sequence of numerals. Such a numbering system does not imply standardization of the direction of rotation of the motor shaft. This principle will now be used to show the terminal marking of a three-phase single-speed induction motor in Figure 2–34a through f.

Step 1: Draw a schematic vector diagram showing an inverted wye connection with two individual circuits in each phase arranged for series connection with correct polarities.

Step 2: Starting with T1 at the outside and top of the diagram, number the ends of the circuits consecutively in a clockwise direction, proceeding on a spiral toward the center of the diagram. This is shown in Figure 2–34b.

Step 3: Show the schematic vector diagram of the particular interconnection of the circuits for the (two circuits per phase) motor and terminal markings as determined in steps 1 and 2. Arrange the vector diagram to give the correct polarity relation of the circuits. For example, connect the two circuits in parallel per phase; the vector diagram is shown in Figure 2–34c.

Step 4: When two (or more) terminals are premanently connected together, the highest terminal number is dropped and only the lowest number is retained. In our example, suppose that it is desired to have three line leads and three neutral leads brought out; the terminal markings are as

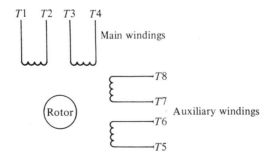

FIGURE 2–33.
Single-phase, dual-voltage terminal marking.

shown in Figure 2–34d. If it was desired to have the windings in series or multiple connections with the neutral point brought out, the vector diagram and terminal markings are as shown in Figure 2–34e.

Step 5: Where the ends of three coils are connected together to form a permanent neutral, the terminal markings of the three leads so connected are dropped. If the neutral point is brought out, it is always marked as T0, as shown in Figure 2–34e.

Step 6: Where the windings are to the connected delta, the inverted-wye diagram shown in Figure 2–34a is rotated 30° counterclockwise. The outer end of the top leg is assigned the terminal marking T1 and the remaining windings are numbered in accordance with step 2. The vector schematic is then constructed in which the T1 leg of the rotated delta becomes the right side of the delta, the T2 becomes the bottom (horizontal) side, and T3 the left side of the delta. This is shown in Figure 2–34f.

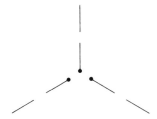

FIGURE 2–34a.
Diagram for two circuits per phase (step 1).

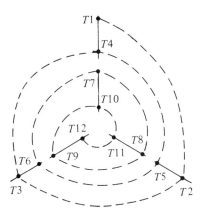

FIGURE 2–34b.
Terminal markings for two circuits per phase (step 2).

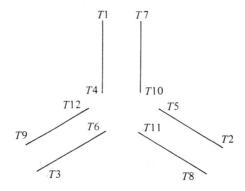

FIGURE 2–34c.
Terminal markings for two circuits in parallel per phase (step 3).

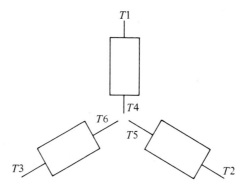

FIGURE 2–34d.
Terminal markings for two windings in parallel per phase, permanently connected (step 4).

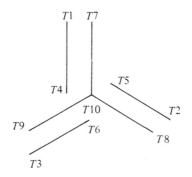

FIGURE 2–34e.
Terminal markings with neutral brought out (step 5).

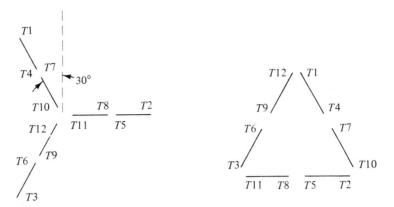

FIGURE 2–34f.
Terminal markings for two circuits per phase, delta connection (step 6).

Many polyphase motors have dual voltage and are connected as wye or delta connections. The same principles as discussed can be applied to achieve the terminal markings for these types of motors. The wye and delta connections for dual-voltage motors are shown in Figure 2–35a and b.

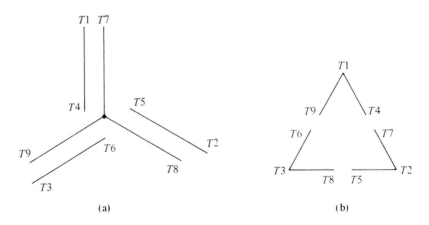

(a)   (b)

FIGURE 2–35.
(a) Wye-connected dual voltage; (b) delta-connected dual voltage.

APPLICATIONS OF MOTORS AND GENERATORS

Motors and generators are applied on the basis that they can carry the rated load and withstand the environmental conditions during their rated life reliably. Because of the different requirements of various industries for motors, each industry has over the years developed different application criteria for motors. Therefore, a wide variety of motor insulation and construction classes are available (manufactured in accordance with NEMA MG1-1978 standards) to satisfy these needs. The actual life and reliability of motors are determined by combining the experience of industry requirements with knowledge of motor mechanical and electrical characteristics. The reliability of a machine can be defined in terms of its electrical and mechanical integrity, which are explained next.

Electrical Integrity

The electrical integrity of a machine can be stated in terms of the dielectric and load-time ratings.

DIELECTRIC RATING
Dielectric rating can be defined as the ability to properly maintain the separation of the conducting and nonconducting parts from the power system supply voltage. To achieve the required dielectric integrity, various insulation systems are used, depending on the type of motor and service conditions. To provide the highest reliability, insulation materials must have a degree of thermal, voltage, mechanical, and environmental endurance. Therefore, insulation systems used for motors and generators are classified on the basis of their ability to withstand the total temperature during the life of the machine without deterioration.

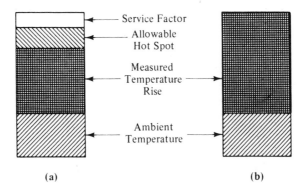

(a)   (b)

FIGURE 2–36.
Total temperature measurements by (a) thermometer and (b) resistance methods.

NEMA standards MG-12.41 describe two methods of temperature-rise measurement. They are (1) thermometer and (2) resistance methods. The resistance method is based upon the ambient and the total temperature rise, which is shown in Figure 2–36b. The thermometer method is based on four factors. These factors are the standard ambient temperature of 40°C, a service factor, the measured temperature rise, and the allowable hot spot. This is shown in Figure 2–36a. The various insulation systems normally used for machines are shown in Table 2–12.

Temperature determined by the resistance method gives an indication of the average total temperature of the motor windings. The life of the insulation system is dependent on both the temperature rise and the total temperature of the motor windings. The total temperature for the various insulation classes is shown in Table 2–12. The motor temperature measurement by resistance method takes into consideration only two factors, the ambient temperature and the temperature rise measured by resistance at service factor load. The sum of these two temperatures makes up the basis of total temperature of the insulation system. The resistance method eliminates the consideration of hot spot allowance, the 10°C allowance for service factor, and temperature rise measured by thermometer at nameplate load. Under the resistance method, the insulation system needed for the motor can simply be specified in terms of the operating ambient temperature and the service factor of the motor.

The use of the resistance method for the measurement of insulation temperature does not change the limitation imposed on the various classes of insulation systems. The resistance method has simplified the specification of the insulation temperature rating system for machine windings. As a result of

TABLE 2–12.

INSULATION-SYSTEM TEMPERATURES FOR MOTORS WITH 1.15 SERVICE FACTOR (°C)

Insulation Class	Ambient Temperature (standard)[a]	Thermometer Method			Resistance Method	Total Temperature
		Temperature Rise		Hot Spot Allowance[b] (average)		
		Measure Rise	Service Factor			
A	40	40	10	15	65	105
B	40	65	10	15	90	130
F	40	90	10	15	115	155
H	40	115	10	15	140	180

[a] The standard ambient is 40°C, whereas for higher temperature applications, 65°, 90°, and 115°C ambient temperatures are standard.

[b] The hot spot allowance is a temperature allowance for the difference between the measured temperature rise of the winding and the estimated hottest location in the winding. This number varies from 5° to 25°C with measured rise, enclosure, and temperature measurement method.

this change in the temperature measurement method, the class B insulation system has been adopted as a standard for motor windings.

LOAD-TIME RATING

The load rating relates to the ability of the machine to carry a load over a period of time. Load ratings can be classified as service-factor duty, short-time duty and overload duty.

Service-factor duty is defined as the multiplier that is multiplied by the nameplate horsepower; the result is used for temperature testing with continuously applied load until the temperature equilibrium is reached. For example, a service factor of 1.0 means that the motor cannot carry an overload on a sustained basis without exceeding the insulation temperature. A service factor of 1.15 has been established as a standard for open and dripproof general-purpose motors below 200 hp. Larger motors have a service factor of 1.0. A service factor of 1.15 usually translates into a 10°C higher temperature with 15 percent overload.

Short-time duty is defined by a motor operating at continuous load over a period of time less than that required to reach thermal equilibrium. The short-time duty ratings are usually 15, 30, or 60 min. Motors should be allowed to cool down to ambient temperature when they are operated in this manner before the next load cycle is applied; otherwise, the motor will overheat.

Overload duty is defined as the ability of the motor to continuously carry an overload for an extended period of time. A common rating is an overload of 25 percent for 2 hours. It is expected that the motor will not reach thermal equilibrium for the time specified for the overload rating.

Mechanical Integrity

Mechanical integrity involves mechanical stresses, vibrational forces, and the ability to keep moving parts separate from stationary parts. The mechanical stresses imposed on motors are due to motor torques and loads. Motors that are switched frequently are more susceptible to these stresses. Vibrations are a result of improper alignment, incorrect mounting, and improper installation, which will tend to deteriorate the motor life performance.

However, the most critical mechanical part of the motor is the bearings, where stationary and rotating parts meet. To ensure optimum performance, the bearings should be properly matched to the load, kept clean, lubricated, and aligned properly. Motor bearings include babbitted, sleeve, and ball types. The fatigue life of ball bearings varies inversely with the cube of the load. The load usually imposes a side force on the shaft extension owing to driven-equipment connections such as belts, gears, or chains. The fatigue life of sleeve bearings is infinite and if maintained properly they will last indefinitely.

Motors and generators conforming to NEMA standards are designed to operate in accordance with ratings under usual service conditions as listed in

NEMA MG1-14.02. Motors and generators operated under service conditions other than those specified in NEMA may involve some hazard. The severity of this hazard depends upon the degree of departure from the usual conditions. Hazards usually result from overheating, abnormal deterioration of the insulation, mechanical failure, corrosion, and fire. Therefore, the manufacturer should be consulted for further information concerning the usual service conditions.

AC Motors

Criteria used as guides for the application of ac motors are discussed next.

ENVIRONMENTAL CONDITIONS
The usual service conditions that a motor is exposed to are the following:

- Ambient temperature not to exceed 40°C and areas with adequate ventilation.
- Altitude not to exceed 3,300 ft.
- Machine installed on a rigid mounting and with belt, chain, or gear drive.

Unusual service conditions for motor operation or exposure can be listed as the following:

- Combustible, explosive, abrasive, or conducting dust.
- Excessively dirty operating conditions where accumulation of dirt will interfere with motor ventilation.
- Chemical fumes and explosive or flammable gases.
- Abnormal shock, vibration, or mechanical loading from external sources.
- High humidity areas, oil vapors, steam, or salt-laden air.
- Excessive departure from rated voltage, frequency, or both.
- Supply voltage is unbalanced.
- Operation above rated speed.
- Poor ventilation.

DIRECTION OF ROTATION
Synchronous, universal, single-phase, and nonreversing dc motors have counterclockwise rotation when facing the end of the machine opposite the drive. For ac and dc generators, the rotation is clockwise.

OPERATION AT ALTITUDES ABOVE 3,300 FEET
The temperature rises for motors and generators are based on a maximum altitude of 3,300 ft with a maximum ambient temperature of 40°C. Motors and generators having a class A or B insulation system and temperature rises shown in Table 2–12 will operate satisfactorily at altitudes above 3,300 ft with ambient temperatures as shown in Table 2–13.

VOLTAGE AND FREQUENCY

- General induction and synchronous motors are designed for a rated voltage, frequency, and number of phases. The supply voltage must be known in order to select the proper motor. For ac motors, the motor nameplate voltage will normally be less than the nominal power system voltage, as shown in Table 2–14 for three-phase 60-Hz motors:

- *Voltage and frequency variations:* When the voltage at the terminals of a motor varies from nameplate rating, the performance or life of the equipment is sacrificed. The effect may be serious or minor depending upon the amount the voltage deviates from the nameplate rating. NEMA standards provide a ±10 percent tolerance from the nameplate rating for operation of induction general-purpose motors. However, even small deviations of voltage from nameplate ratings have an effect on the performance of the motor. The following are some of operating results caused by variations of frequency and voltage.

  High voltage on induction motor: The most significant effects of too high a voltage are increased torque, starting current, and heat, and decreased power factor.

  Low voltage on induction motor: The most significant effects of too low a voltage are reduced starting torque, increased power factor, and increased heating. The increased heating at low voltage and full load reduces the life of the insulation system of the motor.

  High and low frequency of induction motor: An increased frequency of the induction motor above the rated frequency will usually improve the power factor, decrease locked rotor torque, and increase the speed, friction, and windage loss. A decreased frequency below nameplate

TABLE 2–13.
AMBIENT TEMPERATURE VERSUS ALTITUDE

Ambient Temperature (°C)	Maximum Altitude (ft)
40	3,300
30	6,600
20	9,900

TABLE 2−14.
MOTOR VOLTAGE RATINGS

Nominal Power System Voltage (V)	Motor Utilization (Nameplate) Voltage (V)
208	200
240	230
480	460
600	575
2,400	2,300
4,160	4,000
6,990	6,600
13,800	13,200

rating will have the opposite effects. When variations of frequency and voltage occur at the same time, the effects are superimposed. NEMA standards allow a combined voltage and frequency deviation of ±10 percent.

Voltage unbalance: The voltage supplied to the motor should be equal because voltage unbalance will produce circulating negative-sequence currents, which in turn produce heating in the motor. Two to three percent unbalance voltages to the motor will produce the same heating as a 10 percent overload on the motor. A motor should be derated when the unbalance voltage reaches 4 percent.

HORSEPOWER, TORQUE, AND SPEED CONSIDERATIONS
The horsepower of a motor can be defined as the capability of the motor to do a given amount of work. Motors are rated as fractional or integral horsepower. The torque of a motor can be defined as the turning force developed by the motor, or it can be referred to as the resistance offered to the turning force by the driven load. Usually, torque for motors is expressed in terms of percentage of rated full-load torque. The speed of the motor is expressed as revolutions per minute (rpm), that is, a rate of measure of motion. The several definitive speed terms (as outlined in the section on the classification of motors according to variability of speed) that are common to all motors are standardized in order to relate the delivery of torque at a given speed for purposes of application. For ac motors the synchronous speed can be computed as

$$\text{synchronous speed }(N_s) = \frac{120 \times \text{frequency}}{\text{no. of poles}}$$

Induction motors, however, operate at actual speeds that are less than the synchronous speed because of losses in the motor. The difference between synchronous and actual speed is known as slip. Slip is usually expressed as a percentage of synchronous speed and can be calculated as

$$\text{slip (\%)} = \frac{(\text{synchronous rpm}) - \text{actual rpm} \times 100}{\text{synchronous rpm}}$$

The horsepower of the motor can be stated in mechanical or electrical terms. One horsepower is equal to 33,000 ft-lb/min. The torque produced by an electric motor can be calculated as

$$\text{torque} = \frac{5{,}252 \times \text{horsepower}}{\text{actual speed}}$$

Also

$$\text{horsepower} = \frac{\text{watts}}{746} = \frac{\text{kW}}{0.746} = \frac{\text{torque} \times \text{actual speed}}{5{,}252}$$

A typical torque–speed curve for a motor is shown in Figure 2–37. The various NEMA design motor torque–speed curves are shown in Figure 2–38.

In order to apply motors, the first thing to determine is the desired full-load speed and the desired horsepower at that speed. Other factors required when applying motors are type of torque required by the load and the starting current limitations. Motor torque characteristics must match those of the load from starting to the time when the motor reaches its rated speed. The motor must develop net accelerating torque for every point on the load curve in order to reach its actual speed.

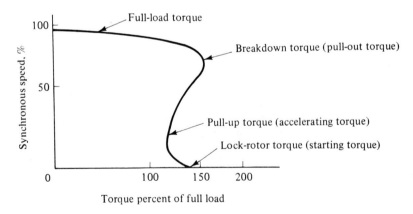

FIGURE 2–37.
Typical torque–speed curve.

To understand the various torques developed by the motor, the following definitions are given; they are shown in Figure 2–37.

- *Lock-rotor torque (starting torque):* The minimum torque developed by the motor for all angular positions of the rotor when the primary winding (stator winding) is energized with ac power supply.
- *Accelerating torque:* The torque developed with rated-power input during the period from standstill to full speed. This is the net positive torque available to the motor beyond the torque required by the load.
- *Breakdown torque (maximum torque):* The maximum torque developed by the motor at rated power input without an abrupt change in speed.
- *Pull-out torque:* The maximum torque developed by a motor for 1 min without stalling. It is frequently referred to as the breakdown torque.
- *Pull-in torque:* The torque developed during the transition from rated speed (slip speed) to synchronous speed.
- *Pull-up torque:* The minimum torque developed with rated horsepower input during the period of acceleration from standstill to rated speed.
- *Full-load torque:* The torque developed at rated speed with rated power input.

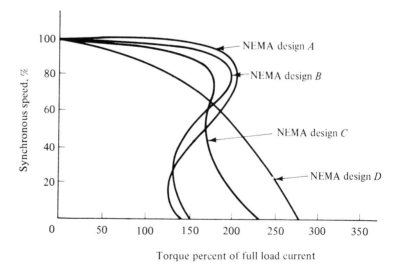

FIGURE 2–38.
NEMA design motors torque–speed curves.

Torque characteristics of various motors can best be described by comparing one motor type with another. Torques are classified as very high, high, medium, low, and very low. The torque–speed curves for the various NEMA designs as listed under classification according to application are shown in Figure 2–38.

POWER FACTOR

The connected motor load in a facility is usually a major factor in determining the system power factor. Low system power factor results in increased losses in the distribution system. Induction motors inherently cause a lagging system power factor and, under certain circumstances, they can cause a very low system power factor.

The power factor of an induction motor decreases as the load decreases. When the load on the motor is increased, the rated load power factor increases; that is, a fully loaded motor has a higher power factor. A number of induction motors, all operating at light load, can cause the electrical system to have a low power factor. The power factor of induction motors at rated load is less for low-speed than for high-speed motors.

A small increase in voltage (10 percent) above rated voltage will decrease the power factor, and a small decrease in voltage (10 percent) below rated voltage will improve the power factor of an induction motor. However, other performance characteristics may be adversely affected by such a change in voltage. Therefore, operation as close as possible to the nameplate voltage and horsepower ratings is recommended.

Power-factor-correction capacitors can be used to improve the power factor of the electrical system. However, if they are used, they should be carefully selected and applied to avoid unsafe operating conditions. It is recommended that the motor manufacturer be consulted for the proper value of corrective capacitance.

The power factor of synchronous motors can range from 1.0 to approximately zero power factor leading, depending on the rated power factor and the load for which they are built. Standard designs are usually rated for either unity, 0.8 lagging, or 0.8 leading power factor. As previously stated, synchronous motors have the capability of improving the power factor of the electrical system.

MOTOR SELECTION

Induction motor. The selection of the induction motor depends on the performance characteristics of the driven machine, and these, in turn, determine the operating characteristics of the motor. Some machines, such as most fans, blowers, centrifugal pumps, and unloaded compressors, require a relatively low starting torque. After starting, the required driving torque increases with increasing speed up to the full-load speed and torque. A design B motor is frequently selected to drive this type of application.

Other machines, such as reciprocating air compressors and loaded conveyors, require relatively high starting torque. The torque needed to start the machine is sometimes greater than the torque required at full-load speed. A design C motor is frequently selected to drive this type of application. For driven machines that impose puslating loads or require frequent starting of the motor, such as punch press and well pumping and hoist applications, a design D is often used.

Synchronous motors. In general, large synchronous motors can be applied to any load that induction motors with design B or C characteristics can handle. They have a higher efficiency than an induction motor of the equivalent rating and are capable of improving the system power factor. When efficiency is a primary consideration in choosing a relatively large motor, a 1.0 power factor synchronous motor may provide the solution. Where system power factor improvement is a primary consideration, the use of a 0.8 leading power factor synchronous motor may provide the solution.

Multispeed motors. Multispeed motors can be designed to have speed–torque characteristics similar to those of design A, B, C, or D motors of the equivalent rating. They can be designed for variable torque, constant torque, or constant horsepower. For the highest efficiency, it is important to select the correct multispeed motor characteristic for the load at all operating speeds. Typical examples of variable-torque loads are fans and centrifugal pumps. Constant-torque motors are used to drive apparatus such as conveyors, positive displacement pumps, and compressors. Machine tools and winches are examples of drives requiring the use of constant-horsepower motors.

AC Generators

Application criteria for ac generators are discussed next.

SERVICE CONDITIONS
The ac generators, like ac motors, should be properly selected with respect to their service conditions. The usual and unusual conditions are the same for generator applications as those listed for ac motors. Some generators may operate in accordance with their ratings under one or more unusual service conditions. However, where some unusual service condition exists, a special-purpose generator may be required. Even though in such cases past experience may be the best guide in selecting the machine, it is recommended that the manufacturer be consulted concerning the mechanical and thermal duty of the machine.

RATINGS
The continuous basis of rating synchronous generators is in kilowatts (kW) or kilovolt-amperes (kVA) at 80 percent power factor. The ratings of kVA, speed, voltage, frequency, and so on, are expressed in NEMA standards MG1-1978,

section 22 for three-phase and single-phase machines. The excitation voltages
for the field windings are also stated in the same NEMA standards; they are
62.5, 125, 375, and 500 V direct current. These excitation voltages apply to
machines with brushes only. Synchronous generators are capable of carrying a
1-min overload of 50 percent of normal rated current with the field set at normal
rated load excitation. A synchronous generator is designed to withstand three-
phase short-circuit current at its terminal for 30 s operating at rated kVA and
power factor, at 5 percent overvoltage with fixed excitation. The phase current
due to faults other than three-phase faults must be limited by external means to
a value that does not exceed the maximum phase currents obtained from three-
phase fault.

The kilowatt (kW) output of the machine depends upon the voltage,
armature current, and power factor. Also, the synchronous generator kVA
ratings may be stated at definite voltage and frequency. The permissible load
output of the synchronous generator depends upon the balance of the load. It
is maximum for balanced loads and minimum for single-phase loads.

TEMPERATURE RISE
The temperature rise under rated load conditions for synchronous generators is
based on the insulation system used for the machines. The temperature rise is
determined in accordance with the latest IEEE standards, Test Procedures for
Synchronous Machines, publication no. 115. The method of temperature determination may be resistance or embedded resistance temperature detector
(RTD). Table 2–15 lists the various temperature rises for the various generator
sizes and insulation systems.

The standard ambient temperature is taken as 40°C, and where the ambient temperature is higher than the standard, it is recommended that the
temperature rise of generators be reduced as follows:

TABLE 2–15.
TEMPERATURE RISE FOR SYNCHRONOUS GENERATORS[a]

Machine Component	Method of Tempera- ture Measurement	Temperature Rise—(°C)			
		A	B	F	H
Armature windings:					
All kVA ratings	Resistance	60	80	105	125
1,563 kVA and less	RTD	70	90	115	140
Over 1,563 kVA					
7,000 V and less	RTD	65	85	110	135
Over 7,000 V	RTD	60	80	105	125
Field windings	Resistance	60	80	105	125

[a] NEMA standard MG1-1978.

- For increases in ambient temperature above 40°C up to and including 50°C, decrease the temperature rise by 10°C.
- For increases in ambient temperature above 50°C up to and including 60°C, decrease the temperature rise by 20°C.

VARIATION IN VOLTAGE

Synchronous generators can operate at rated kVA, frequency, and power factor at voltages above and below the rated voltage not to exceed 5 percent. The maximum voltage any synchronous generator can produce at a definite frequency depends upon the permissible pole flux and field heating. To maintain a rated voltage output, specific field excitation is necessary at some specified load and power factor.

REGULATION

Regulation of a synchronous generator at any given power factor is defined as a percentage rise in voltage, a constant frequency and excitation, when rated kVA load is removed. The regulation depends upon armature reactance, armature effective resistance, change in leakage flux with change in load, and armature reaction.

Direct-Current Motors

Application criteria for dc motors are discussed next.

SERVICE CONDITIONS

Similiar to ac motors, the dc motors should be selected with regard to their environmental conditions. The service conditions may be usual or unusual and may involve environmental as well as operating conditions. The service conditions listed for ac motors also apply to the application of dc motors.

OPERATION OF DC MOTOR ON RECTIFIED ALTERNATING CURRENT

The performance of a dc motor operating on rectified ac current is different than if it were operating on a dc source having the same effective value of voltage. The reason for this is due to the continuous ripple or pulsation of the output voltage from the rectified ac voltage source. The ripple effect appears in the motor armature current and thus affects its performance. The effect of the rectified voltage on the motor armature current becomes significant when the rectifier pulse number is less than 6 and/or the amount of phase control is more than 15 percent. Also when a dc motor is operated from an unfiltered rectifier power supply, bearing currents may result. Ripple currents may flow to ground by means of capacitive coupling between rotor winding and core. Even though these currents are small in magnitude, they may cause damage to antifriction and sleeve bearings under certain circumstances. Measures should be taken to minimize these currents to avoid damage to the motor.

OPERATION OF THE DC MOTOR BELOW BASE SPEED

When a dc motor is operated below base speed by means of reduced armature voltage, the motor will heat up if rated full-load torque is maintained. To avoid overheating of the motor, reduce the load to compensate for the overheating of the motor. The speed of the dc motor is directly proportional to the armature voltage, and the torque is directly proportional to the armature current. Overheating results owing to the insufficient heating-dissipating ability of the motor at these speeds.

OPERATION OF THE DC MOTOR ABOVE BASE SPEED

Direct-current motors are built so that in case of an emergency they can withstand an overspeed of 25 percent above rated full-load speed without mechanical injury.

OVERLOAD CAPABILITY

The general industrial motors of open, forced-ventilation, and totally enclosed water-air-cooled types are capable of carrying, with successful commutation, 115 percent of rated horsepower load continuously at rated voltage throughout their speed range. Refer to NEMA standard MG1-23.41 for momentary duty on these and other types of motors.

Direct-Current Generators

Application criteria for dc generators are discussed next.

SERVICE CONDITIONS

The dc generators should be properly selected with respect to their service conditions. These conditions may be usual or unusual, involving environmental and operating conditions. The typical service conditions that have been listed under the ac motor section in this chapter also apply to dc generators.

RATINGS

The dc generators are classified into industrial dc and other dc integral-horsepower generators and large-apparatus dc generators (larger than 0.6 kW/rpm) of open type. The industrial generator ratings range from 0.75 to 720 kW, speeds range from 720 to 3,450 rpm, and voltages range from 125 to 500 V. The large-apparatus dc generator ratings range from 125 to 6,400 kW, speeds range from 200 to 900 rpm, and voltages range from 250 to 700 V. Refer to NEMA standards MG1-15 and MG1-24 for specific information on generator size, speed, and voltage ratings.

TEMPERATURE RISE

The temperature rise of dc generators under rated load conditions is dependent on the type of insulation system and enclosure used for the various parts of the machine. Either the thermometer or the resistance method is used for the measurement of temperature rise. Refer to NEMA standards MG1-15 and MG1-24 for specific information on temperature rise for the two types of generators.

OVERLOAD CAPABILITY

Industrial-type generators are capable of carrying overload for 1 min, with successful commutation loads of 150 percent of the continuous rated load amperes at rated load excitation. Large-apparatus dc generators of open type are capable of carrying 115 percent of rated current for 2 hours and 200 percent of rated current for 1 minute at rated speed and rated or less-than-rated voltage.

VOLTAGE EXCITATION

Large-apparatus dc generators, when operated at less than rated voltage, shall carry currents equal to those corresponding to their kilowatt and voltage ratings. The load voltage at rated load of a self-excited, flat, compound-wound, dripproof industrial generator, rated at 50 kW and smaller and employing class B insulation, shall not exceed 112 percent of the hot voltage at rated load.

OVERSPEED

Direct-current generators are constructed so that, in an emergency, they will withstand an overspeed of 25 percent without mechanical injury.

2-6 MOTOR CONTROL CENTERS (MCC) AND MOTOR CONTROLS

In this section, motor control centers and basic motor controls are discussed. Motor starters, which are an integral part of MCC, are available in many sizes, which have been standardized by NEMA. Modern motor controls, no matter how complex they may be, are usually combinations of fundamental control circuits. The schematic and wiring diagrams of motor controls are usually required during maintenance and troubleshooting of these circuits. It is imperative that all maintenance personnel dealing with motor controls understand the fundamental control circuits and be able to read these diagrams in order to be able to carry out their assigned maintenance tasks. Because of the nature of this book, it is difficult to treat fully all aspects of motor controls. Therefore, only the basic fundamentals of MCC and motor control circuits are discussed for review purposes.

MOTOR CONTROL CENTERS (MCC)

Motor control centers are comprised of combination motor starters mounted in modular assembly with all associated motor controls. The MCCs include combination starters to meet National Electrical Code requirements, which are either a fusible disconnect switch or a circuit breaker to provide branch circuit protection. The two main elements of MCC (exclusive of motor controls) are MCC bus and enclosure assembly and motor starters.

MCC Bus and Enclosure Assembly

The MCC bus and enclosure assembly consist of groups of motor control equipment and circuits assembled and enclosed in a steel-clad enclosure. Motor control centers generally have a main three-phase bus to distribute the supply power to each unit of motor control equipment. The general arrangement is to have a main horizontal bus and several vertical buses (or some other means of connection such as cables) to distribute the power from the main bus. A fixed or bolt-type connection or a disconnecting-type connection, such as a stab arrangement, are commonly employed in these assemblies. NEMA has defined two classes and three types of motor control centers.

Class I control centers are essentially a mechanical grouping of combination motor controls, feeder tap, and/or other components arranged in a convenient assembly. They include connections from the common horizontal bus to the starting units. They do not include interwiring or interlocking between units or to remotely mounted devices, nor do they include control system engineering.

Class II control centers are similar to class I, but are designed to form a complete control system. They include the necessary electrical interlocking and interwiring between units and interlocking provisions to remotely mounted devices. A connection diagram of the complete control assembly showing remote control devices to illustrate the system and sketches showing overall dimensions are provided.

Type A includes no terminal blocks. Combination-type starters are factory wired and assembled in the structure in the most efficient arrangement. No wiring external to the unit is furnished.

Type B is essentially the same as type A except that all control wires terminate at blocks near the bottom of each unit. Load terminals are all conveniently located adjacent to the control terminal blocks. Plug-in-type terminal blocks for all control wiring and load wiring through size 2 are provided. Control wiring above size 2 can be supplied when specified.

Type C is similar to type B. All control and load wiring is factory wired for up to size 3 and is extended from the unit terminals to master terminal blocks located at the top or bottom of each vertical compartment.

Various combinations of the above-mentioned MCC are available. They are grouped as class I, type A, B, or C and class II, type A or B. NEMA standards have established short-circuit ratings for the horizontal and vertical bus as 10,000, 14,000, 22,000, 30,000, and 42,000 A symmetrical for the standard MCC in the 600-V class equipment.

Motor Starters

A motor starter can be defined as an electric controller for starting a motor from rest to its rated speed. Starters range from simple manual across-the-line start to complex controllers for proper starting and stopping of motors without adverse effect to electric systems or the driven load. Starters consist of manual and magnetic types depending upon their application. NEMA has classified starters into the following classes:

- *Class A:* Alternating-current air-break and oil-immersed manual or magnetic controllers for service on 600 V or less. The short-circuit interrupting capability is up to ten times normal motor rating.
- *Class B:* Direct-current air-break manual or magnetic controllers for service on 600 V or less. They are capable of interrupting short circuits up to their overload capability.
- *Class C:* Alternating-current controllers capable of interrupting faults beyond their operating overload.
- *Class D:* Direct-current controllers capable of interrupting faults beyond their operating overload.
- *Class E:* Alternating-current and oil-immersed magnetic controllers for service on voltages of 2,200 and 4,600 V and capable of interrupting short circuits beyond their operating overloads. Class E starters are further divided into class E1 and class E2. Class E1 is rated for up to 50,000 A symmetrical, whereas class E2 uses current-limiting fuses to provide short-circuit interrupting rating up to 250,000 A symmetrical.

The ac motor starters are available in single phase, two phase, and three phase. Usually, the phases of starters are referred to as either one-, two-, or three-pole starters. The number of poles refers to the power contacts or motor load contacts. The motor starter voltage rating varies from 115 to 600 V for low-voltage ac starters and 2,200 to 4,600 V for high-voltage ac starters. For each voltage class, motor starters have designated horsepower ratings, which are established in accordance with NEMA standards. These ratings are shown in Table 2–16.

The factors to be considered in the application of motor controllers are starting, stopping, reversing, running, speed control, safety of operators, protection, and maintenance requirements. In addition to the factors already mentioned, consideration should be given to whether a manual, remote, or automatic control is required. All these factors must be considered to ensure that the motor control will function properly for the motor and its driven equipment.

Motor starters are intended for repetitive duty, and their normal life is measured in millions of operations. The interrupting capacity of a starter is normally ten times its continuous rating. Where the short-circuit ratings exceed

TABLE 2-16.
NEMA MOTOR STARTER SIZE (CONTINUOUS DUTY)

Phase	Motor Voltage (V)	Motor Minimum Horsepower	Motor Starter Sizes (NEMA)
Single-phase contactors	115	⅓	00
		1	0
		2	1
		3	1P
		3	2
	230	1	00
		2	0
		3	1
		5	1P
		7½	2
Three-phase contactors	230	1½	00
		3	0
		7½	1
		15	2
		30	3
		50	4
		100	5
		200	6
		300	7
		450	8
		800	9
	460/575	2	00
		5	0
		10	1
		25	2
		50	3
		100	4
		200	5
		400	6
		600	7
		900	8
		1,600	9
dc contactors	230	5	1
		10	2
		25	3
		40	4
		75	5
		150	6
		225	7
		350	8
		600	9

the rating of the starter, current-limiting fuses may be used to protect the contractor from high short-circuit currents. Since the starter provides the means of controlling the motor and providing the overload protection, it should be judiciously selected and applied to the motor circuit.

Direct-current starters consist of shunt controllers of constant potential type and include the following devices:

- Nonreversing or reversing line contactors, depending upon the type of application.
- A set of accelerating contactors for the starting of the motor from zero speed to its rated speed.
- Dynamic braking contactors and dynamic brake resistor, if applicable.
- Lock-out contactors, if applicable.
- Starting resistors.
- Mechanical and electrical interlocks.
- Overload, shunt, series, field, timing, and other relays as required.

The application of dc magnetic starters is mostly confined to multimotor and special applications involving many functions and adjustable-speed requirements. The horsepower requirement and ratings for dc contactors are available in 115, 230, and 550 V. The horsepower ratings and the NEMA size ratings for dc contactors are shown in Table 2–16.

Overload Relays

An important element of the starter is overload protection. Several types of overload relays are used in these starters.

THERMAL AND ELECTROMAGNETIC OVERLOAD RELAYS
To protect motors, overload relays are provided as an integral part of the motor starter. Three basic types of overload relays are used. They are thermal (solder pot), bimetallic, and magnetic types. The thermal relays are manually resettable, whereas the bimetallic and magnetic relays are automatically resettable. Air and fluids may be used to retard the motor of the plunger and to provide an inverse time–current characteristic in these relays. The inverse time curve shape is desirable because it tends to match the motor heating capability curve. The inverse time feature means that the greater the overload current is, the shorter the time of relay tripping.

Overload relays (heaters) provide excellent protection against motor overloads and momentary surges but do not provide good short-circuit protection. Therefore, to provide protection against short-circuit currents, a fused disconnect switch or circuit breakers are usually used. This type of application is known as combination starters. The overload heaters are made with different current ratings in order that a given heater element can be used to protect different-sized motors. In general, the heater rating is approximately 120 percent of motor full-load current. However, further adjustments can be made to the heater elements by means of a calibration lever on some overload relays. The application tables provided by manufacturers for heaters provide 115 to 125 percent protection for motors rated at 40°C with a service factor of 1.15 to 1.25.

If the motor operates at higher or lower ambient temperatures than 40°C, the selection of the heater element should be adjusted. The general rule is that, for every 1° rise in motor ambient temperature as compared to the ambient temperature of the motor starter, decrease the rated motor current by 1 percent for selection of heaters. Conversely, if the motor ambient is less by 1° than the motor starter ambient, increase the rated motor current by 1 percent. When motors are rated for a service factor of 1.0 or rated for 55°C, reduce the heater selection by one size. When ambient compensated overload relays are used, the selection of the heater should always be based upon rated motor current. The overload protection, whether it is thermal or magnetic type, should be carefully selected and matched to protect the motor.

MOTOR CONTROLS

AC Motor Controls

Alternating-current motor control circuits can vary from very simple to very complex. Regardless of the complexity of the controls, they are comprised of basic control circuit elements. The following is a description of the basic elements of motor control circuits.

TWO-WIRE CONTROL
The two-wire control circuit is commonly used with maintained contact switches, float switches, pressure switches, and temperature switches. The two-wire control circuit provides a low-voltage release; that is, upon loss of voltage, the coil will deenergize and its associated contacts will open. However, upon restoration of voltage, the coil will be energized (since maintained contacts remain closed), which will immediately close its contacts. Thus maintenance personnel working on such circuits should be aware of this type of condition, which can cause a serious hazard. The circuit for two-wire control is shown in Figure 2–39.

THREE-WIRE CONTROL
The three-wire control circuit uses a momentary push-button station contact for energizing the circuit. Also, there are three wires associated with this circuit. After the coil has been energized through the momentary contacts of the push button, the interlock contacts of the coil seal the circuit after the push button has been released and its contact opened. This circuit provides low-voltage

protection, because once the coil drops out due to loss of voltage, the circuit cannot be energized until the push button is pushed again. The three-wire circuit is shown in Figure 2–40.

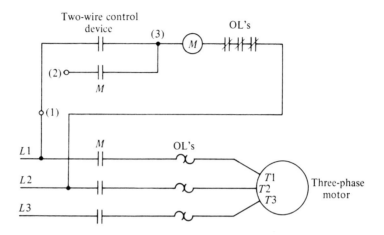

FIGURE 2–39.
Two-wire control circuit for a three-phase motor.

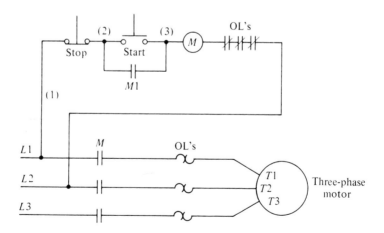

FIGURE 2–40.
Three-wire control circuit for a three-phase motor.

CONTROL CIRCUIT WITH MULTIPLE START–STOP STATIONS

When it is desired to start and stop equipment from more than one location, the start buttons are connected in parallel and stop buttons are added in series. This is applicable to either two or three-wire control. The three-wire control circuit with two start and stop locations is shown in Figure 2–41.

CONTROL CIRCUIT WITH A CONTROL RELAY

This circuit arrangement introduces a control relay in the start sequence of the circuit. It can be either a two- or three-wire control circuit. The control relay coil is energized by a maintained contact or momentary push-button station. The control relay in turn closes its auxiliary control contact to energize the main coil. This circuit arrangement is shown in Figure 2–42.

THERMOSTAT CONTROL CIRCUIT

This circuit arrangement provides thermostatic control of the main circuit. The thermostat single-pole double-throw contacts are wired in parallel with the main coil and its auxiliary contacts, as shown in Figure 2–43. When the thermostat is in its closed position, the coil "M" is energized and its holding contact seal in the circuit. As the thermostat moves from closed to open position, the circuit remains energized until the thermostat completes its open circuit. At this point the coil is short-circuited, thus dropping out the coil and deenergizing the circuit. To prevent burn-out of the coil during its short-circuit cycle, a resistor is added in series with the coil.

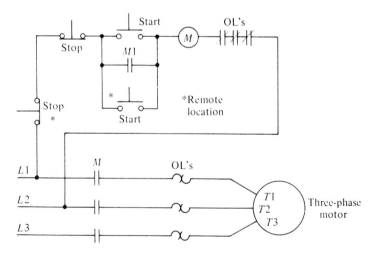

FIGURE 2–41.

Three-wire control multiple start–stop location for a three-phase motor.

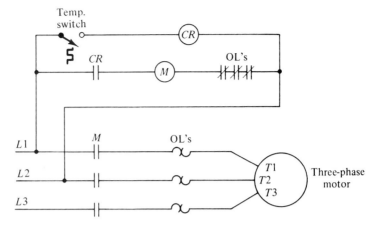

FIGURE 2–42.

Two-wire control with control relay.

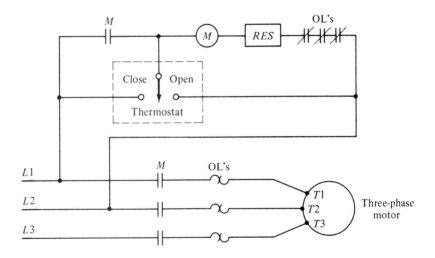

FIGURE 2–43.

Three-wire thermostat control for a three-phase motor.

SELECTOR SWITCH-CONTROL

A"hand-off-auto" selector switch is used with two-wire control applications for starting equipment manually as well as automatically. The pilot device's maintained contact is wired in series with the automatic position to energize the circuit automatically. The starter coil can also be energized manually through the "hand" position. This circuit is shown in Figure 2–44.

THREE-WIRE CONTROL WITH FUSED CONTROL TRANSFORMER

When high-voltage equipment is used, the control circuit used is wired through the step-down transformer. This circuit can also be used when control voltage needs to be less than line voltage for safety reasons. This circuit is shown in Figure 2–45.

THREE-WIRE CONTROL WITH JOGGING CONTROL

The jogging (or inching) of a motor is momentary operation of the motor where small movement of the driven machinery is required. This circuit can be used either with a control relay or selector switch. When used with the control relay, the pushing of the jog button energizes the motor starter coil independently of the control relay. This circuit is shown in Figure 2–46.

THREE-WIRE CONTROL WITH FORWARD AND REVERSE CONTROL

In many applications, forward and reverse control is required. This type of control can be accomplished with a forward-reverse stop push-button station. Mechanical and electrical interlocks can be incorporated into the control circuit. Also, limit switches in both directions may be used to stop motor overtravel. This control circuit is shown in Figure 2–47.

THREE-WIRE CONTROL FOR TWO-SPEED MOTOR

In applications of two-speed motor control, low and high speed push buttons are used. The motor can be started from rest at either speed or changed from

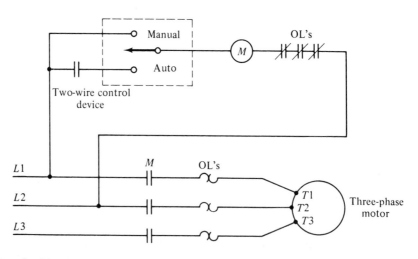

FIGURE 2–44.

Two-wire control with selector switch for a three-phase motor.

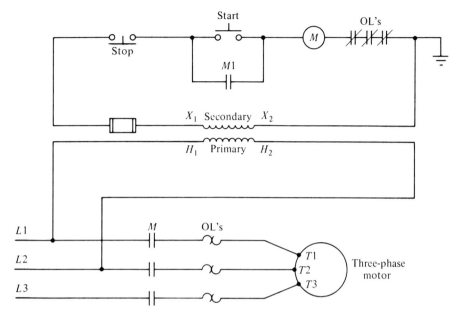

FIGURE 2–45.
Two-wire control with fused control circuit transformer.

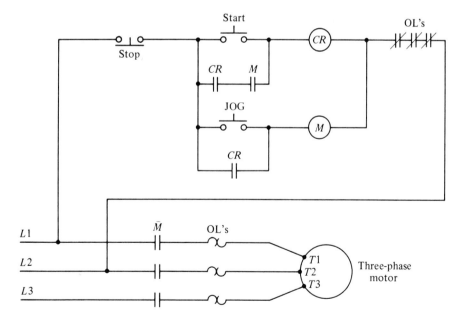

FIGURE 2–46.
Three-wire control with jogging control.

low to high speed. The control circuits prevent the connection of the motor from high to low speed in order to prevent excessive shock to motor and driven machinery. The motor has to be shut down from high speed before low speed control can be energized. This control circuit is shown in Figure 2–48.

DC Motor Controls

Direct-current motors are started gradually by limiting the motor armature current by means of inserting resistance in series with the motor armature circuit. The purpose of the resistance in the armature circuit is to limit the current drawn by the motor during the initial and each accelerating step. As the motor comes up to speed, the resistance is short-circuited in predetermined steps until the motor reaches its rated speed. The control methods used for acceleration of dc motors can be classified into two categories: (1) current-limit acceleration and (2) time-limit acceleration. Each method uses various forms of control principles for accelerating the dc motor.

CURRENT-LIMIT ACCELERATION

- Counter-emf acceleration.
- Lock-out contactor acceleration.

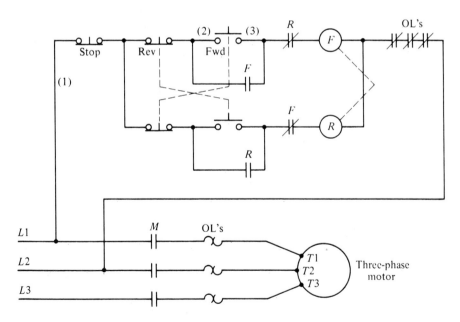

FIGURE 2–47.
Three-wire control forward–reverse for a three-phase motor.

- Series relay acceleration.
- Voltage drop acceleration.

TIME-LIMIT ACCELERATION

- Individual timing elements.
- Time of contactors only.
- Dashpot relays.
- Capacitor discharge.
- Inductive time limit.

Current-limit accleration methods employ devices that sense the motor current or voltage during starting and then cut out the necessary resistance required for each step in a predetermined order. These methods use the fact that, as the motor comes up to speed, the current drawn by the motor from the line decreases. The current-limit acceleration method is load dependent; that is, the time required to accelerate the motor will depend entirely on the load and will be constant only if the load is constant. When the load is light, the motor will accelerate rapidly, and if the load is heavy, the motor will accelerate slowly.

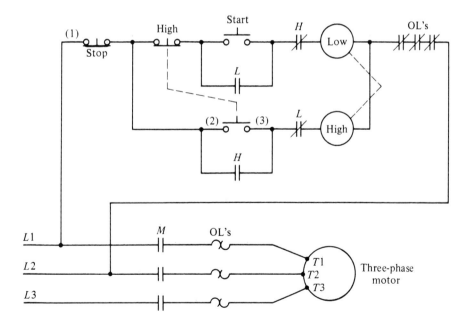

FIGURE 2–48.
Three-wire control for two-speed motor.

The time-limit acceleration method uses predetermined time periods for cutting out the resistance steps necessary for acceleration of the dc motor. The relays and other control devices employed in this method are time dependent and independent of the motor current, voltage, or load. The time-limit acceleration method, if adjusted properly, will limit the current peaks better than the current-limit acceleration method. Furthermore, the time-limit acceleration method is simpler and requires less relays and other control devices. The use of the time-limit acceleration method is almost universal.

CHAPTER 3

PREVENTIVE MAINTENANCE OF ELECTRICAL EQUIPMENT

3-1 INTRODUCTION

The objective of this chapter is to outline the recommended work practices that are usually performed for preventive maintenance of electrical equipment. The recommended procedures specified in this chapter do not pertain to equipment major overhaul and repair. However, many tasks performed during routine maintenance and major overhaul of equipment may be the same. The maintenance practices discussed in this chapter are applicable to equipment that has not reached an advance stage of deterioration. Moreover, these recommendations are written for the average conditions under which the equipment is required to perform and operate. It is further implied that all personnel associated with the maintenance are suitably trained and have experience in the maintenance of electrical equipment.

The recommended practices offered in this chapter are similar to those that manufacturers recommend for their equipment. If detailed instructions are required for particular equipment, the reader should consult the instruction manuals of the manufacturer for the equipment under consideration. The preventive maintenance of electrical equipment involves routine inspection, adjustment, testing, minor repairs, and special handling instructions. In addition, the successful operation of the equipment over its life is dependent upon proper installation and operation. Therefore, this chapter discusses these factors for transformers, insulating fluids, cables, switchgear, motors and generators, and other associated electrical equipment.

3-2 TRANSFORMER INSTALLATION, ACCEPTANCE, AND MAINTENANCE

The successful operation of transformers is dependent on proper installation, loading, and maintenance, as well as on proper design and manufacture. As with all electrical apparatus, neglect of certain fundamental requirements may lead to serious troubles, if not to the loss of the equipment.

The following guide is provided for the installation and maintenance of distribution and power transformers. The transformers are divided into dry and liquid types for the purposes of this guide.

DRY-TYPE TRANSFORMERS

Installation

Factors that should be kept clearly in mind in locating dry-type transformers are accessibility, ventilation, and atmospheric conditions.

Ventilated dry-type transformers (Figure 3–1) normally are designed for application indoors in dry locations. They will operate successfully where the humidity may be high, but under this condition it may be necessary to take precautions to keep them dry if they are shut down for appreciable periods.

FIGURE 3–1.

Type QL general-purpose UL-listed transformer with front panel removed. (Courtesy of General Electric Company, Specialty Transformers, Fort Wayne, Ind.)

Locations where there is dripping water should be avoided. If this is not possible, suitable protection should be provided to prevent water from entering the transformer case. Precautions should be taken to guard against accidental entrance of water, such as might occur from an open window, by a break in a water or steam line, or from use of water near the transformers. Adequate ventilation is essential for the proper cooling of transformers. Clean, dry air is desirable. Filtered air may reduce maintenance if the location presents a particular problem. When transformers are installed in vaults or other restricted spaces, sufficient ventilation should be provided to hold the air temperature within established limits when measured near the transformer inlets. This usually will require a minimum of 100 cubic feet (ft³) of air per minute per kilowatt (kW) of transformer loss. The area of ventilating openings required depends on the height of vault, the location of openings, and the maximum loads to be carried by the transformers. For self-cooled transformers, the required effective area should be at least 1 ft² each of inlet and outlet per 100 kVA of rated transformer capacity, after deduction of the area occupied by screens, gratings, or louvers.

Ventilated dry-type transformers should be installed in locations free from unusual dust-producing mediums or chemical fumes. Transformers above 75 kVA should be located at least 12 in. from walls or other obstructions that might prevent free circulation of air through and around each unit. The distance between adjacent transformers should not be less than this value. Smaller transformers can be mounted directly on the wall but should still be mounted at least 12 in. apart. Also, accessibility for maintenance should be taken into account in locating a transformer. If the transformer is to be located near combustible materials, the minimum separations established by the National Electrical Code should be maintained.

The transformer case is designed to prevent the entrance of most small animals and foreign objects. However, in some locations it may be necessary to give consideration to additional protection.

In general, a flat, level industrial floor is adequate and no special preparation is necessary because of the base construction used on these transformers, which completely eliminates the complicated process of grouting sills into concrete floors. If noise is a factor in the location and operation of any transformer, special consideration should be given to the installation of the equipment.

The impulse strength of these transformers is less than that of liquid-immersed units of the same voltage class. If there is any likelihood that transformers will be exposed to lightning or severe switching surges, adequate protective equipment should be provided.

Transformers of standard temperature rise are designed to operate at altitudes up to and including 3300 ft. Dry-type transformers are dependent upon air for dissipation of their heat losses; consequently, the effect of decreased air density due to high altitude will increase the transformer temperature. Standard transformers can be used at altitudes greater than 3,300 ft if the load to be carried is reduced below nameplate rating as follows:

- If the transformer is dry type, self-cooled, class AA, reduce the nameplate rating by 0.3 percent for each 330 ft above the altitude of 3,300 ft.
- If the transformer is dry type, forced air cooled, class AA/FA, reduce the nameplate rating by 0.5 percent for each 330 ft above the altitude of 3,300 ft.

If the maximum 24-hour average temperature of the cooling air is reduced below design levels, the altitude limitation of 3,300 ft can be safety exceeded without reducing the nameplate rating of the transformer within the limitations of Table 3–1.

Inspection

New transformers should be inspected for damage during shipment when received. Examination should be made before removing from cars or trucks, and if any injury is evident or any indication of rough handling is visible, a claim should be filed with the carrier at once and the manufacturer should be notified.

Subsequently, covers or panels should be removed and an internal inspection made for injury or displacement of parts, loose or broken connections, cracked porcelain, dirt or foreign material, and for the presence of free water or moisture. Corrective measures should be taken where necessary. Shipping braces should be removed if provided. After a transformer is moved, or if it is stored before installation, this inspection should be repeated before placing the transformer in service.

After making all the necessary primary and secondary connections, the equipment should be thoroughly inspected. Before placing in service, the operation of fans, motors, thermal relays, and other auxiliary devices should be checked. All bolted connections that may have loosened in shipment must be tightened before energizing. The case and core assembly of these transformers should be permanently and adequately grounded.

Acceptance Tests

After the transformer has been installed, the following tests should be conducted for acceptance:

INSULATION RESISTANCE TEST
The insulation resistance test is of value for future comparative purposes and also for determining the suitability of the transformer of energizing or application of the high potential test. The insulation resistance test must be successfully completed for factory warranty to be valid. *The insulation resistance test must be conducted immediately prior to energizing the transformer or begin-*

TABLE 3−1.

MAXIMUM 24-HOUR AVERAGE TEMPERATURE OF COOLING AIR, °C

	Altitude			
Type of Apparatus	3,300 Feet (1,000 Meters)	6,600 Feet (2,000 Meters)	9,900 Feet (3,000 Meters)	13,200 Feet (4,000 Meters)
Dry-type, class AA				
80°C rise	30	26	22	18
115°C rise	30	24	18	12
150°C rise	30	22	15	7
Dry-type, class AA/FA				
80°C rise	30	22	14	6
115°C rise	30	18	7	−5
150°C rise	30	15	0	−15

ning the dielectric test. These values, *corrected to factory test temperature* in degrees Celsius, must be either 1,000 megohms (MΩ) or a minimum of one half or more of the values obtained in the factory test when this value is less than 1,000 MΩ. If the corrected field test values at 20°C are less than the above minimum, the transformer is considered unsafe to energize and must be dried, using procedures described in this chapter.

AC HIGH POTENTIAL (DIELECTRIC) TEST
The dielectric test imposes a stress on the insulation since the dielectric test voltage is higher than the normal operating voltage. The insulation resistance test must be successfully completed immediately before performing the dielectric test to prevent the possibility of transformer failure due to moisture. The dielectric test supplements the insulation resistance tests by determining the suitability of the transformer for operation at rated voltage. Field test voltages should not exceed 75 percent of factory test values. The high potential test set must be variable to allow a gradual increase of test voltage from zero and a gradual decrease after the test is completed. These test values are shown in Table 3-2.

TRANSFORMER TURNS RATIO TEST (TTR)
The TTR test is used to determine the turns ratio of the transformer. It measures the number of turns of the primary winding with respect to the number of turns in secondary winding. The accepted values of the TTR test shall be not greater than 0.5 percent as compared with calculated values.

TABLE 3–2.
DIELECTRIC TEST VALUE FOR ACCEPTANCE AND PERIODIC
MAINTENANCE OF DRY-TYPE TRANSFORMERS

Transformer Winding Rated, AC Voltage (kV)	Factory Test, AC Voltage (kV)	Acceptance Field Test, AC Voltage (75%) (kV)	Maintenance Periodic Test, AC Voltage (65%) (kV)
1.2 and below	4	3.0	2.6
2.4	10	7.5	6.5
4.16	12	9.0	7.8
4.8	12	9.0	7.8
6.9	19	14.25	12.35
7.2	19	14.25	12.35
8.32	19	14.25	12.35
12.0	31	23.25	20.15
12.47	31	23.25	20.15
13.2	31	23.25	20.15
13.8	31	23.25	20.15

Maintenance

Like other electric equipment, these transformers require maintenance from time to time to assure successful operation. Inspection should be made at regular intervals and corrective measures taken when necessary to assure the most satisfactory service from this equipment. The frequency of inspection depends on operating conditions. For clean, dry locations, an inspection annually, or after a longer period, may be sufficient. However, for other locations, such as may be encountered where the air is contaminated with dust or chemical fumes, an inspection at 3- or 6-month intervals may be required. Usually, after the first few inspection periods, a definite schedule can be set up based on the existing conditions.

With the transformer deenergized, covers over openings in the case should be removed. Inspections should be made for dirt, especially accumulations in insulating surfaces or those which tend to restrict air flow, for loose connections, for the condition of tap changers or terminal boards, and for the general condition of the transformer. Observation should be made for signs of overheating and of voltage creepage over insulating surfaces, as evidenced by tracking or carbonization.

Evidence of rusting, corrosion and deterioration of the paint should be checked, and corrective measures taken where necessary. Fans, motors, and other auxiliary devices should be inspected and serviced.

CLEANING

If excessive accumulations of dirt are found on the transformer windings or insulators when the transformer is inspected, the dirt should be removed to permit free circulation of air and to guard against the possibility of insulation breakdowns. Particular attention should be given to cleaning top and bottom ends of winding assemblies and to cleaning out ventilating ducts.

The windings may be cleaned with a vacuum cleaner, blower, or with compressed air. The use of a vacuum cleaner is preferred as the first step in cleaning, followed by the use of compressed air or nitrogen. The compressed air or nitrogen should be clean and dry and should be applied at a relatively low pressure (not over 25 psi). Lead supports, tap changers and terminal boards, bushings, and other major insulating surfaces should be brushed or wiped with a dry cloth. The use of liquid cleaners is undesirable because some of them have a solvent or deteriorating effect on most insulating materials.

TESTING FOR ROUTINE MAINTENANCE

Following are the tests that are required for routine maintenance of dry-type transformers.

- Insulation resistance test of winding to winding and winding to ground. This test is similar to the test listed under installation and acceptance.
- Dielectric absorption test should be made winding to winding and winding to ground for 10 minutes. The polarization index should be above 2.0 for acceptable limits.
- Turns ratio test (TTR) should be conducted similarly to that under acceptance.
- Alternating current overpotential test should be made on all high- and low-voltage windings to ground. This is an optional test for routine maintenance testing. The recommended values of test voltage are shown in Table 3–2.
- Insulation power factor test can be conducted for each winding to ground and winding to winding. The acceptable value is less than 3 percent.

Drying out Methods

For the purpose of drying out, transformers can be considered as consisting of core and coil assembly. When it is necessary to dry out a transformer before installation or after an extended shutdown under relatively high humidity conditions, one of the following methods may be used.

- External heat.
- Internal heat.
- External and internal heat.

Before applying any of these methods, free moisture should be blown or wiped off the windings to reduce the time of the drying period.

DRYING BY EXTERNAL HEAT

External heat may be applied to the transformer by one of the following methods:

- By directing heated air into the bottom air inlets of the transformer case.
- By placing the core and coil assembly in a nonflammable box with openings at the top and bottom through which heated air can be circulated.
- By placing the core and coil assembly in a suitably ventilated oven.
- By placing incandescent lamps in the transformer enclosure.

It is important that most of the heated air be blown through the winding ducts and not around the sides. Good ventilation is essential in order that condensation will not take place in the transformer itself or inside the case. A sufficient quantity of air should be used to assure approximately equal inlet and outlet temperatures.

When using either of the first two external heating methods, heat may be obtained by the use of resistance grids or space heaters. These may either be located inside the case or box or may be placed outside and the heat blown into the bottom of the case or box. The core or coil assembly should be carefully protected against direct radiation from the heaters. It is recommended that the air temperature should not exceed 110°C.

DRYING BY INTERNAL HEAT

This method is relatively slow and should not be used if one of the other two methods is available. The transformer should be located to allow free circulation of air through the coils from the bottom to the top of the case. One winding should be short-circuited, and sufficient voltage at normal frequency should be applied to the other winding to circulate approximately normal current.

It is recommended that the winding temperature not be allowed to exceed 100°C, as measured by resistance or by thermometers placed in the ducts between the windings. The thermometers should be of the spirit type, because mercury thermometers give erroneous readings due to the generation of heat in the mercury as a result of induced eddy currents. The end terminals of the windings (and not the taps) must be used in order to circulate current through the entire winding. Proper precautions should be taken to protect the operator from dangerous voltages.

DRYING BY EXTERNAL AND INTERNAL HEAT

This is a combination of the two methods previously described and is by far the quickest method. The transformer core and coil assembly should be placed in a nonflammable box, or kept in its own case if suitable; external heat is applied as described in the first method, and current is circulated through the windings as described in the second method. The current required will be considerably less than when no external heating is used but should be sufficient to produce the desired temperature of the windings. It is recommended that the temperatures attained do not exceed those stated in previous two methods. Drying time depends on the condition of the transformer, size, voltage, amount of moisture absorbed, and the method of drying used.

The measurement of insulation resistance is of value in determining the status of drying. Measurements should be taken before starting the drying process and at 2-hour intervals during drying. The initial value, if taken at ordinary temperatures, may be high even though the insulation may not be dry. Because insulation resistance varies inversely with temperature, the transformer temperature should be kept approximately constant during the drying period to obtain comparative readings. As the transformer is heated, the presence of moisture will be evident by the rapid drop in resistance measurement. Following this period the insulation resistance will generally increase gradually until near the end of the drying period, when it will increase more rapidly. Sometimes it will rise and fall through a short range before steadying, because moisture in the interior of the insulation is working out through the initially dried portions. A curve with time as abscissa and resistance as ordinate should be plotted and the run should be continued until the resistance levels off and remains relatively constant for 3 to 4 hours.

Insulation resistance measurements should be taken for each winding to ground, with all windings grounded except the one being tested. Before taking insulation resistance measurements, the current should be interrupted and the winding should be short-circuited and grounded for at least 1 min to drain off any static charge. All readings should be for the same time of application of test voltage, preferably 1 min.

Constant attendance during the drying process is desirable. It is advisable to have a suitable fire extinguisher convenient for use in the event of an emergency.

Storage

Ventilated dry-type transformers preferably should be stored in a warm dry location with uniform temperature. Ventilating openings should be covered to keep out dust. If it is necessary to leave a transformer outdoors, it should be thoroughly protected to prevent moisture and foreign material from entering. Condensation and the absorption of moisture can be prevented or greatly reduced by the immediate installation of space heaters or other small electric heaters. If more convenient, incandescent lamps may be substituted for the space heaters. For transformer ratings of 750 kVA three phase and below, use six 150-watt (W) lamps; above 750 kVA three phase, use six 300-W lamps or the equivalent. Two lamps should be located under each coil, one on each side of the core. Lamps or heaters should be kept 4 to 6 in. from transformer coils and should never be allowed to come in contact with transformer coil installation.

LIQUID-TYPE TRANSFORMER

The following guide covers general recommendations for installation and maintenance of liquid-filled transformers (Figure 3–2). Many factors listed for dry-type transformers are also applicable to liquid-filled transformers and will not be discussed.

Installation

The transformer should be installed in accordance with NFPA Document 70, National Electrical Code (NEC) Article 450. Because of the ban on askarel for use as a transformer insulating fluid, liquids such as silicone, RTemp and others are being used. The fire point of these new liquids falls somewhere between oil and askarel, and it is very important that local and NEC regulations be followed.

FIGURE 3–2.
A liquid (silicone) filled transformer. (Courtesy of General Electric Company, Medium Transformers, Rome, Ga.)

One factor of importance for transformer installation is ventilation. Adequate ventilation should be provided in transformer rooms and vaults to carry transformer heat away. Self-cooled transformers should have adequate (2 to 3 ft) space between each unit to provide free air movement. The ventilation should be dustfree, dry, and noncorrosive, and should not contain any detrimental contaminants. As with dry-type transformers, precautions should be taken to prevent leakage of water into transformer rooms. The tank of the transformer should be permanently grounded by means of 4/0 cable or larger to the substation grounding bus. The transformer should be protected against lightning and other overvoltage conditions by proper lightning arresters.

Inspection

New transformers should be inspected when received for damage during transit. Examination should be made before unloading from the shipping carrier for indication of rough handling and injury to the transformer. After the transformer is removed from the truck or railcar, an internal inspection should be made for displacement of parts, broken or loose connections, dirt or foreign material, and the presence of water or moisture. If oil or transformer fluid was installed at the factory, check the transformer for leaks. Also check for positive gas pressure if the transformer is equipped with an inert gas. Inspection should include the examination of the transformer case, bushings, anchor and tie rods, grounding straps, drains, covers, valves, and other accessories shipped with the transformer. There should be enough ventilation in the transformer tank before entering to make visual inspection. It is essential that there be at least 16 percent oxygen content before entering the transformer tank. The inspection port cover should not be opened under wet conditions. It is good practice not to expose the transformer liquid to the atmosphere if the relative humidity is above 65 percent.

Acceptance Tests

Before a transformer is energized, it should be given the following tests for acceptance.

INSULATION RESISTANCE TEST
The insulation resistance test is valuable for determining if the transformer is in good condition and also to establish a bench mark for future comparative tests. The insulation resistance values measured are a function of temperature, whether the coils are immersed in the transformer liquid or not, or whether the windings are cold or hot. The measured values should be corrected to 20°C by multiplying them by correction factors as given in Table 3–3. The method of measuring insulation resistance is by megohmmeter, commonly called Megger®, which indicates the insulation resistance directly in ohms or megohms. A 1,000-V Megger is recommended for this test. Before this test is commenced,

TABLE 3–3.
INSULATION RESISTANCE CONVERSION FACTORS TO 20°C

Temperature (°C)	Transformer Oil	Dry
0	0.25	0.40
5	0.36	0.45
10	0.50	0.50
15	0.75	0.75
20	1.00	1.00
25	1.40	1.30
30	1.98	1.60
35	2.80	2.05
40	3.95	2.50
45	5.60	3.25
50	7.85	4.00
55	11.20	5.20
60	15.85	6.40
65	22.40	8.70
70	31.75	10.00
75	44.70	13.00
80	63.50	16.00

make sure that the tank and core are grounded and each winding is short-circuited, except the one that is being tested, at the bushing.

INSULATING LIQUID DIELECTRIC TEST
The insulating liquid should be sampled in accordance with ASTM D-923 standard for determination of its dielectric strength. This test is performed to ensure that the insulating liquid has not varied from its established levels or that dielectric strength has not been lowered through accumulation of contaminants. The oil samples are taken from the bottom of the tank, and samples for askarel, silicone, and RTemp are taken from the top of the tank.

TRANSFORMER TURNS RATIO TEST (TTR)
The TTR is performed to ensure that the turns ratio of the transformer is correct; that is, none of the transformer windings is shorted out. Basically, it compares the number of turns in winding 1 with the number of turns in winding 2. The test should be performed for each tap position for transformers equipped with tap changers. The TTR test can also verify the polarity of the transformer. The TTR test value for acceptance should not be greater than 0.5 percent as compared to calculated values.

HIGH-POTENTIAL (HI-POT) TEST

The hi-pot test (also called the overpotential test) should be made on all high- and low-voltage windings of the transformer to ground. Either ac or dc voltage can be used. However, the accepted practice is to apply either an ac or dc high-potential test to transformers up to 34 kV. For transformers above 34 kV, only the ac hi-pot test is used. For acceptance of the transformer, the ac hi-pot test can be applied at rated transformer voltage for 3 min. This is a go or no-go test. If the hi-pot voltage is held without any failure or malfunction of the transformer, the transformer is considered to have passed the test.

Maintenance

The objective of transformer maintenance is to safeguard against breakdowns by detecting potential causes and eliminating them. Therefore, periodic transformer maintenance will ensure many years of trouble-free operation. The transformer is a very simple, rugged device and is often ignored and forgotten until transformer failure occurs. However, transformers are a vital link in the electrical distribution system and should be given proper care and attention. Transformer maintenance schedules should be determined according to the critical or noncritical nature of the transformer and the load that is connected to it. Large power transformers are obviously more important than small lighting and distribution transformers; thus they warrant more attention and care. Proper maintenance of the transformer should include routine inspection and repair, transformer liquid maintenance and testing, transformer winding insulation maintenance and testing, and any other special maintenance that is recommended by the manufacturer of the transformer. A power transformer maintenance and testing guide with recommended frequency is given in Table 3–4.

ROUTINE INSPECTION AND REPAIR

Routine inspection and repair of the transformer involve the visual observation of the operating conditions of the transformer and necessary repair. The frequency of these observations depends upon the critical importance of the transformer, the environmental conditions, and/or the operating conditions. Various organizations such as the National Fire Protection Association (NFPA), National Electrical Testing Association (NETA), and manufacturers of transformers have published guides for interval of inspection and what to inspect. Following are typical schedules for conducting a routine inspection.

- *Load current:* The transformer loading determines the heating of the transformer. The temperature of the transformer determines its life expectancy, and it is important on large units to monitor load on an hourly basis. For proper loading of transformers, refer to ANSI standard C57.92 for liquid-immersed transformers and ANSI C57.96 for dry-type transformers. For small power transformers, a reading can be taken on a daily or weekly basis.

- *Voltage:* The voltage of the transformer should be monitored similarly to load current. To maintain rated secondary voltage, proper primary voltage would have to be applied. Voltage readings can be taken in conjunction with load current or recording voltmeters can be used. On transformers of lesser importance, voltage readings can be taken on a weekly basis.
- *Liquid level:* Liquid level is important since it not only supplies the cooling medium but also insulates the windings. Liquid loss may occur due to the evaporation of the fluid or due to leakage. Liquid-level

TABLE 3—4.
TRANSFORMER INSPECTION AND MAINTENANCE CHECKLIST

General Inspection Items	*Frequency*
Load current	Hourly or use recording meters
Voltage	Hourly or use recording meters
Liquid level	Hourly or use recording meters
Temperature	Hourly or use recording meters
Protective devices	Yearly
Protective alarms	Monthly
Ground connections	Every 6 months
Tap changer	Every 6 months
Lightning arresters	Every 6 months
Pressure-relief devices	Every 3 months
Breather	Monthly
Auxiliary equipment	Annually
External inspection	Every 6 months
Internal inspection	Five to ten years
INSULATING LIQUID	**FREQUENCY**
Dielectric strength	Annually
Color	Annually
Neutralization Number	Annually
Interfacial tension	Annually
Power factor test	Annually
SOLID INSULATION (WINDING)	**FREQUENCY**
Insulation resistance	Annually
Power factor	Annually
Polarization index (PI)	Annually
Hi-Pot (ac or dc)	Five years or more
Induced voltage	Five years or more
Gas-analysis test	Annually

readings can be taken when load readings are being taken. Any liquid lost by the transformer should be replaced promptly.

- *Temperature:* The load-carrying ability of the transformer is dependent upon its thermal capability. The total temperature of the transformer is the sum of the ambient temperature, winding insulation temperature, and hot-spot temperature. Normally, the average ambient is 30°C; the temperature rise above ambient for class A insulation is 55°C with a permissible hot-spot rise of an additional 15°C, which then gives a total temperature of 100°C. Any time the transformer is operated above its temperature rating, loss in transformer life can be expected. An 8° rule for class A insulation and 12° rule for class B insulation are quoted in the industry for determining the transformer life. In other words, if transformers with class A insulation are operated above their temperature ratings by 8°C, the transformer life can be expected to be cut in half; likewise, operating transformers with class B insulation 12°C above their temperature ratings will cut the transformer life in half. To monitor the temperature for large critical transformers, it is recommended that the following readings be taken on a daily basis.

Liquid temperature.

Ambient air temperature.

Water temperature (for water-cooled transformers).

Oil temperature (for forced oil-cooled transformers).

- *Protective devices:* Basic transformer protection is covered by the NEC. This protection is supplemented with additional protective relays and devices. It is important that protective devices are inspected and maintained on a regular basis to ensure that these devices will operate in case of transformer malfunction or failure. The following protective devices should be inspected and maintained on an annual basis.

Overcurrent phase and ground relays.

Differential relays.

Sudden pressure relays.

Under- and overvoltage relays.

Alarm and auxiliary relays.

Wiring and current-transformer associated with the protective relays.

- *Protective alarms:* Transformers come with various types of alarms, such as overtemperature, liquid temperature, and pressure-relief devices. These are usually open-type contacts that can be connected to either alarm or trip the circuit breaker. The alarm contact and associated wiring should be inspected on a monthly basis.

- *Ground connections:* The transformer tank is always solidly grounded to eliminate electric shock per the NEC. The grounding straps for transformer tanks should be checked for loose, broken or corroded connections. The ground resistance of the substation will depend upon the type and size of the substation. The ground resistance may vary from less than 1 Ω for large-sized substations to 25 Ω for very small-sized substations. The frequency of this inspection and test should be annual.

- *Lightning arrester:* When transformers are supplied from overhead lines, lightning arresters are used to protect the transformer from lightning and other surges. Lightning arresters should be inspected for looseness, broken parts, dirt, and other deposits. All dirt and deposit should be cleaned, loose connections tightened, and broken parts replaced during this check. The inspection should be done annually.

- *Pressure-relief device:* Most transformers are equipped with pressure-relief devices to relieve excessive pressure in the tank due to the internal arcing. This device is set to open at a pressure of 10 to 15 psi. Routine inspection of pressure-relief devices should include checking for leaks around joints, diaphragm cracking, and the like. This inspection should be done quarterly.

- *Breather:* Many transformers have breathers of either the open type or dehydrating type. The function of the dehydrating agent is to prevent moisture from entering the transformer tank. Most dehydrating breakers contain silica gel, which will change from blue when dry to pale pink when wet. Inspection can be made through a glass window provided for the purpose. The breathers should be checked monthly and the dehydrating agent replaced or reconditioned if found restrictive or wet.

- *Auxiliary equipment:* Auxiliary equipment required for cooling, such as fans, oil pumps, control devices, and wiring, should be checked on an annual basis. The equipment should be cleaned and damaged parts replaced.

- *External inspection:* The transformer should be given an external inspection on a semiannual basis. The inspection should include checking the tank, radiators, auxiliary equipment, gasket leakage, and metal parts for corrosion. Also, the electrical connection should be checked for tightness and overheating. Transformer bushings should be checked for mechanical damage, cleanness, and leakage. Bushings should be wiped clean on a regular basis to minimize flashovers.

- *Internal inspection:* This inspection involves the internal investigation of the tank and core. On open-type liquid-filled transformers, the look-in port cover can be removed to examine for evidence of moisture or rust around the bushing supports and transformer top cover. To examine the tank and core, the liquid can be drained out. Examination of the core should be made to check for sludge deposits, loose connections, and any damage to the transformer parts. Evidence of carbon may indicate internal problems. The winding inspection should be checked for damage to terminal panels, barriers, loose connections, and overall connection of the winding. Obviously, such things as untanking the transformer for internal inspection would have to be judiciously made and would depend on the age of the transformer and its overloading and trouble history. The frequency of this inspection should be 5 to 10 years or more.

- *Transformer liquid:* All transformer fluids are subject to deterioration, and the main contaminants are air, moisture, and heat. These contaminants react with transformer fluid and produce acids and sludge. The acid, in turn, attacks the winding insulation, and sludge deposits tend to decrease cooling. Moisture in the transformer fluid tends to lower the dielectric strength of the fluid, which, combined with sludge, will lower the flashover value of insulators and terminal boards inside the transformer tank. As discussed earlier, regular inspection of the transformer is needed to maintain the fluid in a contaminant free state. For proper maintenance of insulating fluids refer to Section 3–3.

Drying-out Methods

Similar to dry-type transformers, the liquid insulating transformer can be considered as consisting of core and coil assembly, except that the assembly is immersed in an insulating fluid. Elaborate measures are taken to prevent and detect the infiltration and increase of moisture content in the transformer. Before the transformer liquid becomes saturated with water, the paper insulation of the winding in a transformer has already absorbed a concentration of moisture because of its great affinity for water. The water in the paper insulation accelerates the degradation of the insulation and lowers its electrical integrity.

We have discussed in the previous sections several tests to judge the dryness of the transformer, such as insulation resistance, polarization index, and power factor. One simple method for detecting the water content in the transformer oil can be made by an approximate method known as the cloud test. It consists of cooling a test tube sample of oil in an ice bath. If a cloud appears in the test tube above 0°C, the transformer contains excessive moisture. Confirmation of the water content in the transformer can be made by a laboratory test.

The distribution of moisture in the transformer is always in a state of unequilibrium. Through the cooler range of temperatures, the solid insulation of the transformer winding will tend to absorb more moisture than the transformer liquid. However, as the transformer is loaded, the rise in winding temperature will release this moisture. This change due to varying loads and temperature is constant, regardless of whether there is an excess of water or only a very small quantity of moisture in the transformer. Also, transformer liquids such as oil tend to hold more water with an increase in temperature. In other words, there will be more moisture in the transformer oil when it is carrying a load than when it is unloaded. Other factors, such as decomposition of paper insulation and contaminants, will tend to generate more moisture in the transformer liquid.

When it becomes necessary to dry out liquid transformers, the following methods can be used: (1) heat alone, or (2) heat followed by vacuum.

HEAT ALONE

This method involves application of heat to the transformer alone. One form of heat application is oven drying, which can be done at any of the service shops of major manufacturers. When the transformer is oven dried in the service shop, it is important to monitor the winding resistance to see when the transformer reaches oven temperature (100 to 120°C). Power factor and insulation resistance measurement should be made at about 6-hour intervals to see when drying is achieved, that is, when at least four readings are of the same value.

HEAT FOLLOWED BY VACUUM

The heating of the transformer with liquid can be performed by applying short-circuit to the transformer or by circulating hot oil by means of an external system. As in the previous method, power factor and insulation resistance measurement should be made at about 6-hour intervals. Completed drying is indicated by at least four readings that are the same. The field drying methods may involve heating the transformer liquid, removing the liquid, and immediately applying high vacuum. Another method may involve removing the liquid and heating the transformer by circulation of hot air. Once the winding reaches 90 to 100°C, a high vacuum of about 0.5 torr is applied. When the temperature drops below 50°C, drying is stopped. The normal length of time to apply heat and vacuum may be a week or more, depending on the size of the transformer. Once the transformer is dried and the vacuum pulled, clean transformer liquid can be introduced into the transformer. Precautions to observe during this process are as follows:

- Before the vacuum is pulled, make sure the tank is braced for full vacuum.
- The air temperature for drying should not exceed 100°C.
- If new undried coils are used for replacement purposes, the coil clamps should be checked after drying is complete since shrinkage may occur during drying.
- When drying is performed on an energized transformer, precautions should be taken to prevent formation of bubbles during the degassing phase. Otherwise, immediate failure may occur.

- The transformer liquid level should be carefully watched because unintentional lowering of transformer liquid level may cause a transformer failure.

Storage

Transformers should be stored in a safe, dry, ventilated location with uniform temperature. In locations where no controls for uniform temperature exist, condensation and absorption of water can be minimized by installation of space heaters or incandescent lamps.

Because of new regulations on the use, disposal, and storage of askarel, transformers using askarel as an insulating liquid will require special storage facilities. The reader is urged to consult regulations put out by the Environmental Protection Agency (EPA).

Transformer Diagnostic Guide

For troubleshooting purposes, the following diagnostic guide is provided. This guide is by no means complete, and the reader is urged to check and test for the problem and its cause. In general, the following conditions will cause the troubles indicated:

- *Overtemperature:* Overtemperature can be caused by an overcurrent, overvoltage, insufficient cooling, low liquid level, sludge in the transformer liquid, high ambient, or short-circuited core. In dry-type transformers, this condition can be due to clogged ducts.

- *Winding insulation failure:* This is an electrical fault in the transformer winding insulation where it can involve phase to ground, phase to phase, three phase and/or ground, or turn-to-turn type short-circuit. The causes for this type of failure may be due to a short-circuit fault, lightning, overload or overcurrent condition, or transformer liquid containing moisture and contaminants.

- *Incorrect secondary voltage:* This condition can be due to improper turns ratio, abnormal primary voltage, and/or shorted turns in the transformer.

- *Bushing failure:* Bushing failure can be caused by flashover due to dirt accumulation and/or lightning strikes.

- *Internal arcing:* Internal arcing can be caused by low liquid level exposing live parts of the transformer, loose connections, or failure of the transformer dielectric. Usually, internal arcing can become audible and cause radio interference.

- *Core failure:* This condition is due to the failure of core laminations, core, bolts, clamps, and so on.

- *High exciting current:* Usually, high exciting currents are due to short-circuited core and/or open core joints.

- *Low dielectric strength:* This condition can be caused by condensation and penetration of moisture due to improper ventilation, broken relief diaphragm, leaks around transformer accessories, or cooling coil leakage.

- *Oxidation of oil:* Oxidation usually results in the formation of acids and sludge in the transformer liquid. It is mainly due to exposure to air and high operating temperatures.

- *Pressure-relief diaphragm broken:* This is due to an internal fault causing excessive internal pressures or the transformer liquid level being too high or excessive internal pressure due to loading of transformer.

- *Discoloration of transformer liquid:* Discoloration is mainly caused by carbonization of the liquid due to switching, core failure, or contaminations.

- *Leakage of transformer liquid:* Leakage can occur through screw joints, around gaskets, welds, casting, pressure-relief device, and so on. The main causes are improper assembly of mechanical parts, improper filters, poor joints, improper finishing of surfaces, defects in the material used, or insufficient tightness of mechanical parts.

- *Moisture condensation:* The main causes for moisture condensation are improper ventilation in open-type transformers and a cracked diaphragm or leaky gaskets in sealed-type transformer.

- *Gas-sealed transformer troubles:* In gas-sealed transformers, additional problems can be the loss of gas, oxygen content above 5 percent, or gas regulator malfunctions. These problems are caused by gas leaks above the oil, leaky valve seats, insufficient gas space, and/or insufficient flushing of gas space with nitrogen.

- *Transformer switching equipment troubles:* Many transformers are equipped with tap chargers and other switching equipment. The problems associated with these transformers may be excessive wearing of contacts, mechanism overtravel, moisture condensation in mechanism liquid, and others. Excessive contact wear is due to loss of contact pressure from weakened springs or a contact-making voltmeter set at too narrow a bandwidth or insufficient time delay. Mechanism overtravel usually is due to defective or improper adjustment of controller contacts. Moisture condensation is due to improper ventilation, and carbonization is due to excessive operation and lack of filtering. Other problems such as control fuse blowing and mechanism motor stalling are due to short-circuits in the control circuit, mechanical binding, or low-voltage conditions in the control circuitry.

3-3 INSULATING LIQUIDS MAINTENANCE

The liquids used in transformers are mineral oil and synthetic liquids such as askarel, silicone, RTemp and Wecosol. The use of askarel, which is a poly-chlorinated biphenyl (PCB), has been banned owing to its toxicity. However, there are a great number of transformers in use that have askarel in them. New liquid, such as silicone and RTemp, have been in use for the last several years. Both silicone and RTemp are of 50 centi-stokes viscosity and are specially manufactured for transformer use. To properly maintain the transformer liquids free of contaminants, regular inspection of the transformer is needed. A brief discussion on the deterioration of insulating fluid is undertaken for maintenance purposes.

DETERIORATION OF INSULATING OIL

Effect of Oxygen on Oil

Moisture contamination is the most common cause of deterioration in the insulating quality of oil. This contamination can be readily corrected by purification. A slow but more serious deterioration, the formation of acids and sludge, is caused by oxidation. Thus, the exclusion of oxygen is of prime importance. In open-breather transformers, the oxygen supply is virtually unlimited and oxidative deterioration is faster than in sealed transformers. Atmospheric oxygen and oxygen contained in water are the sources available for the oxidation of insulating oils. When water is present in insulating oils, oxidation of the oil will take place. Therefore, leaking gaskets constitute a very real hazard since a water leak is, in effect, an oxygen leak. The rate of oxidation also depends on the temperature of the oil; the higher the temperature is, the faster the oxidative breakdown. An increase in temperature of 10°C or 50°F generally doubles the rate of oxidation. This fact points to the importance of avoiding overloading of transformers, especially in the summertime. Oxidation results in the formation of acids in the insulating oil and the formation of sludge at a more advanced state of oxidation.

Moisture in Oil

Water can be present in oil in a dissolved form, as tiny droplets mixed with the oil (emulsion), or in a free state at the bottom of the container holding the oil. Demulsification occurs when the tiny droplets unite to form larger drops, which sink to the bottom and form a pool of free water. Emulsified water or water in the free state may be readily removed by filtering or centrifugal treatment. However, dissolved water is not removed by centrifugal treatment; the filtration process can partially remove dissolved water if the filter papers are thoroughly dried before filtration.

The effect of moisture on the insulating properties of oil depends upon the form in which the moisture exists. A very small amount of emulsified water has a marked influence in reducing dielectric strength of oil. Free moisture in oil usually shows up above 50 to 60 parts per million (ppm) depending upon temperature. Accepted levels of water in oil are shown in Table 3–5. The amount of moisture that can be dissolved in oil increases rapidly as the oil temperature increases, as shown in Figure 3–3. Therefore, an insulating oil purified at too high a temperature may lose a large percentage of its dielectric strength on cooling, because the dissolved moisture is then changed to an emulsion.

Oil Deterioration in Transformers

In transformers, sludge sticks to the surface through which heat should be dissipated; the sludge forms a blanket barrier to the flow of heat from the oil to the coolant and from the core and coils to the cool oil. If allowed to continue long enough, the sludge may even block off the flow of oil through the cooling ducts. As a result, the transformer insulation gets too hot and is damaged, particularly between turns of the windings. Deterioration of the turn insulation may eventually lead to short circuits between turns and the breakdown of the transformer. When oxidation progresses to the point where sludge is being precipitated, the first step should be to remove the sludge from the transformer by a high-pressure stream of oil and to either replace the sludged oil or treat it with activated clay to remove the acid. Under favorable conditions, complete treatment of the oil is less costly than replacing it with new oil.

Absorption of Moisture by Insulating Materials

Solid insulation in transformers is very porous and thirstily absorbs water. Some of the water that is dissolved in the oil is absorbed from the oil by the insulation. As more water is dissolved in the oil, more water is absorbed. Once absorbed, it is difficult to remove. The most effective method for drying out the insulation in transformers is with heat and vacuum. Sometimes a vacuum cannot be applied in the field; then the transformer insulation must be dried by

TABLE 3–5.
MAXIMUM ALLOWABLE MOISTURE IN OIL

Voltage Level (kV)	Maximum Moisture (ppm)
5	30
15	30
35	25
69	20
138 up	15

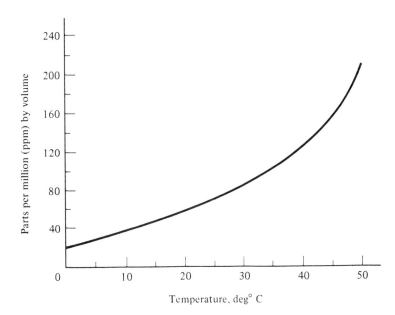

FIGURE 3–3.

Maximum amount of water dissolved in mineral oil as affected by temperature.

circulation of hot, dry oil. This oil should then be cooled and dried. Since the dielectric strength of insulation is reduced by moisture, it is important that the insulation not be allowed to absorb the moisture in the first place.

Absorption of Nitrogen by Oil

Special precaution should be taken in operating transformers with nitrogen over the oil to avoid bubbling of the oil due to release of dissolved nitrogen when the pressure drops. Experience has shown that the automatic gas-pressure regulating system should be adjusted to limit the nitrogen pressure range from ½- to 3-psi (lb/in.²) gauge to avoid formation of these bubbles and subsequent troubles due to corona deterioration.

RECONDITIONING USED INSULATING OILS

Natural Precipitation

Oil that has low dielectric strength or contains deposits of sludge or other contamination should receive maintenance attention. Low dielectric strength indicates the need for drying by mechanical filter or vacuum dehydrator. High acidity, high power factor, or low intrafacial tension (IFT) values indicate the need for reclaiming treatment. When used insulating oils are to be subjected to reconditioning and/or reclaiming processes, every advantage possible should be taken of natural precipitation. Considerable savings can frequently be realized in processing used oil if it is allowed to remain in its container undisturbed for at least 24 hours so that water and suspended solids can settle out. The oil can then be removed without disturbing the residue in the bottom of the container, thus obviating the necessity of removing this residue from the processing machinery.

Filter Presses

Filter presses (Figure 3–4) vary somewhat in form, but are based upon the principle of forcing oil under pressure through a series of absorbing materials, such as paper, fuller's earth, etc. Filters of this type are capable of removing carbon, water, sludge, and the like, when they are in suspension, but except for certain special arrangements, they cannot remove them effectively when they are dissolved or in colloidal form. These devices (particularly those with centrifuges) will not remove air but, in fact, tend to aerate the oil.

FIGURE 3–4.
Fuller's earth (attapulgus clay) filter press system: Stokes Model No. 900-820-225. (Courtesy of Stokes Division, Penwalt Corp., Philadelphia, Pa.)

Experience has shown that the most efficient temperature at which to filter insulating oil is between 20° and 40°C. Below 20°C the viscosity increases rapidly, while at temperatures above 40°C the moisture is more difficult to separate from the oil.

FILTER PRESS OPERATION
When the oil is to be purified by the use of a filter press using blotting paper, the paper should be well dried to obtain the most efficient operation; otherwise, the paper may actually add moisture to the oil. An oven should be used for drying the paper, and the sheets should be separated as they are hung on rods in the oven to permit free circulation of air and to ensure the most rapid drying. The filter paper should be dried from 6 to 12 hours at a temperature of 101° to 105°C. After drying, the paper should be taken from the oven directly to the filter, or it may be stored in dry transformer oil for future use. When transferring the paper, care should be taken to handle it as little as possible to avoid the absorption of moisture from the hands and to minimize the time of exposure to the air.

When purifying very wet oil with a filter press, the back pressure will not increase appreciably as the filter paper absorbs moisture. Therefore, the operator should make frequent dielectric tests of the oil discharged from the filter press to determine when the paper should be replaced. When purifying oil containing materials such as sludge or small carbon particles, considerable back pressure will develop as the filtering progresses because of the materials clogging up the filter paper. When the back pressure reaches about 75 psi, the paper should be replaced.

Cartridge Filters

In recent years mobile cartridge-type filters (Figure 3–5) for reconditioning transformer oil are being used. These units are available in various sizes with oil-processing capacities ranging from 10 to 75 gal/min and utilize disposable cartridges with filter densities ranging from 1 to 25 micrometers (μm). (*Note:* six-micrometer filters are recommended for transformer oil.) These mobile filter units are smaller, lighter, and more portable than large filter presses, have greater oil-flow capacities, and in most cases provide better water and particle removal. In addition, a drying oven is not required since the filter cartridges are hermetically sealed in plastic for shipment and storage.

Centrifuges

Another means of separating free and suspended contaminants, such as carbon, water, and sludge, from oil is the continuous centrifuge [Figure 3–6(a) and (b)]. In general, the centrifuge can handle much greater concentrations than can the conventional filter press, but it cannot remove some of the contaminants as completely as a filter press. Consequently, the centrifuge is generally used for rough bulk cleaning where large amounts of contaminated oil are to be handled.

FIGURE 3–5.
Mobile filter cartridge blotter-paper type dryer filter press (capacity to 7,500 gal/hr)—Hilco Model No. D-100S. (Courtesy of Hillard Corp., Elmira, N.Y.)

Frequently, the output of the centrifuge is put through a filter press for the final cleanup. The centrifuge cannot remove dissolved water from oil; since the centrifuge is sealed with water, the oil leaving the centrifuge may be saturated at the temperature of operation and conceivably could contain more dissolved water than when it entered. Neither the centrifuge nor the filter press is designed to treat oil chemically.

Coalescers

Throughout the power industry, coalescers are replacing centrifuges for use in removing free water from both lubricating and insulating oils. Coalescing is a relatively new technique that has been borrowed from the aviation fueling field. Fiberglass cartridges trap small water particles; increasing differential pressure across the filter media forces the particles of water together, and the large water drops are extruded at the outer suface of the fiberglass element. Large water drops are retained within a water-repellent separator screen and collect, by gravity, at the bottom of the filter while dry oil passes through the separator screen. This method is quite similar to centrifuging with respect to performance and limitations: however, coalescing filters have no moving parts and, therefore, are simpler in operation and maintenance and suitable for unattended and automatic operation.

FIGURE 3–6.

(a) Super centrifuge for transformer oil purifier—Model No. AS18V; (b) super centrifuge, feeder and discharge pumps, a blotter press, indirect heat exchangers, and electrical controls mounted on top of the tool drawer table—Model No. AE18VIH. (Courtesy of Sharpless-Stokes, Penwalt Corp., Warminster, Pa.)

Vacuum Dehydrators

The vacuum dehydrator (Figure 3–7) is efficient in reducing the water content of an insulating oil to a very low value. In this apparatus the oil is exposed to a vacuum and heat for a short interval of time. Vacuum dehydrators can be used to treat oil without removing associated equipment from service. In addition to removing water, vacuum dehydrators will degas the oil and remove the more volatile acids. Vacuum dehydrators are frequently used by the manufacturer during initial filling of new transformers.

LESS FLAMMABLE INSULATING FLUIDS

There has been a great increase in the use of less flammable liquids as an insulating and cooling medium in transformers. As these liquids are chemically different from mineral oils, they cannot be substituted in equipment designed for the use of mineral-oil type liquid. The National Manufacturers Association has officially designated these synthetic liquids as less flammable. They are PCBs, silicone, RTemp, Wecosol R113, and others. As is the case with mineral oil, the dielectric strength of askarels, silicone, RTemp, Wecosol, and other less-flammable fluids is reduced by the presence of emulsified water. Silicone, Wecosol and RTemp characteristics are similar to those of askarel, except that they are heavier than water and more viscous than mineral oil.

Maintenance of Askarels

INSPECTION
Visual inspection and dielectric strength tests should be made on askarel when installing equipment and on a regular schedule at 1-year intervals thereafter. Visual inspection that reveals a clear, faint yellow or light brown color indicates good askarel condition. The presence of a green, red, or blue cast, cloudiness, or turbidity indicates the presence of insulation or moisture contamination, and further tests on the askarel and inspection of the associated equipment should definitely be made. If the askarel sample appears black or contains suspended carbon particles, severe arcing has occurred. The askarel should be discarded and a thorough inspection of the equipment performed.

SAMPLING
Samples of askarel should be taken in a clean, dry glass quart bottle. If the sample is to be stored indefinitely or sent to a service laboratory for moisture content tests, the bottle should be filled only to within 1 in. of the top; the

FIGURE 3–7.
Vacuum dehydrator oil unit shown with optional heater, graphic panel, gauges, etc.—Model No. 820-40. (Courtesy of Stokes Division, Penwalt Corp., Philadelphia, Pa.)

sample should be sealed by wrapping the top and the threads of the jar with aluminum foil before tightly securing the cap. When the sample is to be sent to a laboratory, indicate the temperature of the askarel when the sample was taken. Samples of askarel should be taken when the relative humidity of the environment is low and when the temperature of the askarel is as high or higher than the surrounding air. It is best to take the sample when the unit is near operating or maximum temperature. Samples taken during regularly scheduled intervals should be taken at nearly the same temperature as previous samples. Samples should be taken as close to the top of the liquid surface as possible because askarel is heavier than water.

TESTING
The testing procedure for askarel is the same as for mineral oil, but care should be taken to see that there is no mineral oil in the test cup. The dielectric strength test for askarel is the most important maintenance test. A higher dielectric strength indicates that the insulating efficiency of the askarel is high and that any cloudiness or turbidity present is not due to damaging moisture contamination. If the dielectric strength of the askarel decreases abruptly or a decreasing trend is observed, inspections should be made at more frequent intervals. When the dielectric strength is 26 kV or less, a sample of askarel should be sent to a laboratory for a moisture content test (ASTM D 1533, Karl Fischer method). A high power factor alone is an insufficient criterion for replacing or reconditioning askarel; however, where abnormally low values of dielectric strength occur, the power factor of the askarel can be expected to be abnormally high. Power factors of 20 percent and more are frequently encountered in askarel transformers during normal service. Although this is an indication that some contamination has occurred, experience has shown that askarel is serviceable long after power factor test values increase greatly. Again, the determining criterion that indicates the serviceability of askarel is the dielectric strength. Reconditioning askarel to obtain a lower power factor is usually not justifiable.

CONTAMINATION
Water contamination is the primary cause of deterioration of askarel dielectric strength. Inspect all askarel-filled equipment for possible areas that would allow the equipment to "breathe" moisture-laden air. Numerous sealing compounds are available for sealing these areas. Where gaskets are located, use silastic seals at the flanges, viton for an elastomeric seal, and Teflon tape on pipe threads. On older equipment, cork-type gaskets should have the outside edges sealed with epoxy cement.

RECONDITIONING ASKAREL
The fact that the transformer tanks are generally sealed and that any condensation will float on top of askarel makes filtering by a blotter press rarely necessary. If such filtering is necessary, it can be done with an ordinary press from

which all mineral oil has been removed. A centrifugal purifier designed for mineral oil will not function on askarel. Special combination activated clay purifiers and blotter presses are manufactured for askarel.

HANDLING AND DISPOSAL OF ASKAREL

While askarel is generally considered to be noncombustible, under arcing conditions gases are produced that consist predominately of noncombustible hydrogen chloride and varying amounts of combustible gases depending on the askarel composition. Care should therefore be taken to handle askarel-filled apparatus as potentially combustible when accumulated gases are released.

Askarels consisting of PCBs (polychlorinated biphenyls) have been used in many applications for over 40 years, but only recently was evidence discovered that PCBs are widely dispersed in the environment. Studies have shown that PCBs are an environmental contaminant. Simultaneously, significant steps have been taken by the Environmental Protection Agency (EPA) to limit further releases of PCBs to the environment. The National Electrical Manufacturers Association (NEMA) prepared Publication No. TR-P6-1973 (January 25, 1973), "Proposed American National Standard Guidelines for Handling and Disposal of Capacitor and Transformer-Grade Askarels Containing Polychlorinated Biphenyls." This proposal is an approved ANSI Standard C107.1-1974. The guidelines in this official standard should be rigidly followed by all personnel when handling or disposing of askarel-soaked materials.

The following important excerpts from the official standard are presented as a handy reference:

Safety Precautions: Based on about 40 years of industrial usage, askarels are considered harmful materials to humans. There has been no known instance of human injury when askarels are used under the normally prescribed conditions of precaution and handling. Nevertheless, exposure to askarel should be avoided at all times.

Vapors: The odor of askarel is noticeable well below the maximum safe air concentrations. Depending upon the composition of the askarel used, from 0.5 to 1.0 mg/m^3 of air has been determined to be the upper safe level of exposure during an 8-hour workday. (See American Industrial Hygiene Association Hygienic Guide Series January/February, 1965.) Breathing vapor or fumes from heated askarels should be avoided. High concentrations of vapors can cause irritation of the eyes, nose, throat, and upper respiratory tract. Provision should be made for adequate ventilation and regulation of manufacturing operations to avoid open exposure of hot askarels (55°C or higher). The gases produced when askarel is decomposed by very high temperature (such as that of an electric arc) in the presence of air or organic insulating materials contain a high percentage of hydrogen chloride and small percentages of other gases. Minute concentrations of this combination of gases are very unpleasant and irritating, thus giving ample warning of their presence.

If exposure to high concentrations of askarel or its arced products is necessary under emergency conditions, an approved gas mask of the organic canister-type or self-contained breathing apparatus must be worn. Such exposure should be under the surveillance of other personnel capable of rescue in case of accident. If the odor of askarel or its arced products is detected by the person wearing protective equipment, he should immediately go into fresh air. All gas masks, respirators, and replacement parts should be approved for the purpose and be maintained on a regular schedule in accordance with the manufacturer's recommendation.

Liquid: Unlike mineral insulating oil, there is no fire hazard in handling askarels. A limited solvent action (similar to that for paint thinner) on the fats and oils of the skin with prolonged contact may lead to drying and chapping of the skin. As with insulating oil, some people are allergic to askarel, and continued exposure may result in skin irritation. Both the liquid and vapor are moderately irritating to eye tissue.

Operating procedures should require avoidance of contact with any askarels. The use of porous gloves that can absorb and retain askarels is to be avoided. Resistant gloves and aprons of the neoprene, polyethylene, or viton type should be used if contact is unavoidable. In case of spillage, clothing should be removed as soon as practical, the skin washed, and the clothing discarded. Medicinal washes or mild detergents followed by the application of cold cream will reduce the irritation resulting from the contact of an open cut or abrasion with askarel.

Safety glasses with side shields or face shield should be worn when handling askarel. Eyes that have been exposed to liquid askarel should be irrigated immediately with large quantities of running water for 15 min and then examined by a physician if the irritation persists. (A drop of castor oil has been found to reduce irritation.)

Persons developing a skin irritation or respiratory tract irritation while working with askarels should be placed under supervision of a physician. Ingestion or swallowing of askarels is not generally regarded as a problem of the industry. Should accidental ingestion occur, a physician should be consulted. Hands should be washed with warm water and soap before eating, drinking, smoking, or using toilet facilities.

Maintenance of RTemp

As a general rule, RTemp transformers may be handled in the same manner as conventional oil-filled transformers. However, some of the characteristics of RTemp fluid require special attention. The maintenance of RTemp fluid can be carried out similarly to that for oil and askarel. The sampling procedures for RTemp are similar to askarel. Special maintenance instructions for RTemp are the following:

FILTERING

If it is necessary to filter RTemp fluid to remove excess moisture, sludge, and the like, it can be filtered through conventional filtration systems. The filtering system should be flushed before connection.

Care should be taken to assure that the pump has sufficient capacity to handle the relatively high viscosity of RTemp fluid at lower temperatures. Heating of the fluid and piping system will increase the speed and ease of filtration and is completely acceptable.

COLD START

RTemp fluid has a pour point of −30°C. At this point, the dielectric strength is still sufficient to allow safe energization of the transformer. Because the possibility exists of energizing a transformer into a fault, RTemp transformers should not be energized if the fluid temperature (top oil) is below −15°C. At −15°C top oil temperature or above, full load may be applied to the transformer.

If the top oil temperature is below −15°C, immersion heaters placed near the bottom of the tank, external heating blankets, or some other means should be used to raise the top oil temperature to −15°C, thus assuring adequate cold spot temperature.

PRECAUTIONS

RTemp transformers are high fire point liquid insulated transformers. Relatively small quantities of conventional transformer oil or other low fire point materials can substantially reduce the fire point of RTemp fluid. Care must be taken in processing and handling RTemp transformers not to introduce such contaminants. External systems, such as filtration systems, should be thoroughly flushed with RTemp fluid before connection to a RTemp transformer.

Maintenance of Silicone

Silicone insulating fluid is used in transformers to provide heat transfer. Transformers containing silicone should be installed, operated, and serviced by competent and trained maintenance personnel who are familiar with good safety practices. The sampling procedures for silicone are similar to askarel. The following are special maintenance instructions relating to silicone-filled transformers.

RECEIVING AND HANDLING

Immediately upon receipt of shipping drums or a transformer filled with silicone fluid, an examination should be made for leaks. If leakage is evident either at this time or at any time thereafter, the cause should be corrected and the spillage soaked up with absorbent materials such as sawdust or fuller's earth, followed by a cleanup of the affected area with rags soaked with kerosene or other approved solvent, such as 1,1,1-trichloroethane. Adequate ventilation must be provided when using such solvents.

On those infrequent occasions when silicone fluid is removed for shipment, the transformer may be shipped gas filled and is to be liquid filled at installation. If the transformer is located outdoors, adequate precautions must be taken to ensure that no dirt or moisture enters the liquid during the filling operation. Before opening a container of silicone fluid, allow it to stand until the liquid is at least as warm as the surrounding air.

Before placing the liquid in the transformer, take a sample from each container and make dielectric tests as outlined under Sampling and Testing in Chapter 5. If the tests are unsatisfactory, restore the dielectric strength by filtering before placing the liquid in the transformer. When transferring from containers to the transformer, it is recommended that the liquid be passed through a filter press to remove any undetected moisture or sediment that may be present.

Silicone fluid must be handled in containers, pipes, oil-resistant hoses, and the like, that are free from oil, grease, pitch, or other foreign materials, since these contaminate the liquid and decrease its nonflammable properties. All apparatus used in sampling, filtering, storing, or transporting silicone fluid must be maintained for exclusive use with silicone fluid, since it is extremely difficult to remove all traces of oil or other silicone fluid contaminants from equipment of this type. Also, mineral oil is completely miscible in silicone fluid, and it is practically impossible to separate the two liquids after they have been mixed.

Use kerosene or other approved solvent to remove all traces of silicone fluid on the outside of the transformer tank. This precaution should be taken since silicone fluid has a tendency to affect adhesion of additional coats of paint.

STORAGE

Shipping drums should be stored indoors in an area specially selected for this purpose. If it is necessary to store drums or cans containing silicone fluid outdoors, protect the containers from the weather and direct contact with water. Regardless of location, all drums should be stored in a position that results in the bungs being under a positive pressure. Do not open a drum or can until the liquid is actually needed. Any change in temperature while the containers are open will cause an exchange of air, with the possibility of moisture entering the liquid. Partially emptied drums must be tightly resealed and stored in the same manner outlined previously.

PERIODIC INSPECTION

The insulating liquid must be maintained at the proper level, and for the longest possible service life of the transformer, the dielectric strength of the silicone fluid should be maintained at a high value. It is recommended, therefore, that the liquid be sampled and tested after the first few days of operation, again after 6 months, and yearly thereafter. Keep accurate records of the tests, and filter or replace the liquid as indicated. The entire transformer should also be thoroughly checked for leaks at these same intervals. If the pressure-vacuum gauge consistently reads zero, a leak in the gas space is indicated. If there is any reason to believe that water may have entered the transformer, check a top sample immediately for water.

FILTERING

If test results indicate that moisture or other contaminants are present, they can usually be removed by passing the insulating liquid through a filter press. This device may be used either as a paper filter press for drying or with fuller's earth and paper for purifying. All apparatus used in sampling, filtering, storing, or transporting silicone fluid must be maintained for exclusive use with silicone fluid, since it is extremely difficult to remove all traces of oil or other silicone fluid contaminants from equipment of this type. Filtration can be accomplished in the transformer or other container by circulating the silicone fluid from the bottom to the top through a filter press. Filtering can be done faster and more efficiently by passing the liquid from the transformer through the filter and into a separate, clean, dry container and then back through the filter again to refill the transformer. In this manner all the liquid will be given two complete passes through the filter press. If additional filtering is still required, the entire procedure can be repeated. As moisture is extracted from the liquid during the filtering process, the filtering medium will become wet. Frequent samples of the outgoing liquid should be tested to determine when the filtering medium should be replaced.

The filter press will not remove large quantities of free water from the silicone fluid. When a large quantity of free water is introduced into the filter, it will be passed on through, emerging as finely divided droplets dispersed throughout the liquid. Therefore, if free water is present, it should be removed before filtering is started. A transformer contaminated with moisture may not only have moisture suspended in the insulating liquid, but also in the windings and insulation. The most efficient temperature for filtering moisture from the liquid is between 20° and 40°C, but at this temperature the transfer of moisture from the windings and insulation to the insulating liquid is quite slow. If free water is present in the transformer or if the dielectric strength of the silicone fluid is still below 30 kV after filtering, consult the nearest office of the transformer manufacturer for additional information.

SAFETY PRECAUTIONS

As a class, silicone liquids are nontoxic. Silicone fluid in contact with the eyes may cause local irritation, but this irritation is only temporary. If desired, eyes may be irrigated with water, and if irritation persists, consult a physician.

PRECAUTIONS

Static charges can be developed when silicone fluid flows in pipes, hoses, and tanks. Fluid leaving a filter press may be charged to over 50,000 V. To accelerate dissipation of the charge in the liquid, ground the filter press, the piping, the transformer tank, and all bushings or the winding leads during flow into any tank. Conduction through silicione fluid is slow; therefore, it is desirable to maintain these grounds for at least 1 hour after the flow has been stopped.

Arcs can occur from the free surface of the charged liquid even though the previous grounding precautions have been taken. Therefore, explosive gas mixture should be removed from all containers into which liquid is flowing.

Maintenance of Wecosol

Wecosol fluid is a transformer grade of tetrachloroethylene (sometimes called *perchloroethylene*). Wecosol fluid will slowly evaporate to produce Wecosol vapors. It is necessary to use the proper safety procedures to prevent adverse effects resulting from vapor inhalation and skin contact with fluid. Overexposure to Wecosol vapors will result in symptoms such as headaches, confusion, nausea, and lack of coordination. Extreme overexposure to Wecosol vapors could result in fatal personal injury. The fluid is considered as less than 50 PPM polychlorinated biphenyl (PCB) dielectric fluid in accordance with Federal PCB regulations 40CFR761, dated May 31, 1979. It is considered a nonflammable fluid with boiling point of 121 degrees C at atmospheric pressure. The safe limits of vapor exposure are shown in Table 3–6.

Low lying areas such as pits can slowly accumulate vapors which are nearly six times heavier than air. When the tank is open in those areas which may accumulate the vapors should be ventilated to prevent excessive vapor concentrations. The odor of Wecosol vapors are noticeable at concentrations of 50 PPM and often as low as 10 PPM. Do not use odor to determine vapor concentrations since odor threshold varies between individuals. Also, the ability to recognize Wecosol vapors diminishes after exposure, due to temporary desensitization.

Wecosol fluid is a solvent. Like any solvent, contact will dry out the skin by removing its natural oils. The natural oils can be replaced by the use of

TABLE 3–6.
MAXIMUM WECOSOL VAPOR EXPOSURE[a]

Parts per Million (PPM)	Hours per Day
33	24
50	16
80	10
100	8
133	6
200	4
Greater than 200	0

[a] Reference OSHA Standards Part 1910.1000, Table Z2

common hand lotions. Gloves resistant to Wecosol fluid should be worn to avoid skin contact and transformer fluid contamination.

Fluid splashed into the eyes may cause pain and irritation. Safety goggles should be worn if tasks to be performed risk splashing of fluid into the eyes. If the fluid is splashed into the eyes, flush the eyes with water for approximately 15 minutes and consult a physician. The following are special maintenance instructions for Wecosol.

RECEIVING AND HANDLING

Immediately upon receipt of drums or a transformer filled with Wecosol fluid, examine for leaks. Take the necessary action and precautions so that PCB contamination is not introduced from the leaks or any filling or maintenance of the transformer. If the fluid is received in drums, they must be stored in ventilated dry area in an upright position. Before a drum is used to fill the transformer, it must be sampled and tested for dielectric strength. The dielectric strength must be at least 30 kV for drummed fluid to be used.

SAMPLING

Samples should be taken to prevent air from entering the tank. To prevent air from being drawn into the tank, the tank pressure must be greater than zero psi. If necessary, increase the tank pressure by injecting dry nitrogen until a positive pressure of about one half psi is reached. The sample should be taken when the unit is warmer than the air to avoid condensation.

Care should be taken to procure a sample which fairly represents the liquid in the tank. All samples must be taken from the top liquid sampler near the top fluid level. A sufficient amount of liquid should therefore be drawn off before the sample is taken to insure that the sample will not be that which is stored in the liquid sampler. If the sample taken contains free water, it is not suitable for dielectric tests and the sample must be discarded. A second sample should then be taken after at least two quarts of liquid have been withdrawn. If free water still exists, all transformer fluid must be dried as explained in the following section.

DRYING

The transformer fluid can be dried by either chemical drying or insulation drying methods. Take the necessary precautions so that PCB contamination is not introduced during field filling or maintenance of the transformer. In the chemical drying method use hoses, gaskets, and threaded fitting seals made of viton rubber and teflon lined copper or steel. The liquid temperature must be less than 60°C for chemical drying procedure to be used. Circulate the tank fluid through glass or paper filters and calcium sulfate. The filters should be a 50 micron filter on the calcium sulfate inlet with a one micron absolute on the exit (filter will pass no particle larger than one micron). Continue the drying process until the water content is less than 35 parts per million, and the dielectric breakdown is greater than 26 kV.

In the insulation drying method, the windings, insulation and fluid can be dried by circulating current through the windings. The tank coolers must be blanketed off to reduce heat loss. The low voltage winding is short circuited and sufficient voltage is impressed across the high voltage winding to circulate current through the windings to maintain a liquid temperature between 90°C and 100°C. The voltage necessary to accomplish this task is approximately one third the rated impedance divided by one hundred and multiplied by the rated voltage. Current requirements are approximately one third the rated current. During the heating, monitor the liquid level to make certain the liquid level is at least to the 25°C level. Stop the heating if the liquid level falls below the 25°C level. When the liquid has reached the required temperatures, purge the gas space with dry nitrogen. Minimize the Wecosol vapor exhaust. Continue the purging and heating until the liquid water content is less than 35 parts per million, and dielectric breakdown is greater than 26 kV.

REPROCESSING

If necessary the Wecosol fluid can be reprocessed by filtering. When reprocessing, use hoses and tubing lined with teflon or made of copper or steel. All gaskets and threaded fitting seals used during this process must be made of viton rubber. Circulate the fluid through paper or glass filters and fuller's earth. The inlet filter should be a 50 micron filter. The exhaust filter must be a five micron absolute filter.

INSPECTION AND MAINTENANCE

Periodic inspection and maintenance test conducted to determine whether a transformer fluid should continue to be used, be dried or reprocessed. The various tests which are to be conducted on the fluid are outlined in Chapters 5 and 6.

3-4   CABLES AND ACCESSORIES

After having made the proper selection of cable to meet load requirements and other system characteristics, it is important that cables be installed and maintained properly. A good understanding of local conditions, installation crews, and maintenance personnel is essential to assure that the selected cable system will operate satisfactorily. Many times cable insulation is damaged or weakened during installation by applying the incorrect pulling tensions. Designs of conduit systems not only should minimize the number of conduit bends and distances between manholes, but should also specify the pulling tensions. The inspection personnel should ensure that installation crews do not exceed these values during installations. It is also important that proper bending radius be maintained in order to avoid unnecessary stress points. Once a proper installation is made, routine inspection, testing, and maintenance should be carried out on a regular basis to chart the gradual deterioration and upkeep of the cable system. Cable systems are the arteries of the electric power distribution system and carry the energy required for the successful operation of a plant. Following is a brief discussion on cable installation and maintenance.

INSTALLATION OF CABLE SYSTEM

There are several types of cable systems available for carrying electrical energy in a given distribution system. The selection of a particular system may be influenced by local conditions, existing company policies, or past experience. No set standards or established guidelines can be given for the selection of a particular system. Following is a general discussion of the various types of installations, bending data, and pulling tensions that, combined with sound engineering judgment, will be helpful in selecting a system for a particular installation.

Outdoor Installations

Cable can be installed underground or overhead. Today most cable is installed underground in conduit banks or direct burial, even though the trend for outdoor overhead installation is becoming popular. The underground installation of cables in fiber ducts will result in smaller impedance than for cables in metallic ducts. Since conduits may become flooded, only cable constructions approved for this purpose should be installed in ducts. Cable failures in underground ducts are difficult to locate and repair. Therefore, maintenance personnel should be trained and equipped with proper equipment to troubleshoot cable faults and make repairs.

Several types of cable construction are available for direct-burial service. Cable selected for direct-burial service should have excellent mechanical strength in order to withstand rough environmental surroundings. Cables without jackets should be avoided for direct-burial service.

Low- and medium-voltage aerial cable is becoming popular for overhead installations because of its many advantages, such as low reactance, adaptability, better appearance, and voltage regulation. Another type of overhead installation that is gaining popularity is interlocked armor on ladders or cable trays because of advantages such as flexibility, ease of installation, and good mechanical and chemical protection.

Indoor Installations

The conventional installation of indoor cables has been in conduit [Figure 3–8(a)]. However, interlocked armor cable is gaining popularity recently, especially in industrial plants. This cable can be installed overhead in racks or ladder trays [Figure 3–8(b)], thus eliminating the expensive conduit systems. The racks bonded together provide the ground circuit similar to the conduit system.

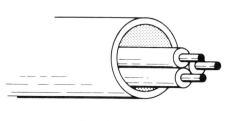

(a) Cable in conduit

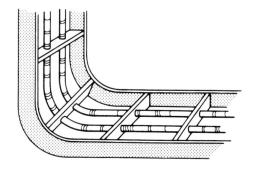

(b) Interlocked armor cable in racks

FIGURE 3–8.
(a) Cable in conduit; (b) interlocked armor cable in racks.

Because of this cable being installed in open air, it has higher current rating. An overall jacket of PVC is available for this cable for installations where corrosive atmosphere may be present.

Bending Data

The Insulated Cable Engineering Association (ICEA) recommended values of minimum bending radii for rubber and rubberlike compounds and varnished cambric cables are given in Table 3–7. As mentioned before, it is important to install cables without sharp bends to minimize stress points. The ICEA recommended bending data do not apply to conduits in which cables may be pulled under tension. In cases of conduit bends, larger radius bend should be required.

Pulling Tensions

Since cables can be damaged by applying excessive pulling tension or by sharp bends in poorly constructed duct banks, the following are some of the cautions that should be considered to minimize damage to cables during installation.

- Do not exceed the required fill as set by the NEC.
- Avoid sharp bends of the cable during pulling.
- Use adequate lubrication to avoid friction. (Use proper kind of lubricant.)
- Check end seals for intactness after installation.
- In rack-type installation, use rollers to prevent cable from dragging on the rack.

TABLE 3–7.
RECOMMENDED BENDING DATA FOR CABLE

Type of Cable	Insulation Thickness (in.)	Minimum Bending Radii as a Multiple of Cable Diameter		
		1 in. or less	1.01–2.00 in.	2.00 in. and Over
Thermosetting and				
thermoplastic	$^{10}/_{64}$ and less	4	5	6
without metallic	$^{11}/_{64}$ to $^{20}/_{64}$	5	7	7
shielding	$^{21}/_{64}$ and over	—	7	8
Varnished				
cambric cable	Up to $^{10}/_{64}$	5	6	7
without armor,	$^{11}/_{64}$ to $^{20}/_{64}$	6	6.5	7
single conductor,	Over $^{20}/_{64}$	6.5	7	7
and nonbelted				
multiconductor				
Multiconductor	All thicknesses	5	6	7

THERMOPLASTIC AND THERMOSETTING WITH SHIELDING OR ARMOR

Multiconductor interlocked armor, 7× diameter	Flat tape and wire armored 12× diameter	Tape shield, 12× diam. up to 15 kV; 10× diam., up to 35 kV	Portable cable over 5 kV, 8× diameter	Portable cable below 5 kV 6× diameter

VARNISHED CAMBRIC ARMORED CABLES

Interlocked armor cambric, 7× diameter	Flat tape and wire armored cable, 12× diameter

In duct and conduit runs, the tension for a straight pull can be calculated by the formula

$$T = Lwf$$

where T = pulling weight
   L = length to feet pulled
   w = weight of cable in pounds/feet
   f = friction coefficient, approximately = 0.5

To pull cables in conduits and ducts, the cables can be gripped directly by a pulling eye or basket-weave pulling grip. The basket-weave grip is usually used for relatively light pulls, whereas pulling eye is used for heavier pulls. The following tension limitations apply when pulling cables:

■ *Direct pull of conductor:* When pulling force is applied directly to the conductor, the maximum pull should not exceed 0.008 lb/circular mil area of cross section for copper and 0.75 for hard-drawn aluminum.

- *Grip over lead sheath:* When a grip is applied over lead-sheathed cable, the pulling force shall be limited to 1,500 psi of sheath cross section.

- *Grip over nonmetallic sheath:* When a grip is applied over a nonmetallic sheathed cable, the pulling force should not be over 1,000 lb provided it does not exceed the force calculated in a direct pull of conductor.

- *Pulling around bends:* The pulling force around bends in conduit should not exceed 300 times the radius of the bend in feet.

Acceptance of Cable

After a new cable has been installed and before it is energized, acceptance proof testing should be performed. Acceptance proof tests are conducted at 80 percent of final factory test voltage. Normally, dc test voltage is used for proof testing of cables. To find the equivalent dc test voltage for 80 percent of final test factory voltage, conversion charts for the various types of cables are given in Section 4-3. For acceptance of newly installed cable, the following tests are performed: (1) insulation resistance measurement, and (2) dc overpotential test. These two tests are described in Chapter 4, Section 4-3.

MAINTENANCE OF CABLES

Visual inspection of the cable, conduit, manholes, and so on, and electrical maintenance proof testing are the major maintenance procedures for cable systems.

Visual Inspection

Visual inspection can be made on energized cables, but if cables are to be touched or moved they should be deenergized. Cables in vaults, substations rooms, manholes, and at other locations should be inspected for the following on a yearly basis:

- Physical damage, sharp bends, and excessive tension.
- Oil leaks, soft spots, and insulation swelling.
- Poor ground connections, metallic-sheath bonding deterioration, corroded cable supports, and continuity of main grounding system.
- Cracked jackets of nonleaded cables.
- Damage to fireproofing.
- Tracking of corona.
- Soft spots in terminations and splices.
- Inspect the manhole for spalling concrete.

- Potheads should be inspected for oil or compound leaks. Dirt and grime should be cleaned off and connections checked for tightness.

Aerial cable should be inspected for mechnical damage caused by vibration or deterioration of support and suspension system. Inspection should be made of cables for insulation abrasion and cable being bent or pinched.

CABLE FAILURES AND THEIR ANALYSIS

Cables can fail due to many reasons. Some of the major causes are discussed next.

Mechanical Failures

Mechanical failures can be due to breaks and defects of sheath material, mechanical punctures by people or machines, or cracks due to sharp bending or vibration. Whenever mechanical damage occurs in the cable sheath, the entrance of moisture will produce slow deterioration of insulation material, resulting in eventual failure of the cable. It is important therefore to take every precaution that either direct or indirect mechanical damage be eliminated or minimized by proper selection, installation, and maintenance of cable systems.

Corrosion of Sheath

Sheath corrosion can occur due to the following factors:

- Dissimilar soil effects.
- Galvanic action.
- Acidity and alkali in conduits.
- Chemical contamination in the soil.

Corrosion of sheath will eventually allow moisture to penetrate into the insulation system and cause an eventual failure. Sheath corrosion can be minimized by proper application of cathodic protection, application of insulating paints, providing proper drainage, and removing the source of chemical contamination.

Moisture in the Insulation

Because of mechanical damage or for other reasons, entrance of moisture into the insulation system will deteriorate the cable, and all precautions should be taken to prevent such entrance. Damage due to moisture can be indicated by the following:

- Bleached or soggy paper.

- Resistance to tearing of tapes.
- Stain on the inside surface of the sheath.
- Visible water.

Heating of Cables

As explained in the section on cable rating, increased heat rise in the cable results in insulation degradation. Heat can be due to overloading, high ambient temperatures, insufficient ventilation, manual heating due to cables being installed too close to each other, or external sources of heat. Care must be taken not to exceed the temperature rise of the cable insulation system. This can be done by first identifying the various environmental and operating factors that will determine the proper selection of the cable insulation and conductor size. Once proper selection and installation are made, routine maintenance and inspection of cable will ensure safe and long operating life of the cable.

FIRE AND LIGHTNING SURGES

Fire in conduit or manholes can cause cable failure in adjacent manholes and junction boxes. Barriers can be installed between large groups of conductors to prevent fire damage. Lightning arresters should be installed to protect the cable where it is connected to overhead lines to minimize failures of cable due to lightning surges.

Electrical Puncture

Once the insulation is weakened owing to any of the reasons already discussed, it may fail electrically. That is, the insulation system cannot confine the flow of electrical current to the conductor inside the insulation system. Failure may be line to ground or three line to ground or line to line faults. Obviously, if the failure is a short-circuit due to defective conductors, it will be detected by the circuit protective device. Some of the not so easy to detect electrical failures can be indicated by the following:

- Bulging of the sheath.
- Tree design marking (dendritic).
- Polymerized compound (wax).
- Lack of compound in the insulation.

The cable failures discussed in the preceding section can be further classified into two classes as follows: (1) inherent causes, and (2) noninherent causes.

Inherent Causes

Inherent causes can be classified as follows:

- Sheath defects.
- Insulation defects.
- Conductor defects.

SHEATH DEFECTS
Sheath defects are due to the following:

- Thin lead (splits under pressure).
- Eccentric lead thickness less than 85 percent.
- Structural defects: radial splits, laminations, gas pockets, and others.

INSULATION DEFECTS
These defects are due to the following:

- *Defects in workmanship:* These can be indicated by the following:
  Wrinkling or creasing of tapes.
  Torn tapes.
  Excessive registrations.
  Knotted or misplaced fillers.
  Soft walls.
- *High dielectric loss:* This can be indicated by the following:
  Scorching or carbonizing of paper.
  Happens in one or more spots.
  Can be determined by power factor at 60°C or higher.
- *Incomplete saturation:* This can be indicated by the following:
  Scarcity of the compound in spaces between adjacent tape edges and surfaces.
  Paper is void of the compound.
- *Unstable compound:* This can be indicated by the following:
  Visible change in the compound.
  Wax, in case of mineral oil.
- *Ionization:* This can be indicated by the following:
  Carbonized paths (tree design).
  Strings or flakes of darkened wax containing carbon.

CONDUCTOR DEFECTS
Conductor defects can be indicated by the following:

- Irregular strands.
- Sharp corners.
- Missing strands.
- Burrs on the strands.
- Poor brazing.

Noninherent Causes

CORROSION OF SHEATH
Corrosion usually proceeds either to complete penetration of the sheath or weakness of the sheath, so that the sheath breaks open. Electrical breakdown takes place owing to the admission of moisture. Corrosion of the sheath can be due to the following:

- Positive potential (anodic), indicated by rough, pitted surface and very thin deposits of white crystals.
- Negative potential (cathodic), indicated by heavy deposit of lead oxides colored red, yellow, or orange.
- Local galvanic action.
- Chemical action.
- Other causes.

LOCAL GALVANIC ACTION
Galvanic corrosion may occur in the presence of an electrolyte and some other metal that is connected electrically to the sheath elsewhere. Such failures are indicated by corroded sheath, which may be identical with either type of decorrosion depending on whether the sheath is anode or cathode.

CHEMICAL ACTION
Chemicals such as alkali attack cable insulation, which comes about from incompletely cured concrete; acetic acid, rotting wood, jute, and other materials. Usually, these can be identified by the chemical known to be present for a particular installation.

EXTERNAL FIRE AND HIGH-VOLTAGE SURGES
These are due to fire in cable circuits and lightning strikes and surges.

OVERHEATING
This is mainly due to heating of a cable that is overloaded or external heat and high temperature.

MECHANICAL DAMAGE

Mechanical damage can be due to the following:

- Vibration.
- Expansion and contraction.
- External causes.
- Injury during installation.

OTHER CAUSES

These can be classified as follows:

- High internal pressure.
- Migration of compound on a slope or riser.
- Moisture admitted through defective joints, terminations, and bonds.

3-5   ELECTRICAL SWITCHGEAR

Switchgear components, such as circuit breakers, disconnect switches, fuses, and insulators, require regular inspection and maintenance. Switchgear can be the indoor or outdoor type and can be from different manufacturers. However, the maintenance of all types of switchgear can be carried out by following the basic maintenance operations. This section provides the fundamental maintenance instructions for an overall maintenance program for switchgear. In cases where detailed instructions are required, the reader is advised to consult the recommendations of the manufacturer of the particular equipment under consideration for maintenance.

MEDIUM-VOLTAGE SWITCHGEAR

Power Circuit Breakers

Medium-voltage circuit breakers consist of air-magnetic circuit breakers either of horizontal drawout type or vertical lift type, oil circuit breakers, and vacuum circuit breakers. The following procedures should be carried out before new power circuit breakers are placed in service.

RECEIVING, HANDLING AND STORAGE

- Inspect the circuit breaker for damage that may have occurred in transit. Check the nameplate data and the packing list provided with the equipment delivered.

- Inspect the arc chutes of the air-magnetic breaker for cracks, damage, or foreign material.
- Inspect the shield on each of the fixed arcing contacts for cracks of the air-magnetic breaker.
- Lift and let down circuit breakers slowly. Do not use the bushing as handles when handling the breaker. Always roll and maneuver the breaker by grasping the top edge of the breaker cover. Avoid any sudden jerks when moving the breaker.
- If the breaker must be stored before it is put into service, keep it in a clean, dry and noncorrosive place. Coat all bare metal surfaces with grease to prevent dusting. If the breaker is to be installed outdoors, make sure power is available for space heaters and that they are working.
- In cases where a breaker is stored for a long period of time, it should be inspected regularly for rusting.

INSTALLATION

- Make an overall examination of the entire breaker to ensure that there are no damaged parts.
- Use a dry, clean cloth to remove dirt and moisture that may have collected on the circuit breaker.
- Cycle the breaker by opening and closing the breaker manually and electrically. Check for proper operation.
- To assure that no damage has occurred during shipment, perform a high-potential test on each breaker pole (or vacuum interrupter) while the breaker is in the open position. Test results should be evaluated on a go, no-go basis by slowly raising the test voltage to the values shown in Table 3–8. Hold the final test value for 1 min.

TABLE 3–8.

HIGH-POTENTIAL VALUES FOR ACCEPTANCE TESTING OF BREAKERS

Voltage Class (kV)	Test Value (ac), kV	Test Value (dc), kV
5	19	27
7.2	36	50
13.8	36	50
23	60	—
38	80	—
Over 38	Consult Manufacturer	—

- Install the breaker into its cubicle in accordance with manufacturer's instructions. Check for proper operation by manually cycling the breaker with control power off.

MAINTENANCE

Power circuit breakers, like other electrical equipment, require preventive maintenance to avoid equipment problems. The schedule for preventive maintenance can vary for each facility depending upon operating and environmental conditions. Frequent inspection and maintenance should be performed if the following factors are present:

- Corrosive atmosphere.
- Excessive dust or dirt.
- High ambient temperature and high humidity.
- Older equipment.
- Excessive repetitive duty.
- Frequent fault interruption.

Generally, the frequency of inspection should be based upon service and operating conditions. As a guide, inspect equipment about 6 months after it is installed and then follow up with scheduled maintenance every 1 to 3 years. In the performance of maintenance routines, all safety precautions should be followed.

Preventive maintenance should include the following areas:

- Circuit breaker:
  Contacts.
  Arc chutes.
  Mechanical parts.
  Auxiliary equipment.
- Cell enclosure:
  Cell joints (i.e., bus joints).
  Cell contacts.
  Insulation.

The following routine maintenance instructions are offered as a general guide for the maintenance of power circuit breakers. If special detailed instructions are required, consult the manufacturer.

Air-Magnetic Circuit Breakers

Before inspecting or performing any maintenance on either the breaker or its mechanism, be sure the breaker is in the open position, is disconnected from all electrical sources, and is removed from the cubicle (Figure 3–9). Both the closing and opening springs should be discharged or blocked mechanically before any maintenance is done.

- Record the number of operations and perform a general visual inspection of the breaker. Report any unusual signs or problems.

- Put circuit breaker in test position and, using a test coupler, operate breaker electrically. Check the operation of all electrical relays, solenoid switches, motors, control switches, and indicating devices.

- Remove circuit breaker from enclosure and perform visual inspection as follows:

  Remove box barriers.

  Wipe clean of smoke deposit and dust all insulating parts, including the bushings and the inside of the box barrier. Use a clean, dry, lint-free cloth; a vacuum cleaner would be helpful.

  Inspect condition of bushing primary disconnect stubs and finger cluster.

  Inspect condition of bushing insulation; it should be clean, dry, smooth, hard and unmarred.

  Check breaker and operating mechanism carefully for loose nuts, bolts, or retaining rings, and ensure that mechanical linkage is secure.

  Inspect insulation and outside of arc chutes for holes or breaks; small cracks are normal.

  Inspect magnetic ''blow-out'' coils (if used) for damage.

  Inspect all current-carrying parts for evidence of overheating.

- Functional inspection:

  Sandpaper throat area of arc chutes until thoroughly clean.

  Ensure that arc chutes are clear of contamination and have no significant damage on grids or ceramics. If ceramics or fins are broken, replace arc chutes.

  Ensure that all brazed, soldered, or bolted electrical connections are tight.

  Inspect contacts of control relays for wear and clean as necessary.

  Check actuator relays, charging motor, and secondary disconnects for damage, evidence of overheating, or insulation breakdown.

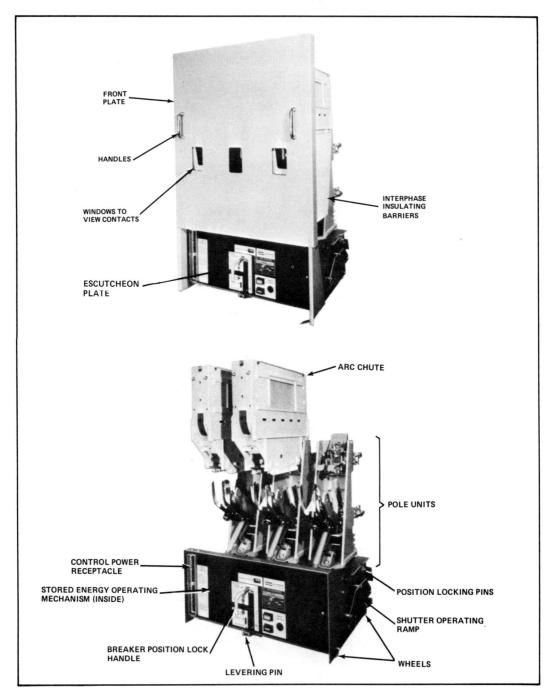

FIGURE 3–9.
Air-magnetic circuit breaker components. (Courtesy of Square D Company, Middleton, Ohio)

Check that all wiring connections are tight and for any possible damage to the insulation. Replace any wire that has worn insulation.

On stored-energy breakers, operate the breaker slowly. By using the spring blocking device, check for binding or friction and correct if necessary. Make sure contacts can be opened or closed fully.

Inspect the arcing contacts for uneven wear or damage. Replace badly worn contacts. Measure the arcing contact wire, using an ohmmeter. Make adjustment if necessary. Refer to appropriate instruction book.

Inspect primary contacts for burns or pitting. Wipe contacts with clean cloth. Replace badly burned or pitted contacts. Rough or galled contacts should be smoothed with a crocus cloth or file lightly. Resilver where necessary.

Inspect primary disconnect studs for arcing or burning. Clean and lightly grease arcing contacts.

Check primary contact gap and wipe. Make adjustment per appropriate instruction book. Grease contacts with an approved grease and operate breaker several times.

Check operation and clearance of trip armature travel and release latch per appropriate instruction book. Replace worn parts.

Inspect all bearings, cams, rollers, latches, and buffer blocks for wear. Teflon-coated sleeve bearings do not require lubrication. All other sleeve bearings, rollers, and needle bearings should be lubricated with SAE 20 or 30 machine oil. All ground surfaces coated with dark molybdenum disulfide do not require lubrication. Lubricate all other ground surfaces such as latches, rollers, or props with an approved grease.

Install box barriers.

Measure insulation resistance of each bushing terminal to ground and phase to phase. Record readings along with temperature and humidity.

Perform hi-pot test for breaker bushing insulation (optional).

Check closed breaker contact resistance (optional).

Perform power factor test (optional).

Perform corona test (optional).

Using test box, operate breaker both electrically and manually. Check all interlocks.

Insert and operate breaker in cabinet. Watch for proper operation of the positive interlock trip-free mechanism. (Breaker should trip if not fully in or in test position.)

Remove breaker from cubicle and check primary disconnect wipe; refer to appropriate instruction book.

Insert breaker into cubicle, ready for energization.

Oil Circuit Breaker

The oil circuit breaker should be maintained on a periodic basis similar to the air-magnetic circuit breakers. To maintain the circuit breaker, mount it on the inspection rack and untank it to expose the internal parts. Check for the following and make adjustments and repairs in accordance with the instruction book.

- Wipe clean all parts, including any carbon markings. Insulating parts should be inspected for damage such as warpage and cracks; replace damaged parts.
- Inspect the contacts for alignment and wear. Replace pitted and burned contacts and file rough contacts. Adjust contacts to ensure that contacts bear with firm and even pressure.
- Take an oil sample and make a dielectric test as explained in Chapter 5 under testing of insulating liquids. If visible carbon particles are evident in the oil, filter oil regardless of the dielectric strength.
- Wipe inside of tank, barriers, and tank linings to remove carbon.
- Inspect and clean operating mechanism similarly to that described in the section on air-magnetic breakers.
- Check the breaker operation by slowly closing with the closing device similarly to the air-magnetic breaker. Also check its electrical operation.
- Replalce tank with proper oil level and make sure that all gaskets, tank nuts, and flange nuts are tightened properly to prevent leakage.

Vacuum Circuit Breaker

The vacuum circuit breaker (see Figure 3–10) maintenance schedule should be based upon operating experience and environmental conditions. If such a schedule has not been determined, it is recommended that the breaker be inspected at least once a year or every 2,000 operations, whichever occurs first. However, a breaker should be inspected every time after a severe fault interruption. The following checks should be performed for the vacuum circuit breaker:

- Check for contact erosion. To determine contact erosion, remove breaker from enclosure. Close the breaker and measure the spring plate overtravel. Consult the manufacturer's instruction book for allowable overtravel. If the specified overtravel is exceeded, the vacuum interrupter must be replaced.
- To check the condition of the vacuum, perform a high-potential test. Consult the manufacturer's instruction book for test value or use 60 percent of the final factory test value.

FIGURE 3-10.
Power/vacuum metal-clad circuit breaker. (Courtesy of General Electric, Burlington, Iowa)

- Using a clean, dry cloth, remove all dirt and moisture from the outside of vacuum interrupters and all insulating parts.
- Check the entire operating mechanism similarly to the air-magnetic circuit breaker.
- Lubricate ground surfaces such as cams, gear teeth, rollers, and pawls when performing maintenance. See the manufacturer's guide on lubrication methods and time periods.
- Operate the breaker manually and electrically several times to make sure that the breaker is operating properly.

Switchgear Enclosure and Bus

An inspection of the switchgear bus and enclosure should be made every year. However, inspection frequency can be increased or decreased depending on operating and environmental conditions. It is good practice to follow the manufacturer's recommendations regarding maintenance procedures. The following are suggestions to supplement the manufacturer's recommendations:

- Check the enclosure housing to ensure that all hardware is in place and in good condition. The purpose of enclosure is to protect the equipment from outside contaminants and prevent exposure of personnel to live parts. A maintenance program should assure that these features are maintained. Lubricate hinges, latches, locks, and so on.

- For outdoor assemblies, check for roof or wall leaks, as well as for damage from previous leaks.

- After the power has been turned off and the bus has been grounded, remove dust and dirt by wiping with a dry, clean cloth or by vacuuming.

- Check for all unnecessary floor openings and any water pools at the bases of enclosures. Seal such openings with duct seal. Check for signs of moisture accumulation, such as droplet depression on dust-laden surfaces and dust patterns. Prevent moisture accumulation by providing heat and ventilation. Therefore, make sure that space heaters and fans are functioning properly.

- Check that ventilators are clear of obstruction and air filters are clean and in good condition.

- The surface of all insulating members should be inspected before any cleaning or dusting, as well as after cleaning for signs of electrical distress, tracking, corona, and thermal heating. Damage caused by electrical distress will usually be evident on the insulating surface as corona markings or tracking parts. The areas most susceptible to electrical distress are the following:

Splices and junction points.

Boundaries between adjoining insulators.

Edges of insulation surrounding mounting hardware grounded to the metal structure.

Bridging paths across insulating surface.

Boundaries between an insulating member and the grounded metal surface.

Hidden surfaces such as adjacent edges between upper and lower members of split bus supports.

Sharp edges in switchgear that are not insulated.

- Check for loose bolted connections in bus bars, splices, and the like, for signs of heating. Tighten in accordance with manufacturer's recommendations.

- Examine grounding connections and ground bus for tightness and cleanliness.

- Check alignment and contacts of primary disconnecting devices for abnormal wear or damage. Check for sulfide deposits and use a solvent such as alcohol for removal of these deposits.

- Repair any paint damage or finishes.

- After cleaning and adjusting, run an insulation resistance testing to measure resistance to ground. Compare the values of test readings with previous readings for any sign of weakening of the insulation system. Readings should be normalized to a common temperature and humidity base before comparison is made.

- Compare equipment nameplate information with latest one-line diagram and report discrepancies.

- Check tightness of accessible bolted bus joints by calibrated wrench method. Refer to manufacturer recommendations for proper torque values.

- Test key interlock systems physically to ensure the following;

  Closure attempt should be made on locked-open devices.

  Opening attempt should be made on locked-closed devices.

  Key exchange should be made with devices operated in off-normal positions.

LOW-VOLTAGE SWITCHGEAR

The low-voltage switchgear discussed in this section involves power circuit breakers and enclosures of indoor or outdoor type. The frequency of inspection and maintenance should be 3 to 6 months when new equipment is installed and 1 to 2 years for existing equipment. However, if problems with switchgear are encountered, the frequency can be shortened. Similarly to medium-voltage switchgear, the conditions that call for frequent inspection and maintenance are high humidity and temperature, corrosive atmosphere, excessive dirt or dust, frequent fault interruption, and age of the equipment. The following guide is provided for the general maintenance of low-voltage equipment; where necessary it should be supplemented by the manufacturer's detailed instructions.

Low-Voltage Draw-out Power Circuit Breakers

Similarly to medium-voltage breakers, low-voltage breakers (see Figure 3–11) should be maintained annually. Moreover, a breaker should be serviced after a severe fault interruption. To conduct maintenance, withdraw the circuit breaker from its enclosure and perform the following:

- Inspect alignment of movable and stationary contacts. Make adjustments as recommended in manufacturer's book. Do not unnecessarily file butt-type contacts.

- Wipe bushings, barriers, and insulating parts. Remove dust and smoke.

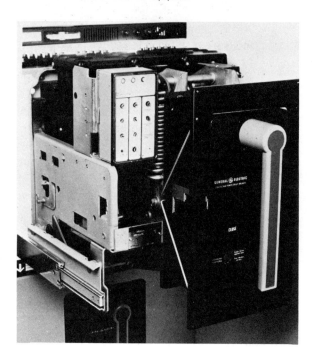

FIGURE 3–11.
Low-voltage draw-out power circuit breaker in fully disconnect position.
(Courtesy of General Electric, Norwalk, Conn.)

- Check arc chutes for damage and blow-out dust. Replace damaged parts.
- Inspect breaker operating mechanism for broken, loose, or excessively worn parts. Clean and relubricate operating mechanism with light machine oil. Use nonhardening grease for lubrication of rollers, cams, latches, and the like. Adjust breaker operating mechanism if required.
- Check control devices and replace if needed. Also replace badly worn contacts.
- Check breaker control wiring and ensure that all connections are tight.
- Operate breaker in fully opened and closed positions after it has been serviced. Check for any binding, and operate breaker manually and electrically before putting back in service.
- Check other items, such as switches, relays, and instruments, during servicing of the breaker.

Low-Voltage Molded-Case Breakers

The maintenance of molded-case breakers consists of inspection of the breaker, its mounting, and electrical connections. The following steps are recommended as a guide:

- Clean all external contamination to permit internal heat dissipation.
- Inspect all surfaces for cracks or damage.
- Check for loose connections, and tighten circuit breaker terminals and bus bar connections. Use the manufacturer's recommended torque values.
- Manually switch off the breaker in order to exercise the mechanism.
- Check for high-humidity conditions since high humidity will deteriorate the insulation system.

Low-Voltage Switchgear Enclosure

The following steps are recommended for servicing the switchgear enclosure, in addition to the maintenance recommendations made under medium-voltage switchgear:

- Turn power off and ground the bus. Vacuum all dust and dirt. Wipe clean buses, insulators, cables, and the like.
- Inspect bus work and disconnect for overheating. Tighten all mounting and splice bolts. Examine all connections for tightness.
- Check for alignment and seating of contacts of disconnecting devices. Look for abnormal wear or damage.
- Clean and lubricate draw-out mechanism. Check operation of shutters, interlocks, and auxiliary devices.
- Clean ventilating openings and filters.
- After servicing, perform an insulation resistance test from phase to ground on each bus. Compare the results with previous tests to see any weakening tendency.
- Refinish damaged paint surfaces.

AIR DISCONNECT SWITCHES, FUSES, AND INSULATORS

The medium- and low-voltage class electrical distribution system is comprised of equipment such as disconnects, fuses, insulators, lightning arresters, in addition to transformers, circuit breakers, and the like. The recommended frequency for maintenance of electrical equipment is a function of environmental conditions. The frequency of maintenance for equipment in dirty, wet, and corrosive environments will always be more frequent than for equipment in clean areas. A general guide for maintaining this equipment is given next.

Air Disconnect Switches

Air disconnect switches come in many varieties and ratings. The disconnect switches are normally not deenergized during routine maintenance of substations and therefore should be approached with caution. Also, service disconnect switches are seldom operated. However, the interrupter switches are specifically designed for making and breaking specified current. The function of the interrupter switch is similar to the circuit breaker, and the maintenance of this switch should be similar to the procedures listed under power circuit breakers.

The air disconnect switch should be inspected and maintained as follows:

- Close the switch several times to ensure the simultaneous closing of the blades and complete seating of the contacts. Check to see if the closing latch is in the fully closed position. Make adjustments if required in accordance with the instruction manual.
- Inspect the contacts for burns, pitting, pressure, and alignment. Also inspect arcing horns for excessive burn marks. If the contacts show minor damage, dress the contact surface with smooth sandpaper. Badly burned contacts and arcing horns should be replaced.
- Inspect the linkages and operating rod for bending or distortion.
- Check all safety interlocks for proper operation.
- Check for any abnormal conditions such as insulation cracks, chemical deposits if the switch is installed in a corrosive environment, flexible braids, and slip ring contacts.
- Perform special inspection and maintenance when the switch has carried heavy short-circuit current.

Power Fuses

The application of power fuses in electrical distribution is quite common. There are many classes of fuses, such as current limiting or noncurrent limiting with various time-current characteristics, silver sand, liquid filled, or vented expulsion type. The frequency of fuse inspection and maintenance must be determined depending upon the environmental conditions of fuse location. Before fuses are removed or installed, deenergize the fuse holders (that is, the total fuse assembly is disconnected from the power source). The following general procedures are suggested for inspection and maintenance of power fuses.

- Inspect the fuse unit and renewable element (if the fuse is a renewable type) for corrosion, tracking, and dirt. Replace those units that indicate deteriorated condition.

- Inspect for dirt, dust, salt deposits, and the like, on insulators for the holders to prevent flashover. Also look for cracks or burn marks on insulators.

- Inspect the seal on the expulsion chamber for vented expulsion-type fuses to ensure that no moisture has entered the interrupting chamber of the fuse.

- Check for any missing or damaged hardware, such as nuts, bolts, washers, and pins.

- Clean and polish contact surfaces of clips and fuse terminals that are corroded or oxidized.

- Tighten all loose connections and check to see if the fuse clips exert sufficient pressure to maintain good contact.

- Generally fuses that show signs of deterioration, such as loose connections, discoloration, or damaged casing, should be replaced.

Insulators

Insulators are used in all switchgear assemblies and equipment. Insulators separate the current-carrying parts from non-current-carrying parts. The integrity of insulators is therefore very important. The following procedures are recommended for maintaining insulators.

- Inspect insulators for physical damage such as cracks or broken parts. Replace those parts that have incurred damage.

- Inspect insulators for surface contamination such as dirt, grime, and dust. Wipe clean all contaminated insulators.

- Check for corona when the switchgear is energized. Normally, corona will produce a sizzling noise accompanied by crackling, spitting, and popping. This noise is due to ionization of air, which is the conversion of oxygen to ozone. Corona can also be identified by a strong, distinct odor.

- Check for all hardware to ensure that the insulators mounting assembly is tight.

3-6 MOTOR AND GENERATOR MAINTENANCE

This section deals with the inspection and maintenance of motors and generators of all sizes except steam and gas turbines. To obtain maximum efficiency and reliability of motors and generators, they have to be operated and maintained properly. When motors and generators are maintained, many precautions must be followed to avoid damage. Usually this damage results from maintenance personnel lacking thorough knowledge of motor design, construction, application, and proper maintenance. The purpose of this section is to provide general maintenance information applicable to all types of motors and generators. The information is divided into several subsections; the first section provides overall general information, and remaining sections deal with particular types of machines and components.

GENERAL

The fundamental justification for the inspection and maintenance of motors and generators is to prevent service interruptions resulting from equipment failure. A definite program of inspection and maintenance should be organized so that all apparatus is assured of attention at stated periods; these periods should be adjusted to meet the actual need that experience over a number of years has indicated is necessary. To assure adequate inspection, it is essential that an inspection record be kept for each piece of apparatus.

Maintenance should be supplemented by visual inspection of all areas that experience has shown to be vulnerable to damage or degradation. Obviously, this necessitates scheduling disassembly of the apparatus at the time the electrical tests are made. Following is a general maintenance guide that is applicable to all motors and generators.

Visual Inspection

The most significant parts on which inspection should be made are the (1) armature windings, (2) field winding, and (3) brush rigging.

ARMATURE WINDINGS
Check for the following signs of deterioration:

- Deterioration or degradation of insulation resulting from thermal aging. Examination of coils might reveal general puffiness, swelling into ventilation ducts, or a lack of firmness of the insulation, suggesting a loss of bond with consequent separation of the insulation layers from themselves or from the winding conductors or turns.

- Girth cracking or separation of the ground wall from wound coils. This is most likely to occur on long stator coil having asphaltic-type bonds. Particular attention should be paid to the areas immediately adjacent to the ends of the slots. Where considerable cracking is observed, it is recommended that the wedges at the ends of the slots be removed, as dangerous cracks may also have occurred just within the slots.

- Contamination of coil and connection surfaces by substances that adversely affect insulation strength, the most common being carbon dust, oil, and moisture contamination.

- Abrasion or contamination of coil and connection surfaces from other sources, such as chemicals and abrasive or conducting substances. Such effects are aggravated in the case of motors used in adverse atmospheric industrial applications, such as chemical plants, rubber mills, and paper manufacturing facilities.

- Cracking or abrasion of insulation resulting from prolonged or abornal mechanical stresses. In stator windings, looseness of the bracing structure is a certain guide to such phenomena and can itself cause further mechanical damage if allowed to go unchecked.

- Eroding effects of foreign substances embedded or lodged against coil insulation surfaces. Particularly damaging are magnetic particles that vibrate with the effects of the magnetic field in the machine.

- Insulation deterioration due to corona discharges in the body of the machine or end windings. These are evidenced by white, gray, or red deposits and are particularly noticeable in areas where the insulation is subject to high electrical stresses. Some experience is required to distinguish these effects from powdering, which can occur as a result of relative vibratory movement between hard surfaces and which can be caused by loose end-winding structures.

- Loose slot wedges or slot fillers that, if allowed to go uncorrected, may themselves cause mechanical damage or reduce the effectiveness of stator coil retention against short-circuit and other abnormal mechanical forces.

- The effects of overspeeding may be observed on dc armatures by distortion of the windings or commutator rises, looseness or cracking of the banding, or movement of slot wedges.

- Commutators should be checked for uneven discoloration, which can result from short-circuiting of bars, or for pin holes and burrs resulting from flashover.

- The rises (connections between commutator bars and coils in slots) may collect carbon deposits and cause electrical leakage and subsequent failure.

FIELD WINDINGS

In addition to insulation degradation from causes similar to those listed under armature windings, close attention should be paid to the following in field windings:

- Distortion of coils due to the effects of abnormal mechanical, electrical, or thermal forces. Such distortion might cause failure between turns or to ground.

- Shrinkage or looseness of field-coil washers. This permits coil movement during periods of acceleration and deceleration, with the probability of abrading turn insulation and breaking or loosening of connections between coils.

- Breakage or distortion of damper bars due to overspeed or abnormal thermal gradients between bars and the connecting end ring. Such breaks are often difficult to observe in machines that have operated in contaminated conditions and usually occur near the end ring or at the end of the pole piece. Low-resistance measurements between bar and end ring by means of a "ducter" or similar instrument provides a means of detection.

- Loose damper bars with related burning of the tips of the pole-piece laminations. Among other causes, this could occur as a result of improper swaging or other means of retention of the bar during manufacture.

- In cylindrical-pole (or round motor) windings, evidence of heating of wedges at their contact with the retaining-ring body and "half-mooning" or cracks on the retaining rings can be caused by high circulating currents due to unbalanced operation or sustained single-phase faults close to the generator, such as in the leads or generator bus.

- The condition and tightness of end-winding blocking, signs of movement of the retaining-ring insulating liner, and any other looseness should be noted.

- Powered insulation in air ducts is evidence of coil movement. Red oxide at metallic joints is evidence of movement of metal parts.

- Check tightness of field lead connections and condition of collector lead insulation.

BRUSH RIGGING

- The brush rigging should be checked for evidence of flashover.

- Before disassembly, the brush boxes should be checked to ensure that the clearance from the collector or commutator surface is in line with the manufacturer's recommendations. They should be checked to see whether the brushes are free riding and that excessive carbon buildup is not present.

- The brushes themselves should be checked to see whether any excessive edge chipping, grooving, or double facing is evident.

- Brush connections should also be checked.

VOLTAGE CHECKS

- Unbalanced voltage or single-phase operation of polyphase machines may cause excessive heating and ultimate failure. It requires only a slight unbalance of voltage applied to a polyphase machine to cause large unbalanced currents and resultant overheating. In such cases, the power supply should be checked and rectified if even the slightest unbalance is found.

- Single-phase power applied to a three-phase motor will also cause excessive heating from failure to start or from unbalanced currents.

- Unbalanced currents may also be caused by attempts to operate machines having one or more coils disconnected or cut out of one or more phases. If the unbalance is appreciable, the machine should be rewound.

DIRECT-CURRENT MOTORS AND GENERATORS AND REPULSION-INDUCTION MOTORS

The following recommendations are given for direct-current motors (see Figure 3–12); they also apply to repulsion-induction motors used on ac circuits.

Cleanliness

One of the principal causes of malfunction and eventual failure in dc and repulsion-induction rotating equipment is dirt, either from an accumulation of day-to-day dust or from contamination by particles from nearby machinery, such as metallic dust, lint, oil vapors, and chemicals. This is particularly true of this type of electrical apparatus because of its commutators, brushes, and brush rigging, which can become fouled with dirt, resulting in unsatisfactory performance, arcing, and subsequent burning.

The electrical conductors in all electrical equipment are separated from the mechanical components by materials that are grouped under the general term "insulation." Insulation is used on coils to isolate individual turns and to separate the coils from the core. Insulation is used in commutators to separate the bars from each other and, on the brush rigging, to isolate it from the frame or end bracket. Here, again, the importance of cleanliness must be stressed since electrical insulation materials are nonconducting only when clean and dry. Accumulations of dust and dirt not only contribute to insulation breakdown, but they operate to increase temperature through the restriction of ventilation and by blocking the dissipation of heat from the winding and frame surfaces.

Armature

The armature is the heart of the dc motor. Through it flows the line current and, if the machine is overloaded, the armature is the first component to show

FIGURE 3–12.
Cutaway view of a direct-current motor. (Courtesy of General Electric, Erie, Pa.)

evidence of damage. If given reasonable attention by scheduled periodic inspection and cleaning, it should give little or no trouble if the unit is operated within its normal rating. Repairs should be entrusted only to a competent person.

When the armature is removed from the frame for either maintenance or repair, the following precautions should be observed to ensure that the armature is not damaged:

- Steps should be taken at all times to protect the commutator and shaft bearing surfaces.
- The armature should not be rolled about the floor since injury to the coils or banding may result.
- The armature should be supported or lifted only by its shaft if possible. Otherwise, a lifting belt should be used under the core.
- The weight of the armature should never be allowed to rest on the commutator or coil heads.

Periodic inspection, varnish treatment, and curing will prolong the life of the winding. Loose slot wedges and banding should be replaced before varnish treatment and curing. Cleaning, varnish treatment, and curing should include the operations listed under Cleaning and Varnishing of Machine Windings. Treatment of this type is definitely recommended for equipment that is subjected to excessive temperatures or contaminants and is desirable even though the equipment is not subject to adverse conditions. Windings dry out and loosen in operation, and loose windings fail rapidly when subjected to centrifugal stresses and vibrations. Varnish treatments fill the pores and crevices. They help to preserve flexibility in the insulation and hold the coils solidly in the slots, thereby keeping failures to a minimum.

If the armature is to be rebanded with steel wire, it is necessary to duplicate very closely the banding originally furnished by the manfacturer with respect to material, diameter of the banding wire, width, and position of each band. Any change in banding width, position, or material could cause heavy current in the bands sufficient to overheat and melt the solder.

Recent developments and tests of the use of resin-filled glass for the banding of armatures have eliminated many of the risks inherent in the use of the metal bands. When properly applied, the strength factor of resin-filled glass is equal to that of steel bands; therefore, replacement of the original banding by resin-filled glass bands can be accomplished in the space provided for steel bands if the magnetic field is not disturbed. Since resin-filled glass is a good insulator, additional heavy insulation under the band is not required and eddy currents are nonexistent. It is imperative that resin-filled glass banding be applied under tension by an expert utilizing the proper equipment.

Commutation

Commutation is the process of collecting current from a commutator, which, at the same time, short-circuits those coils in which the current is reversed (Figure 3–13). Since there is voltage (even though small) generated in each of these short-circuited coils, a circulating current is present in the face of the carbon brush in addition to the load current. The voltage causing this circulating current is proportional to the load current and the speed, and, as the speeds and ratings of modern machines are increased, this becomes a more serious factor. Since this voltage, under some conditions, becomes so high as to cause excessive sparking, it is the designer's problem to control this reactive voltage by designing the machine to minimize the effect of the flux generated in the armature circuit and by the judicious use of commutating poles, sometimes called interpoles. Successful commutation also requires a good continuous contact between the brush and the commutator surface.

It is obvious that successful commutation is not a function of the brush alone or of the commutator or electrical circuit alone, but results from optimum electrical and mechanical brush-to-commutator conditions.

Commutation is such a complex problem that it is necessary to keep the many adverse variables at a minimum. Commutation may be adversely affected by dust, dirt, gases, oil vapor, and the like, and varying atmospheric conditions such as high temperature or low humidity. Where a commutation problem exists owing to one or more of these ambient conditions, it is sometimes possible to arrive at a solution by altering the unit to offset the condition. If the commutation of a unit is not satisfactory and a change in brush grade is indicated, the manufacturer should be consulted. However, in general, this is not a true solution.

The mechanical condition of the unit can also greatly affect commutation. Commutators should be periodically checked for high bars, which will cause flashing and generally poor commutation. Both commutators and slip rings should be smooth, round, and concentric with the axis of rotation. If there is any appreciable vibration, the cause should be determined and corrected.

Some of the most common service problems with commutators and their causes are as follows:

- High commutator bars generally produce sparking, noisy operation, and chipped or broken brushes. The causes are usually a loose commutator, improper undercutting, open or high resistance connections, or electrical shorts.
- Streaking or threading of the commutator surface causes rough surfaces with associated sparking. Primary faults can be:

    Low average current density in brushes due to light machine loading.

    Contaminated atmosphere.

    Oil on commutator or oil mist in air.

    Low humidity.

    Lack of film-forming properties in brush.

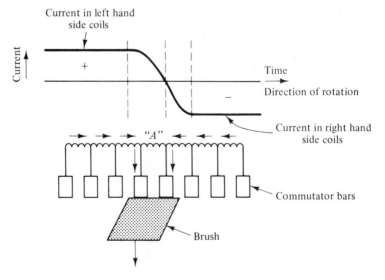

FIGURE 3-13.
Coil "A" undergoing commutation.

Brushes too abrasive.

- Bar etching or burning produces a rough commutator with associated sparking and eventual flashover. Such burning often results from:

High mica.

Operation of machine with brushes off neutral.

Dirty commutator.

Incorrect spring tension.

Machine operating overloaded or under rapid load change such as plugging.

- Bar marking at pole pitch spacing produces a rough commutator with associated sparking and eventual flashover. This burning is generally caused by electrically shorted commutator bars or coils, open armature or field circuits, severe load conditions, misalignment of the coupling, and vibration. The burning in the early stages is generally evident at one-half the number of poles.

- Bar marking at slot spacing produces rough bars at regular intervals around a commutator. Since several coils are imbedded in each armature slot, all the coils may not be equally compensated. The energy unbalance is reflected into the last coil in the slot to undergo commutation and will result in a spark at the brush. Such a spark will cause burned spots on the bars equally spaced according to the bars per slot ratio.

- Selective commutation can occur on machines with more than one brush per brush stud if the resistance path of one brush is lower with respect to the other brushes on the same stud. Due to higher spring pressure, improper staggering of brushes, or a breakdown of the commutator film in one path, the brush with the low contact drop will have a tendency to carry more than its share of the current.

- The exposed portion of the front vee-ring insulation is normally the target for moisture, oil, and dirt, which may cause flashovers and breakdowns to the ground. It is, therefore, essential that the exposed surface of the mica be kept clean and protected by means of other insulation. There are various ways to apply extra insulation at this point, depending upon the individual ideas of the machine designer. In general, however, this consists of a cord or tape of cotton or glass wound in tight layers over the surface of the exposed section of the mica cone or vee ring. The exposed surface is then treated with several coats of varnish suitable for the operating temperature of the machine. These multiple coats of varnish are applied to obtain a smooth, easily cleanable surface. The purpose is to obtain extra insulation that will protect the vee-ring insulation and, so far as possible, seal the joint between the commutator bars and the vee ring.

Field Windings

If the field winding of any type of dc motor is open circuited, the motor will fail to start or it will operate at excessive speed at light loads and serious sparking will occur at the commutator. It should not be concluded that a field is defective until rheostats, switches, and other devices in the motor circuit have been carefully inspected.

To check for grounded fields, a conventional high-potential transformer may be used. If the field circuit is free of grounds and shorted shunt field is suspected, comparative resistance measurements should be made of the individual coils and compared with the resistance of a similar coil that is known to be in good condition. Such a comparative check should preferably be made when the field windings are hot or near their normal operating temperature. A shunt field coil may show the correct resistance when it is cold but may show a lower value when it is hot or near its normal operating temperature. This is due to defective insulation between turns of adjacent conductors, and short circuits may not occur until expansion has taken place because of the increased temperature. If the correct resistance value of good coils is not known, comparative checks made with either a Wheatstone bridge or by the voltammeter method will usually provide a reliable indication of shunt field resistance. If neither a bridge nor an ammeter is available, a check as to the condition of the coils may be obtained by connecting all shunt coils in series to a source of constant potential and measuring the voltage drop across individual coils. For shorts in series and commutating field coils, where the resistance is necessarily low, the use of more sensitive instruments may be necessary to detect defects.

A common cause of field coil failure is overheating, which may result from the following:

- Operation of the machine at low speed, preventing proper ventilation.
- Excitation voltage too high.
- Overloading machine.
- High ambient temperature.

Faulty performance, indicated by poor commutation, improper speed, and overheating, is frequently traceable to defective field coils or to improperly connected field windings.

In removing a shunt or series field coil, the coil should be disconnected from the adjacent coils, and the bolts which secure the pole pieces to the frame should be removed. This will make it possible to remove the pole piece and coil, after which the pole piece, with a new or reinsulated coil, can be installed. Particular care should be taken in replacing the pole with its coil to be sure that the same steel or nonmagnetic shims between the frame and the back of the pole are in the same position to ensure the same air gap that was present in the machine when it was new.

When reconnecting the coil, the proper polarity must be maintained. A simple means of testing the polarity is by the use of a compass, a magnetized needle, or a piece of magnetized steel wire suspended from the middle by a string. The polarity should be alternatively north and south around the frame. When the compass needle is brought within the magnetic field of any pole, one end of the needle will point toward this pole and this end should be repelled by the next pole, and so on around the frame. If this reversal of the needle does not occur, there is a faulty connection of one or more of the field coils.

Since there is a possibility of reversing the poles of a compass with a strong field, similar results can be obtained by putting the compass on a work bench, placing a steel scale against the pole of the machine, and then setting the scale against the compass. The readings will, of course, be reversed as compared to the direct reading with a compass.

INDUCTION MOTOR

There are two types of ac induction motor construction, squirrel cage and wound rotor. Stator design is the same for both; they differ mainly in rotor design. There are no external rotating or secondary connections on a squirrel-cage motor; most wound rotors have a three-phase winding connected through collector rings to an adjustable secondary resistance.

Today's induction motor, especially the squirrel-cage type (Figure 3–14), is a highly efficient machine whose periods of trouble-free service can be considerably prolonged by systematic care. Correct application and installation will minimize maintenance requirements.

Essentially, maintenance of squirrel-cage induction motors centers on the stator windings and bearings. Rotors require little or no special care in normal service, except to make certain that bolts or other fasteners remain tightly secured. For wound-rotor types, rotor construction with the associated brush rigging requires additional maintenance.

Figure 3–14.
Squirrel-cage motor.(Courtesy of General Electric, Schenectady, N.Y.)

Stator windings differ in induction motors, depending on the size of the stator frame. Smaller motors, generally, are known as mush wound and are sometimes called random or wire wound. Mush-wound coils are made by looping wire in an elliptical form without exact dimensions. Coils are inserted, a few wires at a time, in semiclosed stator slots.

Larger motors utilize form-wound coils, constructed by winding magnet wire in a loop, which is then formed to an exact shape to meet specific dimensions of width, height, and pitch. Coils are fitted in open slots in the stator iron.

Since the life of a motor is limited largely by that of its insulation, proper care can greatly extend its service reliability. Maintenance of winding insulation is mostly a matter of keeping the machine clean and dry, providing it with an adequate supply of cool, dry, ventilating air, and operating the machine within its rating.

Stator Windings

A regular schedule of inspection can prevent costly shutdowns and repairs by revealing small defects, which can be corrected before they develop into serious faults. The operating temperature of the machine should be checked at regular intervals. Open-type machines must be inspected more frequently than closed types, with the machines shut down if possible.

The interior of larger machines is often inaccessible because of the end covers, air baffles, and fans. These obstructions should be removed at regular intervals to permit a closer inspection. Under favorable conditions, a machine with a closed ventilating system may require complete inspection and cleaning not more than once a year. On the other hand, a machine operating under less favorable conditions may require a complete inspection and cleaning more often.

The best indication of the condition of the insulation is a record of the insulation resistance taken at regular intervals when the machine is hot. A sudden decrease in the insulation resistance may indicate an approaching breakdown, which may be avoided if the cause is located and corrected in time.

Air Gap

A small air gap is characteristic of induction motors and has an important bearing on the machine's power factor. Anything that may affect the air gap, such as grinding the rotor laminations or filing the stator teeth, may result in increased magnetizing current and lower power factor.

The air gap should be periodically checked with a feeler gauge to ensure against a worn bearing that might permit the rotor to rub against the stator core. Even slight rubbing of the rotor against the stator will generate enough heat to destroy the coil insulation.

Measurements should be made on the drive end of the motor. Openings are provided in the end shields and inner air baffles of some machines for the insertion of feeler gauges for this purpose. This check is needed particularly for sleeve-bearing motors. A change in air gap seldom occurs in antifriction bearing motors unless the bearing fails.

For small sleeve-bearing motors without feeler gauge openings, a check of bearing wear using a dial indicator on the shaft extension should be considered.

A record of air-gap checks should be kept, especially on larger machines. Four measurements should be taken approximately 90° apart. One point of measurement should be made in the direction of load. A comparison of periodic measurements will permit early detection of bearing wear.

Wound-Rotor Windings

Rotor windings of wound-rotor motors have many features in common with stator windings, and the same comments apply to their care and maintenance. However, the rotor requires additional consideration because it is a rotating element.

Most wound rotors have a three-phase winding and are susceptible to trouble from single-phase operation and open circuits. The first symptoms of these faults are lack of torque, slowing down in speed, growling noise, or perhaps failure to start the load.

The first place to look for an open secondary circuit is in the resistance or the control circuit external to the rotor. Short-circuiting the rotor circuit at the slip rings and then operating the motor will usually determine that the trouble is in the control circuit or in the rotor itself.

Some rotors are wave wound, with windings made up of copper strap coils with clips connecting the top and bottom halves of the coil. These end connections should be inspected for possible signs of heating, which could be an indication of a partial open circuit. Faulty end connections are a common source of open circuits in rotor windings. The open circuit may be at one of the stud connections to the collector rings.

A ground in a rotor circuit will not affect motor performance except that, in combination with another ground, it might cause the equivalent of a short circuit. This would have the effect of unbalancing the rotor electrically. Reduced torque is a symptom; others might be excessive vibration of the motor, sparking, or uneven wear of the collector rings. A test for this condition can be made with a 500-V megohmmeter.

Another fairly successful method of checking for short circuits in the rotor windings is to raise the brushes off the collector rings and energize the stator. A rotor winding that is free from short circuits should have little or no tendency to rotate, even when disconnected from the load. If it evidences considerable torque or a tendency to come up to speed, the rotor should be removed and the winding opened and examined for the fault. In making this test, it should be noted that some rotors having a wide tooth design may show a tendency to rotate even though the windings are in good condition.

With the rotor in place, the stator energized, and the brushes raised, the voltages across the collector rings should be checked to see if they are balanced. These voltages bear no particular relation to the line voltage and may be considerably higher. For example, they may be as high as 500 V for a 200-V stator. To make sure that any inequality in voltage measurements is not due to the relative positions of the rotor and stator phases, the rotor should be moved to several positions in taking these voltage measurements.

Brushes and Rings

Brushes and collector rings on wound rotors need special care. Although a certain amount of wear is inevitable, conditions that lead to "grooving" of rings (concentration of wear in narrow rings or ruts) should be prevented, and abrasive dust should be wiped off rings at regular intervals.

Rough or uneven ring surfaces should be remedied as soon as possible, before sparking, pitting, and accelerated brush wear result. Allowing the rotor to oscillate axially will distribute wear more evenly. Unevenly worn brushes should be replaced to assure best operation.

Centrifugal Switches

Basically, all single-phase motors are designed with a special arrangement of winding for starting. To accomplish this, some method is used to automatically change the electrical connections of a motor. This may be one of the following:

- Starting and running windings, with centrifugally operated switches to disconnect the starting winding.
- Centrifugal switch to disconnect or change capacitor circuits.
- Potential relay (occasionally used instead of centrifugal switches).
- Repulsion-induction-type motor with wound rotor and commutator, which utilizes a centrifugally operated switch to short-circuit the commutator at a predetermined speed.
- Repulsion-inductor-type motor with wound rotor and commutator and a squirrel-cage rotor winding that automatically come into use near full speed needs no transfer device.

It is usually more practical to replace defective centrifugal switches than to repair them.

Squirrel-Cage Rotors

Squirrel-cage rotors are more rugged and, in general, require less maintenance than wound rotors. Open circuits or high-resistance joints between the end rings and the rotor bars may give trouble. The symptoms of such conditions are generally the same as with wound-rotor motors, that is, slowing down under load and reduced starting torque. Look for evidence of heating at the end ring connections, particularly when shifting down after operating under load.

Fractures in the rotor bars usually occur between the point of connection to the end and the point where the bar leaves the laminations. Discolored rotor bars are evidence of excessive heating.

Brazing or replacing broken bars requires considerable skill. Unless a capable serviceman is available, the manufacturer's nearest office or an experienced service shop should be consulted before attempting such repairs at the plant.

SYNCHRONOUS MOTORS AND GENERATORS

The stator of a synchronous machine requires approximately the same care as the stator of an induction motor. In large-sized synchronous machines, the windings are generally more accessible and this facilitates cleaning (Figure 3–15).

The rotor field coils of a synchronous machine should be cleaned in the same manner as the field coils on a dc machine. Slow-speed synchronous machines have rotor poles held to the spider with studs and nuts, while in high-speed synchronous machines a dovetail construction is utilized with tapered wedges securing the poles.

Some synchronous machines have the poles bolted to the shaft using bolts through the poles. Some 400-cycle synchronous generators utilize a laminated field structure with coils placed in slots, each tooth representing a pole. Following is a general maintenance guide for synchronous motors:

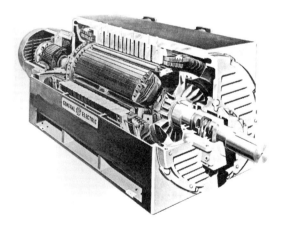

FIGURE 3–15.
Cutaway view of a large synchronous motor. (Courtesy of General Electric, Schenectady, N.Y.)

- During any general overhaul, the nuts on the studs or the wedges for the dovetail poles should be checked for looseness. The amortisseur winding should be checked for loose or cracked connections.

- In dusty installations where collector ring enclosures are not used, the collector rings and brushholders should be blown off weekly with clean dry air. When oil deposits form on the collector ring or brushholder insulation, it should be cleaned by wiping with a suitable solvent and coated with a high-gloss insulating varnish. When cleaning the brushholders, the brushes should be removed to prevent their absorbing the solvent.

- Coat all insulated surfaces of the brushholders and slip rings with a high-gloss insulating varnish. Caution should be exercised. Do not coat brush contact surfaces of the slip rings.

- If the collector rings become eccentric, grooved, pitted, or deeply scratched, this condition can best be corrected by grinding the rings with a rotating-type grinder, with the machine running at rated speed in its own bearing. Fine emery cloth or sandpaper should be used for light scratches on iron or steel rings but not on bronze rings.

- Regardless of the method used, rings should be polished to a high gloss with crocus cloth and oil. After polishing, the rings should be thoroughly cleaned with a solvent to remove all abrasives and foreign materials.

- Inasmuch as the wear due to electrochemical action is not the same on both the positive and negative collector rings, it is suggested that the polarity be reversed about every 3 months of operation to compensate for this condition.

- The field current specified on the nameplate should not be exceeded for continuous operation.

CLEANING AND VARNISHING OF MACHINE WINDINGS

The life of a winding depends upon keeping it in its original condition as long as possible. In a new machine, the winding is snug in the slots, and the insulation is fresh and flexible and has been treated to be resistant to the deteriorating effects of moisture and other foreign matter.

Moisture is one of the most subtle enemies of the insulation on ratating electrical machinery. Insulation should be kept dry. Certain modern types of insulation are inherently moisture proof and require infrequent varnish treatment, but the great majority, if exposed to a damp atmospheric place, should be given special moisture-resisting treatment.

One condition that frequently hastens winding failure is movement of the coils caused by vibration during operation. After insulation dries out, it loses its flexibility. Mechanical stresses caused by starting and plugging, as well as natural stresses in operation under load, sometimes precipitate short-circuits in the coils and possibly failures from coil to ground, usually at the point where the coil leaves the slot.

Periodic varnish treatment and curing, properly done so as to fill all spaces caused by drying and shrinkage of the insulation, will provide an effective seal against moisture and should be a matter of routine electrical maintenance. Varnish treatment and curing of rotating electrical equipment follow a logical procedure.

Cleaning

Some machines are exposed to accumulations of such materials as talc, lint, or cement dust, which, although harmless in themselves, may obstruct the ventilation. The machine will then operate at higher temperatures than normal, and the life of the insulation will be decreased. Such materials can sometimes be blown out with compressed air free of moisture.

The most harmful types of foreign materials include carbon black, metallic dust and chips, and similar substances that not only impair the ventilation, but also form a conductive film over the insulation and increase the possibility of insulation failure. Metallic chips may also work themselves into the insulation because of the ventilation and magnetic fields. When windings are cleaned, inspection should be made for any signs of deterioration.

Epoxy-encapsulated windings, a construction finding increasing favor, are sealed against contaminants. They need little attention other than removing dirt accumulations. The common practice when such windings are damaged is replacement with a new winding.

It is extremely important that all wound stators and rotors be perfectly clean before varnish treatment and curing. Unless all conducting dirt and grease are removed, the varnish treatment will not be fully effective. Also, after varnish treatment, the leakage path caused by conducting materials will be difficult to uncover and remove. Proper cleaning involves the following steps:

- Dirt should be removed from all coil surfaces and mechanical parts. Air vent ducts should be clear. As an alternative, clean, dry air at a pressure of not more than 50 psi may be used. Higher air pressure may damage windings. Do not use air if dust from the machine can damage critical equipment nearby.

- As much oil, grease, and dirt as possible should be removed by wiping the windings with clean, dry cloths and then with clean cloths that have been moistened with a solvent recommended by the coil manufacturer. If the original varnish on the windings is cracked, a brush should be dipped in solvent and used to clean all conducting particles from the cracks.

- For cleaning, armatures or wound rotors should be placed in a vertical position with the commutator or collector ring end up, and a pressure spray gun with solvent should be used to clean under the collecting device and through vent holes. The same procedure should be repeated with the opposite end up, and then repeated again with the commutator or collector ring end up. Most large dc armatures are ventilated through open commutator risers at the front end. The solvent spray should be directed through these risers to reach the inner surface of the armature coils and inner commutator vee-ring extensions.

- Silicone-insulated equipment can be cleaned by the same methods used with other insulation systems. If a liquid cleaner is found to be necessary, the recommendations of the coil manufacturer should be followed.

- For windings other than silicone, there are a number of good commercial cleaners on the market. The manufacturer can recommend the one most suitable for the conditions. Plant safety rules concerning the use of flammable and toxic solvents should be observed and followed.

- Caution should be exercised to remove all liquid cleaners.

Drying

The wound apparatus should be dried in an oven held at a temperature of 115° to 125°C (239° to 257°F) for 6 to 12 hours or until the insulation resistance becomes practically constant. If a vacuum is used, the drying time may be reduced.

The apparatus should be brought up to temperature slowly because excessive moisture may be present in the windings. If heated rapidly, this moisture may vaporize quickly enough to rupture the insulation.

Before treatment, the appratus should be cooled to within 10°C (50°F) above room temperature, but never to a temperature lower than 25°C (77°F). If the apparatus is cooled to room temperature and allowed to stand, it will take up moisture quickly. If placed in the varnish at a temperature higher than that specified, the varnish will tend to harden.

Varnish

The selection of varnish is dependent upon the operating conditions to which the motor is subjected; also, the type of environmental conditions, (i.e., moisture, corrosion, chemical, abrasion) should be taken into consideration.

Varnish must be compatible with the insulation system with which it is to be used. If it is incompatible, it may not adhere and may not give the desired protection. For most applications, the selection of a general-purpose high-bonding, yet resilient, synthetic resin varnish is recommended. The varnish can be either class A, B or F, depending upon the insulation system rating. On large ac stators using class A insulation, the use of a flexible asphalt or oleoresinous varnish is suggested; then, if it becomes necessary to lift a coil, the coil will not be destroyed.

Many types of varnishes are available, and when applying the insulating varnish, the recommendation of the manufacturer should be followed with respect to specific gravity, viscosity, and curing cycle for the particular varnish in question. After the varnish has been adjusted to give the desired film build and drainage characteristics, the specific gravity and viscosity readings should be recorded; then at periodic intervals the varnish should be examined for either specific gravity or viscosity, or both, and adjustments should be made to bring it within the original limits.

The units should be cured in a properly ventilated forced-air circulating oven to remove the solvent vapors. The oven can be either gas fired or electrically heated. Infrared heat can be used if desired.

For the most part, the time and temperature of the cure should follow the varnish manufacturer's recommendations. The time of cure will vary from short bakes of several hours up through 16 to 24 hours, based on the physical dimensions and makeup of the units, and taking into consideration the particular characteristics of the type of varnish that has been applied to the equipment.

Curing temperatures will vary from 75° to 125°C (167° to 257°F) for oleoresinous-type varnishes to 135° to 155°C (275° to 311°F) for classes B and F varnishes. Silicone varnishes usually require a cure temperature range of 185° to 200°C (365° to 392°F) or higher.

Complete rewinding jobs should receive at least two coats of varnish. Baking time can usually be reduced on the first or impregnated coat, with an extended period of time used on the final coat. The use of additional coats is based on what is expected of the unit after it is in operation. If severe conditions are to be encountered, multiple-coat systems are recommended. Also, apparatus such as high-speed armatures should receive multiple coats for the maximum bonding of the conductors. One coat is all that is necessary on older units that have been cleaned up on which no rewind work has been done.

In the case of large stators or rotors where the size is such that dipping is not possible, the varnish must be sprayed on the windings. Old winding surfaces must be completely coated.

For most applications, conventional dip methods are recommended. Other accepted methods are brushing and flooding. However, if the length or depth of the slots is great and the windings tightly packed, it may be necessary to use a vacuum impregnation system.

LUBRICATION, BEARINGS, AND OIL SEALS

Lubrication

Of all the important items of maintenance, lubrication ranks as one of the highest. Improper oiling or greasing will produce as disastrous results as any other type of motor mistreatment.

Excess oil may get into the windings where it will collect dust and other foreign matter. Too much grease in antifriction bearings causes heat and sometimes failure of bearings and may also coat the windings. Most manufacturers furnish data on proper oiling and greasing, and numerous articles have been written on the subject. The important point is to set up a definite lubrication schedule and follow it. Years of experience have demonstrated that it is as bad to use too much as too little oil and grease.

Of equal importance is the type of oil or grease used. In general, the recommendations of the manufacturer or experienced oil companies should be followed. In some cases, for design reasons, manufacturers insist on the use of particular lubricants that have been adopted after exhaustive test by their engineers. It will pay to follow these recommendations.

Sleeve Bearings

Some oil-lubricated machines are shipped without oil and, in the case of large machines, the journals are often packed and treated for protection during shipment. The rotating elements may also be blocked to prevent damage to the bearings and journals during shipment. Where lubrication is required, the bearing must be opened, the packing removed, and the journal cleaned and flushed before filling the housing with oil. All motor and generator bearings should be checked for oil before starting up.

The bearings of all electrical equipment should be carefully inspected at scheduled periodic intervals in order to obtain maximum life. The frequency of inspection, including the addition of oil, changing the oil, and checking the bearing wear, is best determined by a study of the particular operating conditions. Should it ever become necessary to add excessive amounts of makeup oil, an investigation for oil leaks should be started immediately.

The more modern types of sleeve-bearing housings are relatively dust and oil tight and require very little attention, since the oil does not become contaminated and oil leakage is negligible. Maintenance of the correct oil level is frequently the only upkeep required for years of service with this type of bearing.

Older types of sleeve bearings require more frequent inspection and checking for wear, and oil changes should be made more often. Never add oil to bearings when the machine is running.

In most cases, the safe temperature rise for a bearing is considered to be within 40°C above the room ambient.

Small sleeve-bearing motors use either wool packing or fluid wick for transferring the lubricant to sleeve bearings instead of oil-ring lubrication. Some of these small motors have provision for relubrication.

When electrical equipment must operate under extreme differences in air temperatures, the use of a lighter oil may be found desirable during cold weather.

Care should always be exercised in the use of reclaimed lubricating oils. The filtering operation should be positive and should remove all foreign and injurious matter.

A hot bearing is usually due to one of the following causes:

- No oil.
- A poor grade of oil or dirty oil.
- Failure of the oil rings to revolve with the shaft.
- Excessive belt tension.
- Rough bearing surface.
- Improper fitting of the bearing.
- Bent shaft.
- Misalignment of shaft and bearing.
- Loose bolts in the bearing cap.
- Excessive end thrust due to improper leveling. A bearing may become warm because of excessive pressure exerted by the shoulder of the shaft against the end of the bearing.
- Excessive end thrust due to magnetic pull, with the rotating part being "sucked" into the stator or field because it extends farther beyond the magnetic structure or field poles at one end than at the other end.
- Excessive side pull because the rotating part is out of balance.

If a bearing becomes hot, the load should be reduced if possible and lubricants fed freely, loosening the nuts on the bearing cap. If the machine is belt connected, the belt should be slackened. In case relief is not afforded, the load should be removed and the machine kept running slowly, where possible, until the shaft is cool in order that the bearing will not "freeze." The oil supply should be renewed before starting the machine again.

A new machine should always be run unloaded or at slow speed for an hour or so to make sure that it operates properly. The bearings should be carefully watched to observe that the oil rings revolve and carry a plentiful supply of oil to the shaft.

Antifriction Bearings

Ball or roller bearings carry the load by direct contact, as opposed to sleeve bearings, which carry the load on lubricating film. Lubrication is necessary to minimize the friction and generation of heat caused by the balls rubbing on the outer race as they roll over the top or on the retainer of the cage.

Antifriction bearings require considerable care to prevent loss of end clearance, distortion of balls, and marking of races. If too much force is used in pressing the bearing on the shaft, the clearance may be destroyed. It is recommended that antifriction bearings be heated in a hot bath of clean oil rather than by the use of dry heat. When the bearing is pulled off, with all the stress on the outer race, both races may be damaged, with resultant failure when put back in service. The bearing manufacturer's recommendations should be followed when removing and reapplying this type of bearing.

Bearing manufacturers produce a bearing known as the prelubricated shielded bearing. Several years' use of this bearing has demonstrated that, for many applications, no further lubrication is needed. Such bearing construction is usually indicated on the nameplate.

In general, to obtain maximum service, ball-bearing motors should be relubricated at intervals determined by the type, size, and service of the bearing. Many motor manufacturers offer as a guide a table suggesting the intervals between lubrication. These show time intervals between greasing that range from 3 months or so for motors operating in very severe service, as in conditions involving dirt or vibrating applications, those where the end of the shaft is hot, or high ambient temperatures, to 3 years for easy service, where motors operate for short periods or infrequently.

The bearing housing is usually arranged to introduce new grease and purge the bearing of old grease, allowing it to discharge through a partially restricted escape port or relief hole. This will, in general, allow filling to the desired degree, which is one-third to one-half full, leaving some space in the housing to allow for expansion of the grease.

It is again stressed that overgreasing can be just as harmful as undergreasing. Overgreasing causes churning and internal friction, which results in heating, separation of the oil and soap, oxidation of the grease, and possible leakage through the retaining seals.

Installation of Oil Seals

The importance of properly installing an oil seal cannot be overemphasized. Failure to observe correct installation procedures probably accounts for more cases of the improper functioning of oil seals than any other single cause. To secure the ultimate in satisfactory service, it is recommended that the following precautions be observed.

CORRECT SEAL

It is essential that the seal be the correct size for the installation. Oil seals are made for a specified shaft size. When they are installed on a shaft of a larger diameter, there will be drag, frictional heat, and excessive wear on the sealing element and shaft. When installed on a shaft having a smaller diameter, immediate leakage can occur.

FLUID CONTACT

The seal should be assembled with the toe or wiping edge of the sealing element pointing toward the fluid to be retained. Exceptions for unusual applications must be by specification in manuals or instructions furnished with the assembly.

BORE

The bore should be checked for adequate chamfer (30° angle to a minimum depth of $\frac{1}{16}$ in.). The bore should be inspected for scratches and all sharp edges removed. The seal outside diameter should be correct for the bore in the assembly. When a leak at the outer edge of either metal or rubber-covered seals is caused by abrasion of the oil seal, it may be directly related to improper chamfer on the bore or the use of improper installation tools.

SHAFT

The surface of the shaft should be uniform and free from burrs, nicks, scratches, and grooves. The surface finish should be between 10 and 20 microinches (μin.) and, on a repair job, should be buffed to this thickness with crocus cloth.

LUBRICATION

In all cases a lubricant should be applied to the shaft or to the sealing element of the oil seal. This aids installation and reduces heat build-up during the first few minutes of run. The application of a lubricant to the outer periphery of a synthetic rubber-covered seal will reduce the possibility of shearing or bruising.

PRESSING TOOLS

In pressing the seal into the bore, it is imperative that the proper-sized pressing tool be used to localize the pressure on the face of the seal and in direct line with the side walls of the seal case to prevent damage and distortion to the seal cases during the installation. When a seal must penetrate the bore below the surface, the proper pressing tool should be $\frac{1}{32}$ in. smaller than the bore diameter. On installations where the seal is flush with the housing, the proper pressing tool should be at least $\frac{1}{8}$ in. larger in diameter, and more if room permits. Care should be taken to avoid hammer blows, uneven pressure on seal surfaces, and cocking of the seal during this operation.

When an oil seal of open channel construction is pressed-fit heel first into the bore, an installation tool will be helpful. The tool is designed to have contact with the inside diameter of the seal case.

SHAFT END

If the seal is to be installed toe first, the end of the shaft should have a 30° by $\frac{3}{16}$-in. taper, or an installation tool must be used. If the seal is to be installed heel first, no special precautions are necessary other than to remove burrs or sharp edges from the end of the shaft.

SHAFTS WITH KEYWAYS AND THE LIKE

When an oil seal is installed over the keyway, splines, and the like, an installation thimble should be used with the outside diameter not more than $\frac{1}{32}$ in. over the shaft.

PRESSURE-LUBRICATED BEARINGS

Because of speed and bearing loading, it is necessary to pressure lubricate the bearings on some larger motors and generators. Pressure gauge readings may not show the amount of oil flowing, but machines have a sight oil flow detector where oil flow may be checked. Orifices in the feed lines may clog, and oil-flow detection devices will protect the bearings.

BEARING INSULATION

If the bearing is insulated, care must be taken so that the insulated bearing is not grounded by bearing temperature detectors or relays.

BRUSHES

Proper care of brushes, brush rigging, and current-collecting parts is a fundamental necessity if satisfactory performance is to be obtained. Adequate inspection is essential to the maintenance of this equipment, and the following points should be observed:

- The brushholder box should be adjusted between $\frac{1}{16}$ and $\frac{1}{8}$ in. from the face of the commutator.
- Care should be taken to see that dirt and particles broken from the edges of brushes or the commutator have not lodged in the face of the brush.
- The brushes must be correctly aligned, and the commutator brushes must be properly staggered, pairs of arms (+ and −) being set alternately.
- A brush is affected by such adverse conditions as sparking, glowing, rough commutator, severe chattering, no-load running, overload running, improper spring pressure, and selective action.
- A brush on a machine that sparks or glows owing to load conditions, off-neutral operation, or an electrical fault in the machine will be burned and pitted near the sparking edge.
- Severe chattering of the brush is caused by a high-friction film on the surface of the commutator or by improper spring pressure.
- Brush chattering due to a high-friction film occurs on machines where there is considerable no-load or light-load running. The characteristic curve of friction versus load current is of such a shape that minimum friction can be obtained at approximately 55 A/in.^{2}, and as load current is either reduced or increased, the brush friction is increased. Accordingly, it is sometimes good practice, when a machine is running at very light loads for a considerable period of time, to lift one or more brushes per arm to bring the brush friction into the desirable range. Cases where the load current is above the normal values are more serious,

because the higher currents produce sparking, overheating of the machine, and brush chatter simultaneously.

■ Spring pressure has a direct effect on the riding characteristics of a brush. A common error is to reduce spring pressure for brush wear or marking of the commutator. This permits the brush to bounce on the commutator, which, in turn, causes sparking and selective action and produces a rough commutator. On the other hand, excessive spring pressure causes brush wear and commutator wear, and usually lowers the electrical contact voltage drop to the point where satisfactory commutation is not obtained. Correct spring pressure should be 2½ to 5½ lb/in.^{2} for industrial service and 5 to 10 lb/in.^{2} for traction service. The lower range on traction work will be found where spring-supported motors are used; axle-hung motors use the higher range.

■ When checking spring pressure, the action of the brush in the box should be free. Dirt or gummy oil on the brush or in the brush box sometimes causes the brush to stick and, in some cases, to completely break the contact between the brush and the commutator.

■ Commutator wear in various forms is frequently attributed to a brush that is too hard. Actually, the abrasiveness of a brush does not result from its hardness. Some of the most abrasive brushes are soft to the touch or low when measured for scleroscopic hardness. The property in a brush of given grade that causes abrasiveness is controlled by the brush manufacturer, who should be consulted for information as to the relative cleaning properties of the various grades.

Brush Adjustment

The brushes of a new machine are generally adjusted at the factory to the electrically neutral position, and it should not be necessary to change the adjustment. An exception to this rule may occur on large machines where an off-neutral setting is sometimes used to improve commutation. In any case, the method for identifying the proper brush position is given in the manufacturer's instruction book. Various methods may be used for determining the neutral position. The *kick method* is commonly used as is outlined here.

With all brushes raised from the commutator and the machine standing still, voltages will be induced in the armature by transformer action if the shunt field is excited to about one-half of its normal strength and the field current suddenly broken. It will be found that the induced voltages in conductors located at equal distances to the right and left of the main pole centers will be equal in magnitude and opposite in direction.

Hence, if the terminals of a low-reading voltmeter (5 V) are connected to two commutator bars on the opposite side of a main pole and exactly halfway between the center lines of two main poles, the voltmeter will show no deflection when the field current is broken. The spacing of these commutator bars is, therefore, the correct distance between brushes on adjacent brush arms.

The most practical method of making this check is to make two pilot brushes of wood or fiber to fit the regular brushholder, each brush carrying in its center a piece of copper fitted for line contact with the commutator bar. With a lead for the connection of adjacent brush arms, the brush rigging may then be shifted slightly forward or backward, as necessary, until breaking the field current produces no deflection on the voltmeter. By noting the position at which no deflection is obtained for each pair of brush arms, the average of the positions of neutral thus obtained will give the correct running location for the brushes.

A quick and convenient method of locating the neutral position on a dc motor with shunt fields is to check the speed of the motor in either direction with the same impressed line voltage. The position of the brushes that produces the same speed in either direction under the same voltage conditions is the correct neutral position.

Another shortcut is to take a piece of lamp cord and bend it in the middle, bringing the two ends together. The insulation should be removed for ½ in. on each end and the bare wires twisted together, fanning out to form a brush. When this brush is held so that it spans two bars at the outer end of the commutator and moved with and against the direction of rotation, the point of least sparking at the ends of the wires is the proper location for the center line of the brushes.

BALANCING

Electrical failures are often ascribed to deteriorated insulation, open circuit, short circuit, and so on, but in many cases, failure of insulation results from mechanical disturbances.

Unusual noises in electrical apparatus may be the result of grounds, short-circuited coils, changes in voltage or frequency, rubbing or looseness of parts, vibration, defective bearings, and many other causes.

Any unusual amount of vibration or an increase in machine vibration should be investigated immediately. Common causes of undue vibration, other than imbalance, are bearing wear, dirt accumulation, misalignment, an improper or a settled foundation, uneven air gap, parts rubbing the rotating element, sprung shafting, a short-circuited field coil, or imbalanced stator currents in the case of ac machines. These should be investigated before balance weights are added or shifted. If at any time it should be necessary to remove the balance weights, they should be replaced in the same position.

Before disassembling a pole on high-speed machines, the axial position of that pole should be accurately marked so that it can be replaced in the same position. Should it become necessary to replace a field coil, or a complete pole, the balance must be checked.

Need for Balancing

Vibrations produced by unbalanced rotating parts may result in the following:

- Excessive bearing wear.
- Noisy operation of the equipment.
- Failure of structural parts.
- Reduced overall mechanical efficiency.
- Vibration of machine parts or the supporting structure.

Imbalance Measurement

Ounce-inches (oz-in.) is generally the measurement used. An imbalance of 1 oz-in. in a rotating body will produce a centrifugal force equivalent to that produced by 1 oz of weight 1 in. from the rotational axis. A rotor weighing 62.5 lb (1,000 oz) whose mass center is displaced 0.001 from the rotational axis is 1 oz-in. out of balance.

Only force imbalance is measured by static balancing, which is a single-plane correction. The part being balanced is not rotated. Dynamic balancing of a part by rotation is required when there is appreciable axle length because, by this method, force imbalance, moment imbalance, or a combination of both may be measured. This is a two-plane correction.

The balancing process is not complete until corrections have been applied of the size and at the exact location indicated by the balancing machine. Corrections for balance may be made by the addition or removal of metal.

BELTS, GEARS, AND PINIONS

Belts

In most industrial organizations, installation, adjustment, inspection, and care of belts is the responsibility of a specially trained individual or group. The application of belts involves alignment and belt tension, which affect bearing operation. Maintenance personnel must report belt alignments that seem inaccurate, tensions that appear excessive, and splices that look doubtful. Drives having upward belt tension may be questioned. Bearing loads on sleeve-bearing motors should not be against that portion of the bearing where the oil is fed into the bearing. Action should be taken to protect the electrical apparatus when there is evidence of belt-produced static.

Gears and Pinions

Gears and gear trains are among the principal sources of noise and vibration. In designing such mechanisms, the manufacturer strives for the best tooth form to give the least amount of whip and backlash, with the gear center so located that the teeth mesh at the proper pressure points.

It is essential, therefore, that the bearings be so maintained that these gear center distances do not change. Proper lubrication of gears is essential to keep down the wear of teeth. A gear with worn teeth, even though it appears to have considerable life left in it, should be replaced to keep vibration and noise to a minimum.

3-7 MOTOR CONTROL CIRCUITS AND STARTERS

Motor control circuit (MCC) and motor-starter maintenance involves the recognition of causes that result in controller problems. Controller problems could be due to lack of systematic maintenance, improper application, or electrical power distribution system deficiencies. The lack of systematic maintenance can result in catastrophic failure because of neglect of equipment. A well-planned maintenance program will detect early any potential sources of trouble and correct them before they result in major failure. Improper application of control equipment can result in early failure of equipment. Examples are wrong-sized overloads, installation of equipment in poor ventilation locations, overly dirty or dusty areas, or excessive vibrations. To ensure correct selection and application of control equipment, the manufacturer's recommendations should be followed. Deficiencies of electrical systems, such as low-voltage conditions or unbalanced voltages, can cause severe motor heating. Low-voltage conditions can also cause motor starting problems, such as the starting contacts being unable to close fully, which causes arcing and buildup of resistance. As a result, overheating will take place and possibly welding of the contacts.

Preventive maintenance should include regularly scheduled inspections, minor repairs, and good record keeping. The factors that will influence the maintenance program are the level of reliability required, environmental conditions, age of equipment, and type of process the control equipment is controlling.

INSPECTIONS OF CONTROL EQUIPMENT

- Inspect the MCC enclosure, especially those installed in dirty, wet, or corrosive atmospheres for signs of dirt or dust accumulation, rust, and the like; clean off dirt or dust with a vacuum cleaner. The corroded parts of the enclosure should be cleaned, refinished, and painted.
- Inspect the bus bar and terminal connections for proper tightness of all joints and connections. Normally, overheating is due to looseness of connections and will show discoloration in the bus bar. The proper

torque required for tightness is a factor of the materials used in the MCC. Torque values can be obtained from the manufacturer's maintenance and instruction data books. Ensure that all connections are torque tightened in accordance with manufacturer's recommended values. Inspect frequently for loose connections if the MCC is installed in areas where there are excessive vibrations or temperature variations.

- Inspect bus bar insulators for contamination, cracks, and signs of arcing. Replace the cracked and defective insulators and tighten those that are loose.

- Inspect contactor contacts for wear, alignment, and pitting. Replacement of contacts should be done in sets to avoid misalignment. Ensure that all moving parts are functioning properly. Contactors installed in dirty or corrosive environments should be inspected more frequently than those installed in dust-proof enclosures. The dressing of contacts with a file or other abrasive should only be done for alignment purposes.

- Pilot and control devices should be checked for loose wiring, signs of overheating, and proper mechanical operation.

The following list of items should be inspected on a regular basis:

- *Contactors, relays, and solenoids:* Check for excessive heating of parts, control voltage, dust, grease, corrosion, loose connections, and indications of tracking.

- *Contacts:* Check for excessive pitting and roughness.

- *Springs:* Check contact pressure and see if pressure is the same on all contact tips.

- *Arc chutes:* Check for breaks and burn marks.

- *Magnetic parts:* Check shading coil; look for misalignment and clean surfaces.

- *Flexible leads:* Check for frayed or broken strands and brittleness.

- *Enclosure:* Check the interior and exterior for dust, rust and corrosion, mechanical damage, loose nuts and bolts, and all mechanical connections.

- *Overloads:* Check for proper size; inspect for dirt and corrosion, connections, and freedom of movement.

- *Pilot devices and auxiliary equipment:* Check contacts; inspect for dirt, grease, and corrosion; look for signs of overheating and signs of discoloration of current-carrying parts.

- *Control operation:* Check sequence of operation of all control devices and look for sparking of contacts during control operation.
- *Fuses and fuse clips:* Check for proper fuse rating and check for fuse-clip pressure.

MAINTENANCE OF CONTROL EQUIPMENT

The following list is offered as a general guide for control equipment maintenance. For detailed instructions the manufacturer's recommendations should be followed:

- The cleaning of dust, dirt, grease, and grime should be done periodically for the motor starter and control devices. If not cleaned, dust will settle on control device contacts and interlocks, which may prevent a circuit from functioning. Moreover, dust could form unwanted tracking paths, resulting in equipment failure. Dry dust can be vacuumed, whereas sticky dust or grease may have to be wiped clean. Ensure that the control enclosure is suitable for the environment in which the control equipment is installed.
- The contact springs should always maintain the proper contact pressure. The loss of contact pressure will usually result in the contacts wearing too thin or weakening of the spring, thereby resulting in overheating of contacts. Refer to manufacturer's recommendations for proper contact pressure. Moreover, the contact pressure should be the same for all three poles. If pressure at one pole is considerably less, it is due to the spring being considerably weakened and it should be replaced.
- File rough copper contacts with a fine file. Also remove any copper oxide from contact surfaces because it acts as a high resistance, thus causing overheating. Make sure that the contact surfaces retain their original shape when they are filed in order to provide the best operation.
- Do not file silver contacts unless they show extreme roughness. Moreover, do not wipe silver oxide from the contact surface because it has good conducting properties.
- When replacing contacts, always replace them in pairs, that is, both the moving and stationary contacts.
- Maintain proper voltage for the contactor operating coil and other control relays. The higher voltage at the contact coil will cause excessive heat, which will reduce the operating life of the coil. Also, the coil will operate with more mechanical force owing to overvoltage and thus result in more wear and tear of mechanical parts. The normal operating

range of contactor coil voltage is from 85 to 110 percent of its rated voltage. Excessive low voltage will cause the contactor or relays to operate sluggishly because of reduced magnetic force. This can result in the contact not seating firmly, which can result in burning or welding of contacts. Moreover, low voltage will cause the contactor operating coil to draw high current, which may result in coil burnout.

- The protective trips (overloads) should be checked to see that they are properly selected, that is, that they are the right size, rating, and type for the controller. Make sure that the ratings of the overloads have taken into account the ambient temperatures. Calibrate the overload on a periodic basis and check contacts for cleanliness.

MAINTENANCE REPAIRS

Maintenance repairs are performed after the trouble has been diagnosed to indicate the possible causes. Following is a summary of possible conditions that cause trouble in control equipment and will require maintenance repairs.

Low-Voltage Conditions

This condition will cause noisy magnets (humming), overheating of the coil due to failure of the magnets to seal in, failure of the coil to pick up and seal in, and failure of the motor to start. The maintenance repairs for this condition are to check the system voltage during running and starting and correct for proper rated voltage.

Dirt, Rust, or Foreign Matter on Contact Surfaces

This condition will eventually result in short contact life or overheating of tips of contacts; to eliminate this condition, replace or adjust contact springs, and file only copper contacts with fine file.

Dirt, Rust, or Gummy Substance on Pole Faces

This condition will cause an increase in the air gap, which will result in over-heating of the coil, failure of the coil to drop out, and noisy magnets (humming). To remove this condition, the pole faces should be cleaned and realigned.

Loose Connections

Loose connections of the control circuit wiring, such as contacts and overload relays, will cause overheating of contacts, tripping of overload relays, and the failure of the circuit to become energized. All loose connections should be cleaned and tightened.

Weak Contact Pressure

This condition will cause overheating of the contacts. To correct it, replace contact springs.

Excessive Filing or Dressing of Contacts

The copper contacts may be filed with a fine file, but silver contacts should never be filed. Similarly, copper oxide from contact surfaces should be removed, wheras silver oxide should be left on the contact surfaces to provide better conductivity. When excessive filing is done, the contacts may not seat properly, resulting in overheating of the contacts.

Overvoltage or High Ambient Temperature

This condition will result in overheating of the coil; the high ambient temperature may affect the overload relay if it is not ambient compensated; overvoltage will result in motor overtorque. Check for system voltage and correct for proper voltage for all devices. Reduce high ambient temperature or install higher-temperature-rated devices.

Broken Shading Coil

This condition will cause too much chatter of the contacts and humming of the magnets. Replace shading coil to correct this condition.

Sustained Overloads

This condition will result in short contact life and tripping of overload relays. Check to see if the overloads are correct for the starter size, and check for excessive motor currents, grounds, short-circuits, or motor bindings.

Failure of the Overloads to Trip

This condition can cause motor burnout, which results from oversized or wrong trip units, motor or trip units located in different ambient temperatures, mechanical binding, or corrosion. To correct this condition, check for all the causes mentioned under maintenance. Consult the manufacturer for appropriate-sized overloads to match the load.

CHAPTER 4

DIRECT-CURRENT TESTING OF ELECTRICAL EQUIPMENT

4-1   INTRODUCTION

This chapter covers direct-current (dc) tests ordinarily performed in the field for acceptance and maintenance of electrical equipment and apparatus. The information provided by these tests will indicate whether any corrective maintenance or replacement of installed equipment is necessary, assess if the newly installed equipment can be safely energized, and chart the gradual deterioration of the equipment over its service life.

The dc test methods discussed in this chapter cover transformers, insulating liquids, cables, switchgear, motors and generators. It is important to have the proper equipment and trained operators when conducting these tests. Also, if any test is to provide optimum benefits, it is essential to record all test data and maintenance actions for further analysis and future reference. Furthermore, the test equipment should be maintained in good condition and used by qualified operators. When test equipment is used to calibrate other equipment, it should have twice the accuracy of the equipment under test. Moreover, the test equipment should be calibrated at regular intervals to assure the accuracy of test data.

The test voltage levels and methods, as described in this chapter, are mostly in accordance with industry standards for the types of equipment discussed. The dc voltage values correspond to the ac test voltages as specified by the applicable industry standards. It is recommended that the manufacturer of the equipment be consulted for specific test and test voltage levels when the exact construction of the equipment under test is not known. Where definitive information for a particular equipment cannot be obtained, it is advised that the suggested dc test voltage be based on the rated ac circuit voltage in order to avoid possible damage to the insulation system. It is also important to observe certain additional precautions when conducting dc high-voltage tests; these are listed in Section 4-8.

229

4-2   TRANSFORMERS

The dc testing of transformers involves testing of the solid winding insulation and the insulating fluids used in transformers. The testing of insulating fluids is covered in Section 5-3. The testing of solid winding insulation complements other transformer testing. The solid winding insulation tests are not conclusive in themselves, but provide valuable information on winding conditions, such as moisture content, and carbonization. The dc tests are considered nondestructive even though at times they may cause a winding failure. It should be pointed out that a winding failure results from an incipient failure that the test was supposed to detect. If it had gone undetected, it might have occurred at an unplanned time. The dc tests conducted for transformer winding insulation are discussed next in order of priority.

INSULATION RESISTANCE MEASUREMENT

This test is performed at or above rated voltage to determine if there are low resistance paths to ground or between winding to winding as a result of winding insulation deterioration. The test measurement values are affected by variables such as temperature, humidity, test voltage, and size of transformer. This test should be conducted before and after repair or maintenance is performed. The test data should be recorded for future comparative purposes. The test values should be normalized to 20°C for comparison purposes. The factors for conversion are shown in Table 3–3. The general rule of thumb that is used for acceptable values is 1 megohm (MΩ)/1,000 volts (V) of applied test voltage. Sample resistance values of good insulation systems are shown in Table 4–1. The test procedures are as follows:

- Do not disconnect the ground connection to the transformer tank and core. Make sure that the transformer tank and core are grounded.
- Disconnect all high-voltage, low-voltage, and neutral connections, lightning arresters, fan systems, meters, or any low-voltage control systems that are connected to the transformer winding.
- Before beginning the test, jumper together all high-voltage connections, making sure that the jumpers are clear of all metal and grounded parts. Also jumper together all low-voltage and neutral connections, making sure jumpers are clear of all metal and grounded parts.
- Use a megohmmeter with a minimum scale of 20,000 MΩ.
- Resistance measurements are then made between each set of windings and ground. The winding that is to be measured must have its ground removed in order to measure its insulation resistance.

TABLE 4–1.

TYPICAL INSULATION RESISTANCE VALUES FOR POWER AND DISTRIBUTION TRANSFORMERS

Transformer Winding Voltage (kV)	Winding to Ground (MΩ)				
	20°C	30°C	40°C	50°C	60°C
Below 6.6	400	200	100	50	25
6.6 to 19	800	400	200	100	50
22 to 45	1,000	500	250	125	65
66 and above	1,200	600	300	100	75

- The megohmmeter reading should be maintained for a period of 1 minute (min). Make the following readings for two-winding transformers:

  High-voltage winding to low-voltage winding and to ground.

  High-voltage winding to ground.

  Low-voltage winding to high-voltage winding and to ground.

  Low-voltage winding to ground.

  High-voltage winding to low-voltage winding.

  The connections for these tests are shown in Figures 4–1(a) through (e) and 4–2(a) through (e).

- Megohmmeter readings should be recorded along with the test temperature (degrees Celsius). The readings should be corrected to 20° by the correction factors shown in Table 3–3. If the corrected field test values are one-half or more of the factory insulation readings or 1,000 megohms, whichever is less, the transformer is considered safe for the hi-pot test.

- For three-winding transformers, test should be made as follows:

  High to low, tertiary and ground (H-LTG).

  Tertiary to high, low and ground (T-HLG).

  Low to high, tertiary and ground (L-HTG).

  High, low, and tertiary to ground (HLT-G).

  High and tertiary to low and ground (HT-LG).

  Low and tertiary to high and ground (LT-HG).

  High and low to tertiary and ground (HL-TG).

- Do not make the megohm test of the transformer winding without the transformer liquid because the values of insulation resistance in air will be much less than in the liquid. Also, do not make the insulation

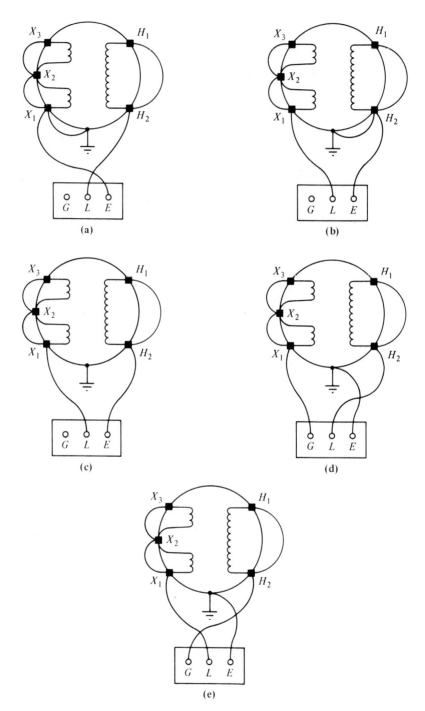

FIGURE 4–1.

Test connections for insulation resistance single-phase transformers.

233

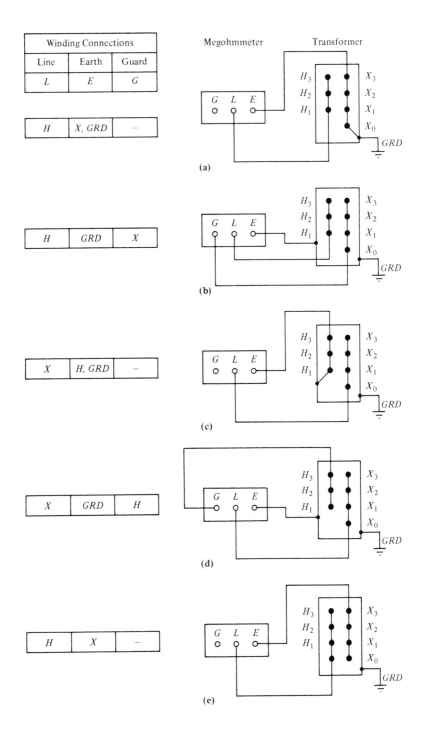

FIGURE 4-2.

Test connection for insulation resistance three-phase transformers: (a) connection for high winding to low winding to ground; (b) connection for high winding to ground and low winding guarded; (c) connection for low winding to high winding to ground; (d) connection for low winding to ground and high winding guarded; (e) connection for high winding to low winding.

resistance test of the transformer when it is under vacuum because of the possibility of flashover to ground.

■ In Figure 4–2, the test connections shown in (a), (c), and (e) are most frequently used. The test connections in Figure 4–2(b) and (d) give more precise results. The readings obtained in the connections in (a) and (b) are practically equal to readings in test connections (c) and (d), respectively.

DIELECTRIC ABSORPTION TEST

The dielectric absorption test is an extension of the transformer winding insulation resistance measurement test. The test consists of applying voltage for 10 min and taking readings of resistance measurements at 1-min intervals. The resistance values measured during this test are plotted on log-log paper with coordinates of resistance versus time. The slope of the curve for a good insulation system is a straight line increasing with respect to time, whereas a poor insulation system will have a curve that flattens out with respect to time. There are two special tests conducted under dielectric absorption test.

Polarization Index Test

The ratio of winding insulation resistance values at 10 min to 1 min is defined as the *polarization index (PI)*. The PI provides information on the moisture and deterioration of the winding insulation. The PI values can vary from above 2 to a low of less than 1. An acceptable value should be at least 2 or higher, values between 2 and 1 indicate marginal condition, and values below 1 indicate poor condition.

Dielectric Absorption Ratio Test

The ratio of winding insulation resistance value at 60 seconds (s) to 30 s is defined as the *dielectric absorption ratio (DAR)*. This test provides information similar to the PI test except that the test duration is shorter. The connections and test procedures for conducting this test are the same as the transformer winding insulation resistance measurement test.

DC HIGH-POTENTIAL (HI-POT) TEST

The dc high-potential test is applied at above rated voltage to evaluate the condition of the transformer winding insulation. The dc high-voltage test is not recommended on power transformers above 34.5 kV; instead the ac high-potential test should be used. Generally, for routine maintenance of transformers, this test is not employed because of the possibility of damage to the winding insulation. However, this test is made for acceptance and after repair of transformers. If the hi-pot test is to be conducted for routine maintenance, the test values should not exceed 65 percent of factory test value, which is equal to 1.6 times the ac value for periodic testing (i.e., $1.6 \times 65 = 104$ percent of ac factory test value). The dc hi-pot test can be applied as a step-voltage test where readings of leakage current are taken for each step. If excessive leakage current is noticed, voltage can be backed off before further damage takes place. For this reason, the dc hi-pot test is considered to be a nondestructive test. Some companies conduct the ac hi-pot test at rated voltage for 3 min for periodic testing instead of the 65 percent of factory test voltage. The hi-pot test values for dc voltages are shown in Table 4–2.

The procedure for conducting this test is as follows (refer to Figure 4–3(a) and (b) for test connections):

- The transformer must have passed the insulation resistance test immediately prior to starting this test.
- Make sure transformer case and core are grounded.
- Disconnect all high-voltage, low-voltage, and neutral connections, low-voltage control systems, fan systems, and meters connected to the transformer winding and core.
- Short-circuit with jumpers together all high-voltage connections to the same potential with respect to ground. Also short-circuit with jumpers together all low-voltage connections to ground.
- Connect high-potential test set between high-voltage winding and ground. Gradually increase test voltage to desired value. Allow test voltage duration of 1 min, after which gradually decrease voltage to zero.
- Remove low voltage to ground jumper and connect high-potential test set between low-voltage winding and ground. Also connect the short-

TABLE 4–2.
DIELECTRIC TEST VALUES FOR ROUTINE MAINTENANCE OF
LIQUID-FILLED TRANSFORMERS

Transformer Winding Rated Voltage (kV)	Factory Test AC Voltage (kV)	Routine Maintenance DC Voltage (kV)
1.2	10	10.40
2.4	15	15.60
4.8	19	19.76
8.7	26	27.04
15.0	34	35.36
18.0	40	41.60
25.0	50	52.00
34.5	70	72.80

circuited high-voltage winding to ground. Gradually increase test voltage to desired value. Allow the test voltage duration of 1 min, after which gradually decrease voltage to zero.

- If the preceding two tests do not produce breakdowns or failures, the transformer is considered satisfactory and can be energized.

- Remove all jumpers and reconnect primary and secondary connections and other system equipment that may have been disconnected.

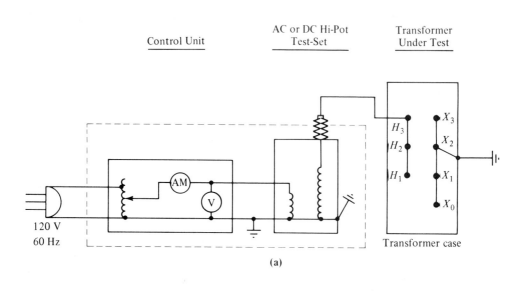

(a)

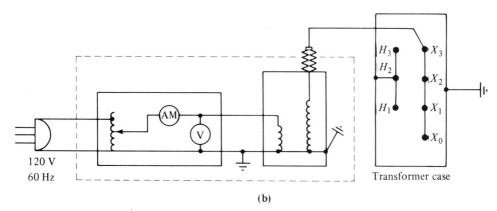

(b)

FIGURE 4–3.

Transformer high voltage (hi-pot) test connection: (a) high winding hi-pot test connections; (b) low winding hi-pot test connections.

■ The following are some cautions and considerations in performing hi-pot tests:

In liquid-filled transformers two insulation systems are in series, that is, solid insulation with oil or synthetic fluid. When ac or dc hi-pot test voltage is applied, the voltage drops are distributed as follows:

Voltage	Paper-Cellulose Insulation	Oil
AC	25%	75%
DC	75%	25%

When using direct current on liquid-filled transformers, the solid insulation may be overstressed.

Insulation that may be weakened near the neutral may remain in service due to lower stress under operating conditions. However, when subjected to hi-pot test voltage, it may break down and require immediate repair. The weakened insulation may usually be detected by the measurement at lower voltages.

If a hi-pot test is to be conducted for routine maintenance, consider the following in advance: (1) assume that a breakdown will occur; (2) have replacement or parts on hand; (3) have personnel available to perform work; (4) is the loss of the transformer until repairs are made beyond the original routine outage?

4-3 CABLES AND ACCESSORIES

Cable testing is conducted to chart the gradual deterioration over the years, to do acceptance testing after installation, for verification of splices and joints, and for special repair testing. Normally, the maintenance proof tests performed on cables are at a test voltage of 60 percent of final factory test voltage. When the exact construction of cable in an existing installation is not known, it is generally recommended that dc maintenance proof test voltage be based on rated ac circuit voltage using the recommended value for the smallest sized conductor in the rated ac voltage range. The dc voltage tests conducted on cables are insulation resistance measurement and dc high-potential test (dc hi-pot test). The dc hi-pot test can be performed as leakage current versus voltage test, leakage current versus time test, or go, no-go overpotential test.

It is always appropriate to conduct the insulation resistance measurement test first, and if data obtained looks good, then proceed with the dc overpotential test.

INSULATION RESISTANCE MEASUREMENT TEST

The insulation resistance is measured by a portable instrument consisting of a direct voltage source, such as a generator, battery, or rectifier, and a high-range ohmmeter that gives insulation resistance readings in megohms or ohms. This is a nondestructive method of determining the condition of the cable insulation to check contamination due to moisture, dirt, or carbonization. The insulation resistance measurement method does not give the measure of total dielectric strength of cable insulation or weak spots in the cable. Generally, the following voltages can be used for the indicated cables.

Voltage Rating of Cables	Megohmmeter Voltage
Up to 300 V	500 V
300 to 600 V	500 to 1,000 V
2,400 to 5,000 V	2,500 V to 5 kV
Above 5,000 V	Above 5 kV

The following is the general procedure when using a megohmmeter (Megger)® for resistance measurement tests.

- Disconnect the cable to be tested from other equipment and circuits to ensure that it is not energized.
- Discharge all stored capacitance in the cable by grounding it before testing, as well as after completing tests.
- Connect the line terminal of the instrument to the conductor to be tested.
- Ground all other conductors together to sheath and to ground. Connect these to the earth terminal of the test set.
- Similarly measure other insulation resistance values between one conductor and all other conductors connected, one conductor to ground and so on. The connections are shown in Figure 4–4(a) through (d).
- The guard terminal of the megohmmeter can be used to eliminate the effects of surface leakage across exposed insulation at the test end of the cable, or both ends of the cable or leakage to ground.

The insulation resistance measurements should be conducted at regular intervals and records kept for comparison purposes. Keep in mind that, for valid comparison, the readings must be corrected to a base temperature, such as 20°C. A continued downward trend is an indication of insulation deterioration even though the resistance values measured are above minimum acceptable limits.

®Biddle Company trademark for megohmmeter.

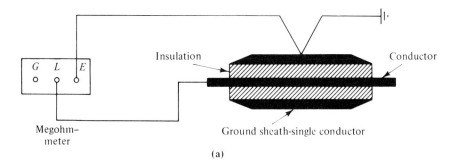

Megohm–
meter

(a)

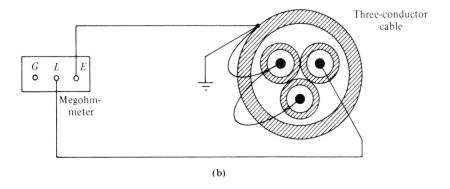

Megohm–
meter

(b)

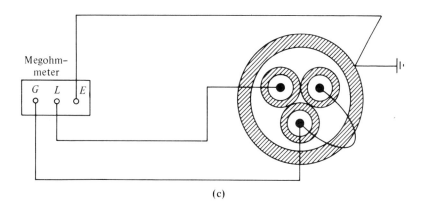

Megohm–
meter

(c)

FIGURE 4–4.

Cable test connections for insulation resistance measurement: (a) Connection for single-conductor cable, one conductor to ground test; (b) connection for three-conductor cable, one conductor to other conductors and sheath to ground; (c) connection for three-conductor cable, one conductor to sheath and to ground and two conductors guarded;

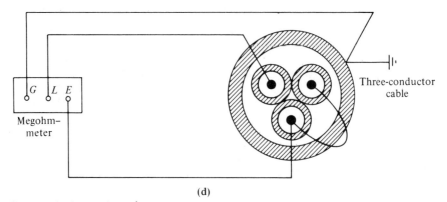

(d)

FIGURE 4—4 continued

(d) connection for three-conductor cable, one conductor to all other conductors without leakage to ground.

DC OVERPOTENTIAL TESTING

This test is extensively used for acceptance and maintenance of cables. It can indicate the relative condition of the insulation at voltages above or near operating levels. This test can be used for identification of weakness in the cable insulation and can also be used to break down an incipient fault. A typical dc test set is shown in Figure 4–5. Generally, it is not recommended that this test be used for breakdown of incipient faults even though some test operators use it for this purpose. Therefore, the incipient fault breakdown probability should be anticipated before and during the hi-pot test. The impending cable failure will usually be indicated by sudden changes in the leakage current, and before insulation is damaged the test can be stopped. The test voltage values for dc hi-pot tests are based upon final factory test voltage, which is determined by the type and thickness of insulation, the size of conductors, the construction of cable, and applicable industry standards. The dc test values corresponding to ac factory proof test voltages specified by the industry standards are usually expressed in terms of the ratio of dc to ac voltage for each insulation system. This ratio is designated as K which when multiplied by the acceptance test factor of 80 percent and maintenance factor of 60 percent yields the conversion factors to obtain the dc test voltages for hi-pot tests. These recommended test voltage conversion factors are shown in Table 4–3.

Many factors should be considered in selecting the right voltage for existing cables that are in service. As a general rule, for existing cables the highest values for maintenance should not exceed 60 percent of final factory test voltage, and the minimum test value should be not less than the dc equivalent

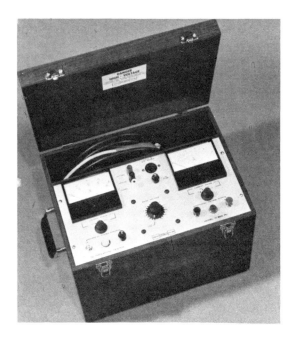

FIGURE 4–5.
Direct-current hi-pot test set, 60 kilovolts. (Courtesy of Hipotronics, Brewster, N.Y.)

of the ac operating voltage. If the cable cannot be disconnected from all the connected equipment, the test voltage should be reduced to the voltage level of the lowest rated equipment connected. The hi-pot test can be conducted as a step voltage test as in the following.

Voltage versus Leakage Current Test (Step-Voltage Test)

In this test, the voltage is raised in equal steps and time is allowed between each step for leakage current to become stable. As explained in Chapter 1, the current is relatively high as the voltage is applied owing to capacitance charging current, surface leakage current, and partial discharge currents. As time passes, these transient currents become minimum with the steady-state current remaining, which is the actual leakage current and a very small amount of absorption current. At each step of voltage, the leakage current reading is taken before proceeding to the next step. Usually, it is recommended that at least eight equal steps of voltage be used and at least 1 to 4 min be allowed between each step. The leakage current versus voltage are then plotted as a curve. As long as this plotted curve is linear for each step, the insulation system is in good condition. At some value of step voltage, if the leakage current begins to increase notice-

TABLE 4–3.
CONVERSION FACTORS FOR DC HI-POT TESTS

Type of Insulation	K	Conversion Factors	
		DC Acceptance Test Voltage (0.8 × K)	DC Maintenance Voltage (0.6 × K)
Impregnated paper, lead covered	2.4	1.92	1.44
Varnished cloth	2.0	1.60	1.20
Ozone-resistant rubber compound	3.0	2.40	1.80
Polyethylene	3.0	2.40	1.80
Polyvinyl chloride	2.2	1.76	1.32
Non-ozone-resistant rubber compound	2.2	1.76	1.32

ably, an increase in the slope of the curve will be noticed, as shown in Figure 4–6 at point A. If the test is continued beyond this test voltage, the leakage current will increase even more rapidly and immediate breakdown may occur in the cable insulation. Unless breakdown is desired, the test should be stopped as soon as the increase of slope is noticed in the voltage versus leakage current curve.

Leakage Current versus Time Test

When the final test voltage of leakage current versus voltage test is reached, it can be left on for at least 5 min, and the leakage current versus time can be plotted for fixed intervals of time as the leakage current during this step reduces from an initial high value to a steady-state value. A curve for good cables will generally indicate a continuous decrease in leakage current with respect to time or steady-state value without any increase of current during the test. This curve is shown in Figure 4–7.

Go, No-Go Overpotential Test

The hi-pot test can be conducted as a go, no-go overpotential test. In this test the voltage is gradually applied to the specified value. The rate of rise of the test voltage is maintained to provide a steady leakage current until final test voltage is reached. Usually, 1 to 1½ min is considered sufficient time for reaching the final test voltage. The final test voltage can then be held for 5 min, and if there is no abrupt increase in current sufficient to trip the circuit breaker, the test has been successfully passed. This test does not provide a thorough analysis of cable condition, but provides sufficient information as to whether the cable meets a specific high-voltage breakdown strength requirement. This type of test

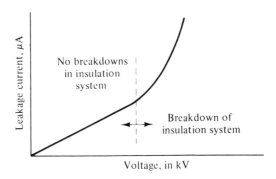

FIGURE 4-6.
Step-voltage high-potential test current.

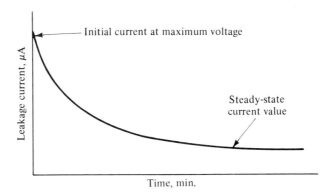

FIGURE 4-7.
Leakage current versus time.

is usually performed after installation and repair, where only cable withstand strength verification without a breakdown is to be certified.

DC OVERPOTENTIAL TEST CONNECTIONS AND PROCEDURES

The test connections for this test are similar to those shown in Figure 4-4(a) and for three-conductor cable are similar to those shown in Figure 4-4(b) and (c). The test procedures are the following:

- Cable to be tested must be deenergized, opened at both ends if possible, and grounded to discharge any electrostatic charge on the cable. Switches, potential transformers, lightning arresters, jumpers from potheads to feeders, fuses, cutouts, and any switchgear should be disconnected. If impossible to disconnect any or some of connected equipment, the test voltage should not exceed the value that could overstress these devices connected to the cable. See Figure 4–8 for equipment to be disconnected.

- The dc test voltage should be applied from phase to ground on each conductor with other conductors, shields, and metallic sheath connected to ground or other conductors guarded with shield and metallic sheath grounded.

- Ensure that the hi-pot set main "on-off" switch is in off position and the high-voltage "on" switch is in the off position with voltage control switch turned to zero position before beginning the tests.

- Connect the hi-pot test set safety ground stud to a good electrical ground and make sure the connections are tight. Never operate the dc hi-pot test set without this ground connection. Also connect the shield ground strap of the shielded cable under test to the test set ground stud.

- Connect the return line from other conductors not under test to the earth ground terminal or to the guard terminal of the test set as desired. The hi-pot grounding switch should be switched into the appropriate position. Normally, 100-V insulation is required on the return line. Connect the shield and sheath to ground and also to the ground terminal of test set. The guard terminal is provided to bypass the current due to corona around the microammeter so that corona current is not included in the test readings.

- Connect one end of the output or line cable to the desired phase of the cable under test, making sure that the connections are tight and without any sharp edges. Where corona currents may be expected owing to the application of high voltages, it is recommended that the connections be taped, covered over with clear plastic bags, or use a corona ring or corona shield. The other end of the output or line cable is connected to the output or line stud of the test set.

- The cable used for connecting the hi-pot test set to the cable under test, that is, the line or output cable, should be short and direct and supported along its length so that it is not touching the ground or grounding materials or surfaces. If extension cables are to be used with the output or line cable to reach the cable under test, shielded cable should preferably be used for this purpose. The shields of the extension cable and hi-pot cable should be connected with a shield jumper, which should be run away from the splice to prevent leakage. In case of the extension cable being nonshielded, care should be taken to keep the nonshielded wire away from the grounding surfaces as explained previously.

- When shielded cable is being tested, it is recommended that the shield be trimmed back about 1 in. for every 10 kV. The shield on the test set

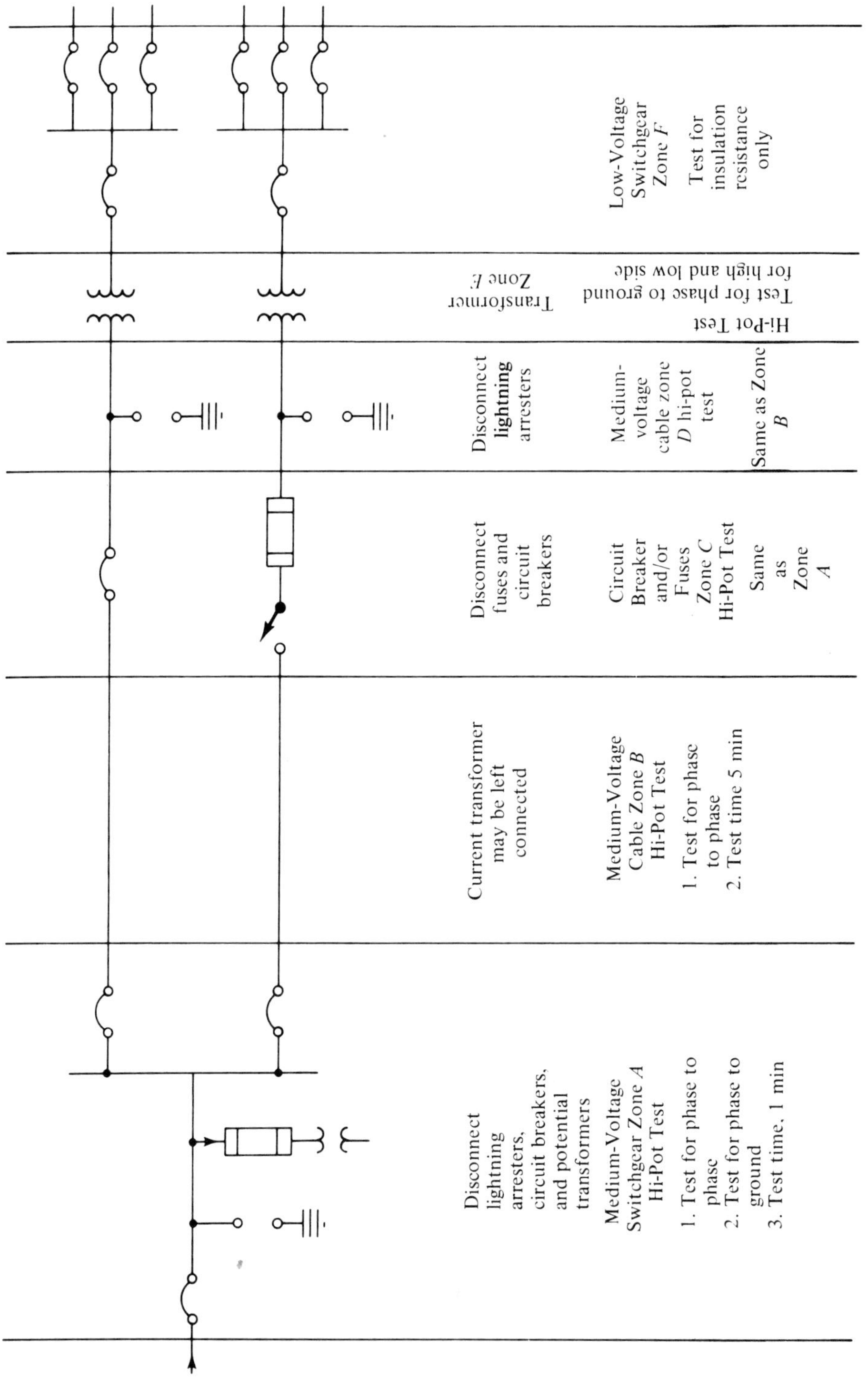

Low-Voltage
Switchgear
Zone *F*

Test for
insulation
resistance
only

Transformer
Zone *E*

Hi-Pot Test

Test for phase to ground
for high and low side

Disconnect
lightning
arresters

Medium-
voltage
cable zone
D hi-pot
test

Same as Zone
B

Disconnect
fuses and
circuit
breakers

Circuit
Breaker
and/or
Fuses
Zone *C*
Hi-Pot Test

Same
as
Zone
A

Current transformer
may be left
connected

Medium-Voltage
Cable Zone *B*
Hi-Pot Test

1. Test for phase
   to phase
2. Test time 5 min

Disconnect
lightning
arresters,
circuit breakers,
and potential
transformers

Medium-Voltage
Switchgear Zone *A*
Hi-Pot Test

1. Test for phase to
   phase
2. Test for phase to
   ground
3. Test time. 1 min

FIGURE 4–8.
Hi-pot test for cables and associated equipment and equipment to be
disconnected during tests.

end of the cable is connected to ground as explained previously. The shield on the other end of cable can be taped and left hanging without any connections made to it.

■ The test set now should be plugged into a 115-V, 60-hertz (Hz) outlet. It is important that the ac supply voltage have good line regulation, because the dc output voltage of the test set depends upon the ac line input voltage. The test voltage kilovolt range should be selected before beginning the test. The power now can be turned on and the test begun either as step-voltage or as a go, no-go test.

■ After the test is completed, turn the high-voltage switch of the test set to "off" position. Allow the cable just tested to discharge either through the internal test set discharge circuit or external ground applied to the cable by means of hot stick or gloves. Do not touch the cable until it is fully discharged.

■ Connect a ground to the cable that was tested and leave it connected for at least twice the length of the test time or until the cable is connected into the system.

4-4   ELECTRICAL SWITCHGEAR

The dc testing of electrical switchgear involves the following:

■ Insulation resistance measurement test.
■ DC high-potential test.
■ Circuit breaker contact resistance test.

The insulation resistance measurement test may be conducted on all types of electrical switchgear using the insulation resistance megohmmeter commonly known as the Megger.® The dc high-potential test is normally not made for ac electrical switchgear.

INSULATION RESISTANCE MEASUREMENT TEST

The insulation resistance test consists of applying voltage (600 to 5,000 V dc) to the apparatus to determine the megohm value of resistance. This test does not indicate the quality of primary insulation. Several factors should be remembered when performing this test. The first is that this test can indicate low values of insulation resistance because of many parallel paths. The other is that an insulation system having low dielectric strength may indicate high resistance values. In view of this, the test results should only be interpreted for comparative purposes. This does not indicate the quality of the primary insulation system from the point of view of dielectric withstandability. The connection

®Biddle trademark for megohmmeter.

diagram for making this test on a power circuit breaker is shown in Figure 4–9. The connection diagram for testing the insulation resistance of each branch circuit in a distribution panel is shown in Figure 4–10. When performing insulation testing, it is recommended that auxiliary equipment, such as potential transformers, and lightning arresters, be removed from the stationary switchgear.

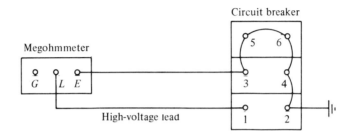

FIGURE 4–9.
Typical connection for insulation resistance test of circuit breaker in open position.

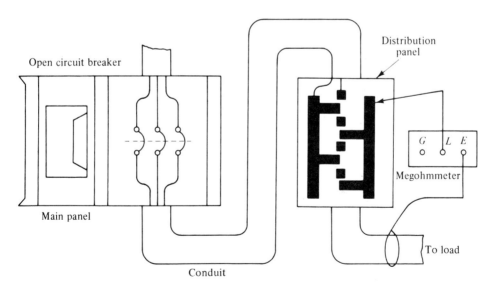

FIGURE 4–10.
Insulation resistance testing of branch circuit to ground of a distribution panel.

Insulation resistance tests are made with the circuit breaker in open and closed position, whereas the insulation test for the switchgear bus is made with one phase to ground at a time, with the other two phases grounded. The procedure for this test is as follows.

- *Circuit breaker open:* Connect high-voltage lead to pole 1. Ground all other poles. Repeat for poles 2 through 6, in turn, with other poles grounded.
- *Circuit breaker closed:* Connect high-voltage lead to pole 1 or 2, as convenient, with either pole of phase 2 and 3 grounded. Repeat for phases 2 and 3 with other phases grounded.
- *Stationary gear (buses):* Connect high-voltage lead to phase 1 with phases 2 and 3 grounded. Repeat the same for phases 2 and 3 with other phases grounded.

DC HIGH-POTENTIAL TEST

The high-potential testing of switchgear involves testing of the circuit breakers and switchgear buses separately. This is a major test and determines the condition of the insulation of the switchgear assembly. The dc high potential test is not preferred for testing ac switchgear because the application of dc voltage does not produce similar stress in the insulation system as is produced under operating conditions. Moreover, the dc high-potential test produces corona and tracking owing to concentration of stress at sharp edges or end points of buses. The corona and tracking are more pronounced in older equipment, and it is therefore recommended that dc high-potential testing be avoided on such equipment.

The test procedures for dc high-potential testing are similar to those of ac high-potential testing, which is described in detail in Chapter 5. If dc high-potential testing is to be performed, the dc voltage test values shown in Table 4–4 are recommended for various voltage-class equipment.

The high-potential test should be conducted under conditions similar to those of commercial testing. The switchgear should be wiped, cleaned, and restored to good condition before the high-potential test is conducted. Temperature and humidity readings should be recorded and the test reading corrected when conducting dc tests.

CIRCUIT BREAKER CONTACT RESISTANCE MEASUREMENT TEST

Stationary and moving contacts are built from materials that provide good resistance to arcing. However, if contacts are not maintained on a regular basis, resistance due to repeated arcing builds up, resulting in the contacts ability to carry current. Excessive corrosion of contacts is detrimental to the breaker performance. One way to check contacts is to apply dc current and measure the contact resistance or voltage drop across the closed contacts.

The breaker contact resistance should be measured from bushing terminal to bushing terminal with the breaker in closed position. It is recommended that for medium and high voltages the resistance test be made with 100-A direct current. The use of a higher current value gives more reliable results than using lower current values. The resistance value is usually measured in microohms ($\mu\Omega$). The average resistance value for 15-kV-class circuit breakers is approximately between 200 and 250 Mμ.

4-5   MOTORS AND GENERATORS

The electrical insulation system is the most prominent part of motors and generators that needs periodic maintenance and testing. The insulation system of machines is subjected to varying degrees of mechanical, thermal, and electrical stresses. The reliability of a machine depends upon the integrity of its insulation system. Therefore, a preventive maintenance program should include an effective testing program, along with visual inspection and routine maintenance, to evaluate the insulating system.

The insulating parts found in motors and generators consist of stator windings, field windings, winding support, collector lead and ring, stator core, and others. The maintenance and testing program should be planned to detect and provide data on deteriorating factors to which motors and generators are subjected. The electrical tests conducted should indicate existing faults and the expected service reliability of motors and generators. The following dc tests can be conducted on motors and generators for the purposes of preventive maintenance.

TABLE 4–4.
DIRECT-CURRENT HIGH-POTENTIAL MAINTENANCE
TEST VALUES

Rated Operating Voltage (V)	One Minute DC Test Voltage
240	1,600
480	2,100
600	2,300
2,400	15,900
4,160	20,100
7,200	27,600
13,800	38,200
23,000	63,600
34,500	84,800

INSULATION RESISTANCE TEST

This test is conducted with voltages from 500 to 5,000 V and basically provides information on the condition of insulation caused by moisture and other contaminants. A clean, dry insulation system has very low leakage as compared to a wet and contaminated insulation system. This test does not assure that the insulation system is physically sound or will withstand a high-voltage test. However, this test is commonly made before the high-voltage test to identify insulation contamination or faults. This test can be made on all or parts of the machine circuit to ground. The following procedures are given for making this test on field winding, stator windings, and individual stator windings. Typical synchronous motor or generator connections are shown in Figure 4–11.

Field-Winding Test Procedures

The test connection is shown in Figure 4–12 and the procedures are as follows:

- Lift brushes on the rotor.
- Disconnect neutral terminal from neutral device or ground.
- Ground all stator terminals, stator frames, and rotor shaft.

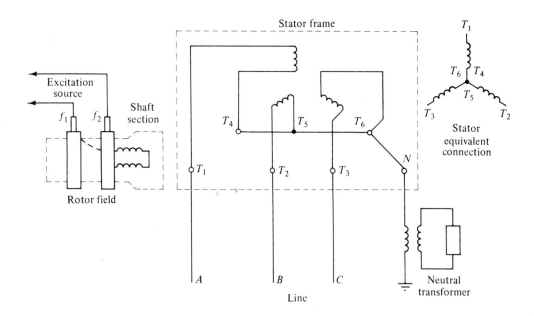

FIGURE 4–11.
Typical in-service connection for synchronous machines.

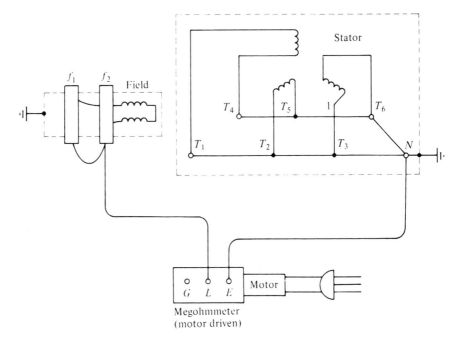

FIGURE 4–12.
Test connections for field winding insulation resistance measurement.

- Ground f_1 and f_2 for 30 min before conducting test to completely discharge winding.
- Disconnect ground from f_1 and f_2, connect test instrument (megohmmeter) ground terminal to ground, and test voltage lead to f_1 and f_2.
- Perform one of the following:

  Ten-minute test to determine polarization index (PI).

  One-minute test to determine dielectric absorption ratio (DAR).

  One-minute test.

Overall Stator (Armature Windings) Test

The following procedures are given for conducting this test, and the connection diagram is shown in Figure 4–13.

- Check that stator frame and rotor shafts are grounded.
- Ground rotor terminals f_1 and f_2.

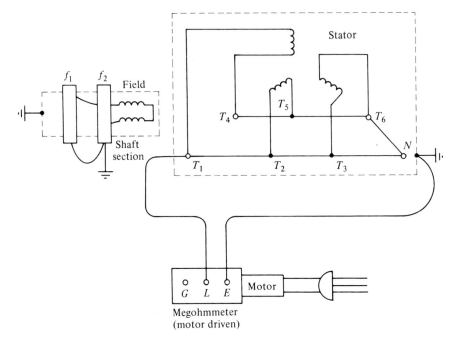

FIGURE 4–13.

Test connection for overall stator winding test.

- Connect ground terminal of instrument to ground and test voltage lead All T terminals are connected together.
- Remove ground connection from stator winding.
- Perform the following:

  Ten-minute test, that is, polarization index test (PI).

  One-minute test, that is, dielectric absorption (DAR) test.

  One-minute test.

Overall System Test for the Motor or Generator

The overall system test includes generator neutral, transformer, all stator windings, isolated phase bus, and low side windings of generator step-up transformer. This test is performed as a screening test after an abnormal occurrence on the machine. If the reading is satisfactory, no further tests are made. If the reading is questionable or lower, the machine terminals are disconnected and further isolation performed to locate the source of the trouble. Similarly, it may be desirable to test a motor including its cables to prevent disconnection of motor terminals unnecessarily. The connection diagrams are shown in Figures 4–14(a) and (b) for generator system and a motor.

Individual Stator Winding Test

The following procedures are given for conducting this test, and the test connection diagram is shown in Figure 4–15.

- Ground stator terminals for 30 min.
- Disconnect all stator terminals T1 through T6 and leave neutral terminal disconnected.
- Test T1-T4 winding with T2-T5, T3-T6, and rotor grounded.
- Test T2-T5 winding with T3-T6, T1-T4, and rotor grounded.
- Test T3-T6 winding with T1-T4, T2-T5, and rotor grounded.

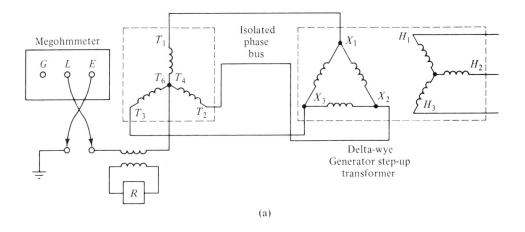

(a)

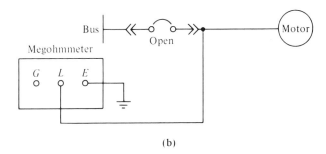

(b)

FIGURE 4–14.

Test connection for an overall system for generator or motor: (a) generator system; (b) motor.

The connections for the four insulation resistance measurement tests are summarized in Table 4–5.

The polarization index value of 2 or more is acceptable for insulating systems such as varnish-impregnated windings and asphalt windings, whereas thermoplastic insulation systems have a higher value than 2. A polarization index value of less than 1.0 indicates deterioration of the windings, which should be investigated. A very high PI value (above 5) indicates dried out, brittle windings such as is the case in very old machines.

DC OVERPOTENTIAL TEST

The dc overpotential test is conducted on motors and generators to assess the insulation dielectric strength. This test can be made during routine maintenance or after repairs have been made on the machine. Either all or parts of the machine can be tested to ground to ensure that the insulation system has sufficiently high dielectric strength for safe operation.

As a general rule the ac voltage used for the factory proof testing of the machine windings of motors or generators is based upon the rated operating voltages of the machine. A commonly used rule for establishing factory test values for stator windings is two times rated voltage (E) plus 1,000 V. For dc field winding it is ten times the excitation voltage. To convert these value to dc overpotential test values, the multiplying factor is 1.7. The recommended dc acceptance test voltage is 75 percent of the equipment ac voltage used for the

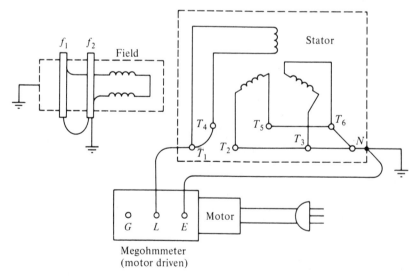

FIGURE 4–15.

Connection diagram for individual stator winding test.

TABLE 4–5.
INSULATION RESISTANCE CONNECTIONS

Winding under Test	Connect Test Voltage	Ground	Figure
Rotor field	f_1, f_2	Shaft, stator frame, T1, T4 T2, T5, T3, T6	4–12
All stator armature	T1, T4, T3, T5, T3, T6	Shaft, stator frame, f_1, f_2	4–13
Overall stator, conductors, transformer	Neutral transformer primary	Shaft, stator frame, f_1, f_2	4–14
Individual stator windings:			
T1-T4	T1, T4	Shaft, stator frame, f_1, f_2 T2, T5, T3, T6	
T2-T5	T2, T5	Shaft, stator frame, T1, T4, T3, T6	4–15
T3-T6	T3, T6	Shaft, stator frame, f_1, f_2 T1, T4, T2, T5	

factory proof test, whereas the recommended dc maintenance test voltage is 65 percent of the factory proof test value. These values can be represented by the following equations:

$$\text{dc acceptance test voltage} = [(2 \times E) + 1{,}000)] \times 1.7 \times 0.75 \text{ V}$$

$$= (2.55E + 1.275) \text{ V}$$

$$\text{dc maintenance test voltage} = [(2 \times E) + 1{,}000)] \times 1.7 \times 0.65 \text{ V}$$

$$= (2.21E) + 1.105) \text{ V}$$

The values mentioned may be varied depending upon the type and size of the machine. The standard duration of the dc overpotential test is usually 1 to 5 min for most electrical machines but may be varied depending upon the type and size. The reader is urged to consult IEEE standard 95, Guide for Insulation Testing of Large A-C Rotating Machinery with High Dielectric Voltage, for further information on this subject. To obtain meaningful results, the dc maintenance test voltage should not be below 50 percent of the equipment ac factory test value.

Voltage versus Leakage Current Test (Step-Voltage Test)

The dc overpotential test is a controlled test; that is, the increase in applied voltage is controlled by monitoring the leakage current to identify any impending failures of the winding insulation with the intention of stopping the test before the breakdown occurs. This test is commonly known as the step-voltage test, and the test connection diagram is shown in Figure 4–16. This test procedure may be described as follows:

- The first voltage step is usually one-third of the calculated test voltage, which is applied to the machine. Readings are taken at 1-min intervals up to a maximum of 10 min.
- The next step is to increase the test voltage in about-equal 1,000-V steps and record the leakage current value for each step. Allow sufficient time between each step for leakage current to become stable.
- At each step, plot the values of leakage current on the vertical axis versus the applied test voltage on the horizontal axis. For a good insulation system, the curve generated by the readings will be smooth with rising slope. Any sudden changes in curve characteristics are indications of impending winding failure.
- Take steps to eliminate the possibility of excessive leakage due to ionization or leakage across bushing in order to measure the true leakage current.

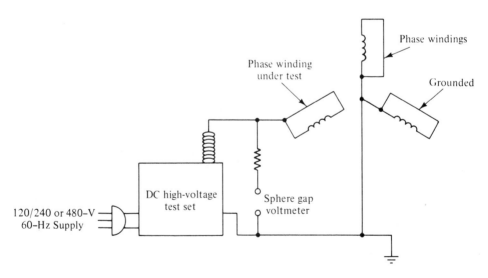

FIGURE 4–16.

Direct-current overpotential test connections for an ac machine armature (stator).

Leakage Current versus Time Test

This test can be made in lieu of the voltage versus leakage current test. In this test the point is to separate the absorption current from the total leakage current. In this test, reasonable time is allowed during each step of applied test voltage to allow the absorption current to disappear before readings are taken. To completely eliminate the absorption current, many hours of test time will be necessary. Therefore, a reasonable time interval is taken to be a 10-min waiting period during each step of applied voltage. The IEEE standard 95 describes this test in its appendix; it may be summarized as follows:

- Apply an initial voltage of about 30 percent on the machine winding and hold for 10 min. The readings are taken at regular intervals and are plotted on a log-log graph, with leakage current on the vertical axis and time on the horizontal axis.
- A curve is generated by the points plotted on the graph. This curve is used to calculate the conduction component of measured current. The total current readings at time intervals of, say, 1, 3, and 10 min are used and substituted into the following formula for calculation of the conduction component (C).

$$C = \frac{(i_{1.0} \times i_{10.0}) - (i_3)^2}{(i_{1.0} + i_{10.0}) - 2i_3}$$

where $i_{1.0}$ = 1-min total current

$i_{3.0}$ = 3-min total current

$i_{10.0}$ = 10-min total current

- The value of C as calculated from this formula is subtracted from the total current at 1- and 10-min-interval readings. The difference of the current readings gives the current due to absorption. These values are used to calculate the absorption ratio N, which is equal to

$$N = \frac{i_{a_{1.0}}}{i_{a_{10.0}}}$$

where $i_{a_{1.0}}$ = absorption current at 1 min

$i_{a_{10}}$ = absorption current at 10 min

- The absorption ratio N is then used to select the time intervals from a precalculated schedule, as shown in IEEE standard 95, December 1962 and here in Table 4–6.

TABLE 4—6.
ELAPSED TIME AT THE CONCLUSION OF EACH VOLTAGE STEP (IEEE 95)

Time at end of first step, 10 min. Voltage increment 20 percent of first step. Absorption ratio, N.

VOLTAGE % OF FIRST STEP	2	3	4	5	6	7	8	9	10	11	12	13	14	15	16	20
100	10'	10'	10'	10'	10'	10'	10'	10'	10'	10'	10'	10'	10'	10'	10'	10'
120	13'14"	13'27"	13'36"	13'44"	13'49"	13'54"	13'58"	14'2"	14'5"	14'8"	14'10"	14'13"	14'15"	14'17"	14'19"	14'25"
140	15'56"	16'21"	16'39"	16'53"	17'4"	17'14"	17'22"	17'30"	17'36"	17'42"	17'47"	17'52"	17'56"	18'0"	18'4"	18'17"
160	18'17"	18'55"	19'21"	19'42"	19'59"	20'13"	20'25"	20'36"	20'46"	20'54"	21'2"	21'9"	21'16"	21'22"	21'28"	21'48"
180	20'24"	21'12"	21'47"	22'14"	22'37"	22'56"	23'12"	23'26"	23'39"	23'51"	24'1"	24'11"	24'20"	24'29"	24'36"	25'3"
200	22'19"	23'12"	24'1"	24'34"	25'2"	25'25"	25'46"	26'4"	26'20"	26'34"	26'48"	27'0"	27'11"	27'22"	27'32"	28'5"
220	24'4"	25'14"	26'4"	26'43"	27'17"	27'45"	28'9"	28'31"	28'50"	29'7"	29'23"	29'38"	29'52"	30'4"	30'16"	30'57"
240	25'42"	27'1"	27'59"	28'45"	29'23"	29'55"	30'24"	30'49"	31'11"	31'31"	31'50"	32'7"	32'23"	32'38"	32'51"	33'39"
260	27'12"	28'41"	29'47"	30'38"	31'21"	31'58"	32'30"	32'59"	33'24"	33'47"	34'8"	34'28"	34'46"	35'3"	35'19"	36'13"
280	28'37"	30'15"	31'28"	32'25"	33'13"	33'54"	34'30"	35'2"	35'30"	35'56"	36'20"	36'42"	37'2"	37'21"	37'39"	38'41"
300	29'57"	31'44"	33'3"	34'7"	34'59"	35'44"	36'24"	36'59"	37'31"	37'59"	38'26"	38'50"	39'12"	39'33"	39'53"	41'1"
320	31'12"	33'8"	34'34"	35'43"	36'40"	37'29"	38'12"	38'51"	39'25"	39'57"	40'26"	40'52"	41'17"	41'40"	42'2"	43'17"
340	32'23"	34'27"	36'0"	37'14"	38'16"	39'9"	39'56"	40'38"	41'15"	41'49"	42'21"	42'49"	43'16"	43'41"	44'5"	45'27"
360	33'31"	35'43"	37'22"	38'41"	39'48"	40'45"	41'35"	42'20"	43'0"	43'37"	44'11"	44'42"	45'11"	45'38"	46'4"	47'32"
380	34'35"	36'55"	38'40"	40'5"	41'16"	42'17"	43'11"	43'58"	44'42"	45'21"	45'57"	46'31"	47'2"	47'31"	47'59"	49'33"
400	35'36"	38'4"	39'55"	41'25"	42'40"	43'45"	44'42"	45'33"	46'19"	47'1"	47'40"	48'16"	48'49"	49'20"	49'49"	51'30"
420	36'35"	39'10"	41'7"	42'42"	44'2"	45'10"	46'11"	47'5"	47'53"	48'38"	49'19"	49'57"	50'32"	51'5"	51'36"	53'24"
440	37'31"	40'14"	42'17"	43'56"	45'20"	46'32"	47'36"	48'33"	49'24"	50'11"	50'55"	51'35"	52'12"	52'47"	53'20"	55'14"
460	38'25"	41'15"	43'23"	45'8"	46'35"	47'51"	48'58"	49'58"	50'52"	51'42"	52'28"	53'10"	53'49"	54'26"	55'1"	57'1"
480	39'17"	42'14"	44'28"	46'17"	47'48"	49'8"	50'18"	51'21"	52'18"	53'10"	53'58"	54'42"	55'23"	56'2"	56'38"	58'45"
500	40'8"	43'11"	45'30"	47'23"	48'59"	50'22"	51'35"	52'41"	53'41"	54'35"	55'25"	56'11"	56'55"	57'36"	58'14"	60'27"
520	40'56"	44'6"	46'30"	48'28"	50'8"	51'34"	52'51"	53'59"	55'1"	55'58"	56'50"	57'39"	58'24"	59'6"	59'46"	62'6"
540	41'42"	44'58"	47'29"	49'31"	51'14"	52'44"	54'3"	55'15"	56'19"	57'18"	58'13"	59'4"	59'51"	60'35"	61'17"	63'42"
560	42'28"	45'50"	48'25"	50'31"	52'19"	53'52"	55'14"	56'28"	57'35"	58'37"	59'34"	60'26"	61'15"	62'1"	62'45"	65'16"
580	43'11"	46'40"	49'20"	51'30"	53'21"	54'58"	56'23"	57'40"	58'50"	59'53"	60'52"	61'47"	62'38"	63'26"	64'11"	66'48"

600	43°54"	47°28"	50°13"	52°28"	54°22"	56°2"	57°30"	58°50"	60°2"	61°8"	62°9"	63°6"	63°59"	64°48"	65°35"	68°18"
620	44°35"	48°15"	51°4"	53°24"	55°22"	57°5"	58°36"	59°58"	61°12"	62°21"	63°25"	64°23"	65°17"	66°9"	66°57"	69°46"
640	45°15"	49°1"	51°55"	54°18"	56°19"	58°6"	59°40"	61°4"	62°21"	63°32"	64°37"	65°38"	66°34"	67°27"	68°17"	71°13"
660	45°53"	49°45"	52°44"	55°11"	57°16"	59°5"	60°42"	62°9"	63°29"	64°41"	65°49"	66°51"	67°50"	68°44"	69°36"	72°37"
680	46°31"	50°28"	53°32"	56°3"	58°11"	60°3"	61°43"	63°13"	64°35"	65°50"	66°59"	68°3"	69°3"	70°0"	70°53"	74°0"
700	47°8"	51°10"	54°18"	56°53"	59°5"	61°0"	62°43"	64°15"	65°39"	66°56"	68°7"	69°14"	70°16"	71°14"	72°9"	75°21"
720	47°43"	51°51"	55°4"	57°42"	59°58"	61°56"	63°41"	65°16"	66°42"	68°1"	69°15"	70°23"	71°27"	72°26"	73°23"	76°41"
740	48°18"	52°32"	55°48"	58°30"	60°49"	62°50"	64°38"	66°15"	67°44"	69°5"	70°20"	71°30"	72°36"	73°38"	74°36"	77°59"
760	48°52"	53°11"	56°32"	59°18"	61°39"	63°43"	65°34"	67°13"	68°44"	70°8"	71°25"	72°37"	73°44"	74°47"	75°47"	79°16"
780	49°25"	53°49"	57°14"	60°3"	62°28"	64°35"	66°28"	68°10"	69°43"	71°9"	72°28"	73°42"	74°51"	75°56"	76°57"	80°32"
800	49°58"	54°26"	57°55"	60°48"	63°17"	65°26"	67°22"	69°6"	70°42"	72°9"	73°30"	74°46"	75°57"	77°3"	78°6"	81°46"
820	50°29"	55°3"	58°36"	61°33"	64°4"	66°16"	68°14"	70°1"	71°39"	73°8"	74°32"	75°49"	77°1"	78°9"	79°14"	82°59"
840	51°0"	55°38"	59°16"	62°16"	64°50"	67°6"	69°6"	70°55"	72°35"	74°7"	75°32"	76°51"	78°5"	79°14"	80°20"	84°11"
860	51°30"	56°13"	59°55"	62°58"	65°35"	67°54"	69°57"	71°48"	73°30"	75°4"	76°30"	77°51"	79°7"	80°18"	81°26"	85°22"
880	52°0"	56°45"	60°33"	63°40"	66°20"	68°41"	70°47"	72°40"	74°24"	76°0"	77°28"	78°51"	80°8"	81°21"	82°30"	86°32"
900	52°29"	57°21"	61°10"	64°20"	67°6"	69°27"	71°35"	73°31"	75°17"	76°55"	78°25"	79°50"	81°9"	82°23"	83°33"	87°41"
920	52°57"	57°54"	61°46"	65°0"	67°46"	70°13"	72°23"	74°22"	76°10"	77°49"	79°21"	80°47"	82°8"	83°24"	84°36"	88°48"
940	53°25"	58°26"	62°23"	65°39"	68°29"	70°58"	73°10"	75°11"	77°1"	78°42"	80°17"	81°44"	83°7"	84°24"	85°37"	89°55"
960	53°53"	58°58"	62°58"	66°18"	69°10"	71°41"	73°57"	75°59"	77°52"	79°35"	81°11"	82°40"	84°4"	85°23"	86°38"	91°1"
980	54°20"	59°29"	63°32"	66°56"	69°50"	72°24"	74°42"	76°46"	78°41"	80°26"	82°4"	83°35"	85°1"	86°21"	87°37"	92°5"

- The test now may be carried out for the remaining steps of test voltage using the precalculated values of time steps. The readings of leakage current versus voltage are taken at the end of each step.

- A new curve may be generated by plotting the leakage current on the vertical axis and voltage on the horizontal axis. The curve obtained should be a straight line if the rate of increase of conduction current component is linear. Moisture in the insulation system will produce a continuous upward slope, whereas void ionization will exhibit minor breaks in the slope of the curve. However, a sharp break in the curve will usually indicate an impending failure.

4-6   EVALUATION OF TEST DATA READINGS

Insulation resistance measurements, coupled with other information, can serve as a guide to determine what action to take on electrical apparatus or cables. The choices are as follows:

- Place or restore the circuit to service until the next scheduled inspection.

- Restore the circuit to service now, but plan to perform indicated repairs as soon as possible.

- Leave out of service until repairs have been made.

What factors should be considered to determine whether insulation is good or bad?

- Rule of thumb: Minimum acceptable value of insulation to place equipment in service is 1 MΩ per rated kilovolt plus 1 MΩ. This is based upon experience rather than the characteristics of insulation. The insulation resistance should never be less than 1 MΩ for all equipment.

- Manufacturers' information when available.

- Comparison with values obtained at acceptance or installation.

- Comparison with values from previous routine tests.

- Comparison with values of several similar units.

What physical factors may influence the readings?

- Contamination, including dirt, moisture, acids, and salts.

- A terminal connection or contamination at an end point can cause a low reading, and the true reading of a winding or cable will be unknown.

- Readings should be compared at a common temperature base, for example, 20°C. Different insulating materials have different temperature correction tables, which are available in manufacturers' literature.

ACCEPTANCE VALUES FOR RATING INSULATION

The following criteria can be applied for rating insulation as to whether it is good, bad, or needs further investigation. The following table provides rule-of-thumb minimum acceptance values:

System Voltage (kV)	Megohms	System Voltage (kV)	Megohms
216 V	1.2	34	35
480 V	1.5	69	70
2.4	3.4	138	139
4.16	5.16	230	231
7.2	8.2	345	346
13.8	14.8	500	501

The following table is an example of evaluating 15-kV cable readings:

Test	Megohm Values			Good	Bad	Investigate
	Phase 1	Phase 2	Phase 3			
1	4,000	4,500	3,500	×		
2	4,000	800	3,500			×
3	4,000	50	3,500		×	
4	4,000	200	3,500		×	
5	4,000	1,000	3,500		×	
6	4,000	4,000	3,500		×	

Test 4 indicates a low value and upon investigation indicated a cracked sheath. Test 5, which was conducted on the second day on the same cable, indicated a higher value of resistance due to drying out. Test 6, conducted on the third day, indicated normal values because of further drying, but sheath crack still was not repaired.

An example for a lightning arrester might be as follows:

Test	Megohm Value		
	Phase 1	Phase 2	Phase 3
1	8,000	8,000	50,000

The 50,000-MΩ value is too high and could indicate damage to the lightning arrester, such as missing elements. The 8,000-MΩ value is good.

An example for a generator might be as follows:

Test	Test Type	Generator Stator	Generator Rotor	Criteria Good	Criteria Bad	Criteria Investigate
1	PI	4.1	2.6	×		
2	PI	4.1	1.2		×	
3	PI	4.1	7.0			×

Test 2 indicates moisture or contamination, whereas test 3 indicates rotor insulation embrittled by heat.

The following lists insulation resistance values for transformers:

Transformer Condition	One-Minute Readings in Megohms (corrected to 20°C)
New mineral-oil transformers	1,000 and up
Service-aged transformers	100 to 1,000
Investigate	Below 100
Askarel-filled transformer with high-voltage switch	10 to 50

Examples for motors and generators are as follows:

Test	Test Type	Good	Fair	Questionable	Poor
1	Dielectric absorption ratio (DAR)	1.4 and above	1.25 to 1.4	1.1 to 1.25	Less than 1.1
2	Polarization index (PI)	3 and above	2 to 3	1.5 to 2	Less than 1.5

4-7   PRECAUTIONS WHEN MAKING DIRECT-CURRENT TESTS

- A dc overpotential test can be conducted any time equipment can be taken out of service for a few hours; however, it is preferred that the test be planned in conjunction with a periodic dismantled inspection of the equipment. This will allow time to investigate the cause of unsatisfactory test results and make necessary repairs with a minimum of interference to normal production.

- The equipment should be taken off the line sufficiently in advance of the test to permit it to cool below 40°C (104°F). Testing at ambient temperature is preferred.

- The insulation of windings should be relatively clean and dry. If excessive foreign matter is present, the windings should be cleaned prior to conducting the test. Any cleaning solvent used should be allowed to evaporate thoroughly so that the surface of the insulation is dry; otherwise, false leakage current readings may result.

- Where it is possible to do so, especially with large rotating machines, phase connections should be opened in order to test each phase separately, phase to phase and phase to ground. All windings not under test should be short-circuited and grounded to the machine frame.

- As a safety precaution, before any dc voltage tests are conducted a ground should be applied to the unit or cable to be tested.

- Allow the dc voltage to discharge sufficiently, especially in cables after tests have been concluded. A common rule of thumb is that the discharge time should be twice as long as the charge time.

CHAPTER 5

ALTERNATING-CURRENT TESTING OF ELECTRICAL EQUIPMENT

5-1   INTRODUCTION

This chapter covers the alternating-current (ac) tests ordinarily used in the field for acceptance and maintenance of electrical equipment and apparatus. The ac methods covered in this chapter pertain to the transformer, insulating liquid, electrical switchgear, and machines. Again, the basic purposes of conducting these tests are to identify and conduct necessary corrective maintenance and repair, determine the adequacy of the installed equipment, and chart the gradual deterioration of equipment over its service life. The ac high potential and power factor are the two most commonly used tests.

The field ac high-potential tests are conducted at voltages above rated circuit voltage, usually some specified value of final ac factory test values, for a short duration. The ac high-potential tests are go, no-go tests; that is, the equipment either passes or fails the test. The final factory test voltage values are in accordance with applicable industry standards. However, manufacturer's instructions and specified test voltage levels should be followed when testing very old equipment or equipment whose construction is unknown.

The power factor test conducted on the insulation system measures the cosine of the angle of charging current and impressed voltage. For low values of power factor, the dissipation factor can be considered to be the same as the power factor. Test equipment commonly used for power factor testing can give direct readings of power factor and dissipation factor or readings of charging volt-amperes and dielectric losses (watts) from which the ratio can be calculated. The test equipment should be able to produce and maintain a sinusoidal wave shape while conducting this test at a minimum of 2,500 volts (V) or at the operating voltage of the equipment under test. The test voltage for the power factor test should in no case be less than 500 V. Evaluation of the test data should be based upon industry standards, comparative evaluation with previous tests at base temperature and humidity, and correlation of data with test results of similar units on a industry-wide basis. The normal base temperature is 32°F and relative humidity is 70 percent for comparative analysis of the power factor test data.

5-2   TRANSFORMERS

Transformers may be tested with ac voltage similar to the dc voltage test. Overall, ac voltage is preferable to dc voltage for testing transformers because ac voltage simulates the internal stress that the transformers experience during operating conditions.

The following ac voltage tests are conducted on the transformer:

- AC high-potential (ac hi-pot) test.
- Insulation power factor test.
- Transformer turns ratio (TTR) test.
- Polarity test.
- Excitation current test.
- Induced potential test.

AC HIGH-POTENTIAL TEST

The ac high-potential test is applied to evaluate the condition of transformer windings. This test is recommended for all voltages, especially those above 34.5 kilovolts (kV). For routine maintenance testing of transformers, the test voltage should not exceed 65 percent of factory test voltage. However, the hi-pot test for routine maintenance is generally not employed on transformers because of the possibility of damage to the winding insulation. This test is commonly used for acceptance testing and after repair testing of transformers. The ac high-voltage test value should not exceed 75 percent of the factory test value. When ac high-potential testing is to be used for routine maintenance, the transformer can be tested at rated voltage for 3 minutes (min) instead of testing at 65 percent of factory test voltage. The ac high potential test values for different voltage systems are shown in Table 5–1. Testing procedures and test connections are similar to the dc high-potential tests described in Chapter 4.

INSULATION POWER FACTOR (PF) TEST

This test is performed on large high-voltage transformers. Basically, this test measures the power loss due to the leakage current through the insulation. Two test sets (as manufactured by Doble Engineering Co., Watertown, Mass.) are shown in Figure 5–1.

TABLE 5-1.

ALTERNATING-CURRENT DIELECTRIC TEST FOR ACCEPTANCE
AND ROUTINE MAINTENANCE FOR ALL LIQUID-FILLED
TRANSFORMERS

Transformer Winding Rated Voltage (kV)	Factory Test AC Voltage (kV)	Acceptance Field Test AC Voltage, 75%, (kV)	Maintenance Periodic Test, 65% (kV)
1.20	10	7.50	6.50
2.40	15	11.20	9.75
4.80	19	14.25	12.35
8.70	26	19.50	16.90
15.00	34	25.50	22.10
18.00	40	30.00	26.00
25.00	50	37.50	32.50
34.50	70	52.50	45.50
46.00	95	71.25	61.75
69.00	140	105.00	91.00

Power factor can be represented as the ratio of watts (W) divided by volt-amperes. Writing PF in an equation form,

$$PF = \frac{W}{EI} = \frac{EI \cos \theta}{EI}$$

where E = phase voltage
I = total phase current
θ = phase angle between E and I
W = watts

The transformer total phase current (I) is made up of resistive (I_R) and capacitive (I_C) currents. However, when the transformer is energized with the secondary side open (i.e., no-load condition), the resistive current is very small and is practically limited to dielectric losses. This is a condition when PF is very low and almost the total current is made up of capacitive current I_C. Therefore we can represent PF as the ratio of the resistive current divided by the capacitive (or total phase) current. Writing in an equation, we can state

$$PF = \frac{I_R}{I} = \frac{I_R}{I_C}$$

where $I_C \approx I$

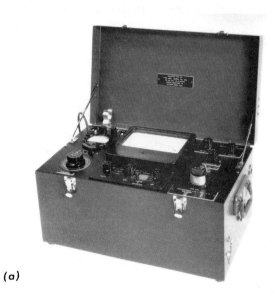

(a)

(b)

FIGURE 5–1.
(a) Doble-type MEU 2500-volt dielectric loss and power factor test set;
(b) Doble-type M2H 10-kilovolt dielectric loss and power factor test set.
(Courtesy of Doble Engineering Co., Watertown, Mass.)

Also we can write resistance $R = \dfrac{E^2}{W}$ and capacitance $C = \dfrac{I_C}{E\omega} \approx \dfrac{I}{E\omega}$ where ω is the angular velocity.

Figure 5-2 shows in simplified form a typical two-winding transformer and the standard series of tests applied to it as recommended by Doble®.

- C_H refers to all insulation between the high-voltage conductors and grounded parts, including bushings, winding insulation, structural insulating members and oil.

- C_L refers to the same parts and materials between the low-voltage conductors and grounded parts.

- C_{HL} refers to all winding insulation, barriers and oil between high- and low-voltage windings.

Tabulated are the standard series of tests (1 to 4), two calculated values, and two supplementary tests—illustrating how data pertaining directly to C_H, C_L and C_{HL} are obtained without need for physical isolation of transformer parts or sections.

Test data are recorded in terms of alternating changing current and watts-loss at 2.5 or 10 kV, from which power factors are calculated.

Power factor readings can depend upon many factors, such as temperature and instrument accuracy. The acceptable values of transformer power factors are based on comparative power factor values of similar transformers. Companies engaged in this service should be consulted or engaged to perform this work. When the values obtained with the power factor test are unacceptable, further investigation may be required. A special test known as a power factor tip-up test can be performed to evaluate whether moisture or corona is present in the insulation system. If the applied test voltage is varied and the power factor value does not change, moisture is suspected to be the probable cause. If the power factor increases as the voltage is increased, carbonization

®Doble Engineering Co., Watertown, Mass.

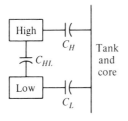

Test	Energized	Grounded	Guarded	Measure
1	H	L	—	$C_H + C_{HL}$
2	H	—	L	C_H
3	L	H	—	$C_L + C_{HL}$
4	L	—	H	C_L
5		Test 1 minus Test 2		C_{HL}
6		Test 3 minus Test 4		C_{HL}

FIGURE 5–2.
Power factor test for two winding transformers.

of the insulation or ionization of voids is the cause. The accepted values for power factor test for transformers are shown in Table 5–2.

TRANSFORMER TURNS RATIO (TTR) TEST

The TTR test applies 8 V ac (hand-crank generator) to the low-voltage winding of a transformer under test and the reference transformer in the TTR set. The high-voltage windings of the transformer under test and the TTR reference transformer are connected through a null detecting instrument. After polarity has been established at 8 V, when the null reading is zero, the dial readings indicate the ratio of the transformer under test. The TTR test provides the following information:

- It determines the turns ratio and polarity of single- and three-phase transformers, one phase at a time.
- It confirms nameplate ratio, polarity, and vectors.
- It determines the ratio and polarity (but not voltage rating) of transformers without markings. Tests include all no-load tap positions on a transformer. Tests include all load taps on load tap changer (LTC) transformers if connected for voltage ratio control. On LTC transformers connected for phase angle control, ratio and polarity are performed in neutral positions only. If tested on load taps, readings may be taken for reference for future comparison, but will deviate from nameplate ratings. LTC taps may be confirmed by application of low three-phase voltage and reading volts and the phase angle for each.

TABLE 5–2.
TRANSFORMER POWER FACTOR VALUES [a]

Test	Percent Power Factor		
	Good	Marginal	Investigate
H winding	0.5 or less	0.5 to 1.0	Above 1.0
X winding	0.5 or less	0.5 to 1.0	Above 1.0
Interwinding	0.5 or less	0.5 to 1.0	Above 1.0
Bushing UST [b]	Below 1.0	—	—
Oil-maintank, tap changer, switch compartment [c]	0.5 or less	Above .5	Replace if above 2

[a] Usually for tests at 10 kV.
[b] UST, ungrounded specimen test.
[c] See Section 5-3.

- Identify trouble in transformer windings, such as open circuit and short circuits of turn to turn sensitivity. The standard deviation as defined by ANSI 57.12.00, section 6.1 states that results should be within 0.5 percent of nameplate markings, with rated voltage applied to one winding. The TTR with accuracy of 0.1 percent is accepted as a "referee."

The following procedures are used for conducting the TTR test:

- Transformer is isolated and tagged and leads disconnected.
- Read transformer nameplate.
- Observe polarities and vectors (phasors).
- Calculate ratios for each no-load and load tap position.
- Set up data test form as follows:

Tap Pos.	Nameplate Volts	Calc. Ratio	Black-Red H1-H2 X0-X2	% Dev.	Black-Red H2-H3 X0-X3	% Dev.	Black-Red H3-H1 X0-X1	% Dev.
			TTR Leads					
1	14,438	5.775						
2	14,094	5.638						
3	13,750	5.500						
4	13,406	5.362						
5	13,063	5.225						

Example:

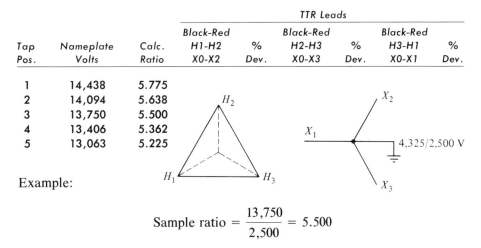

$$\text{Sample ratio} = \frac{13,750}{2,500} = 5.500$$

Make the null check, zero ratio check, and unity ratio check on the TTR.

Null Check

- Set dials to 0.000, anvils (C clamp) open; clip H_1 and H_2 together.
- Crank to 8 V.
- Null detector should not deflect more than 1/16 in.

Zero Ratio Check

- All dials at zero, close anvils; clip H_1 and H_2 together.
- Crank to 8 V.
- Null should read zero.

Unity Ratio Check

- Set dials to 1.000; connect H_1 and X_1, and H_2 and X_2.
- Crank to 8 V.
- Null should balance at 1.000 ratio.

The test connections are shown in Figure 5–3(a) through (c).

Alternative Test for TTR

In case a TTR test set is not available, a quick and rough test can be performed to check the continuity and phase identification of transformer windings. The test consists of the following. The equipment needed for this test is a 100-watt (W) lamp with socket and an extension cord for connection to a 120-V 60-hertz (Hz) power supply, with which three test procedures are performed.

Test 1
Connect the 120-V, 60-Hz power through the lamp to the transformer primary terminals as shown in Figure 5–4(a). Leave the transformer secondary winding open. The lamp will burn dimly.

Test 2
Maintain connections as described in test 1, but now short the secondary winding. The lamp should burn with great brilliance. If the lamp still burns with somewhat less than full brilliance, investigate for problems in the transformer winding. Connections for this test are shown in Figure 5–4(b).

Test 3
This test is similar to tests 1 and 2, but as applied to a three-phase transformer for phase identification and phase continuity check. Conduct tests 1 and 2 for each winding of a three-phase transformer individually with the remaining windings left open. The test connections are shown in Figure 5–4(c).

POLARITY TEST

The polarity test can be performed with the TTR on power, distribution, and potential transformers. However, for current transformers the TTR test is not used. Instead, a test commonly known as the *kick test,* consisting of applying a dc battery and multimeter, is used. The kick test can also be used for power, distribution, and potential transformers; however, the TTR test is preferred. The connections for a kick test for a current transformer are shown in Figure 5–5. The dc battery voltage is usually about 7.5 V, and the multimeter voltage range is set for 3 V full scale. The negative terminal of the battery is connected to current transformer terminal H_2 and the positive side is left hanging for the

(a)

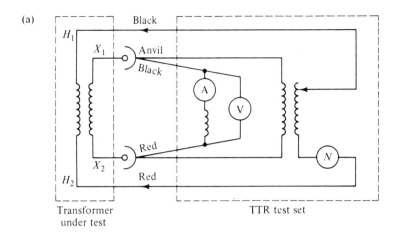

(b)

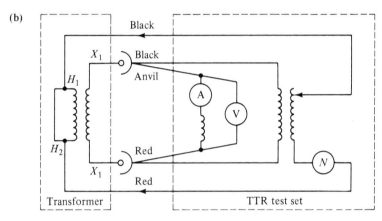

(c)

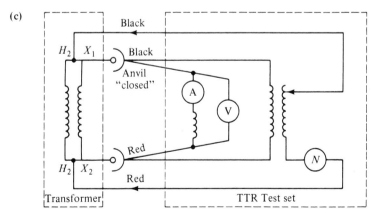

FIGURE 5–3.

(a) Transformer turns ratio test set connections; (b) test connections for null check for TTR; (c) test connections for zero check for TTR.

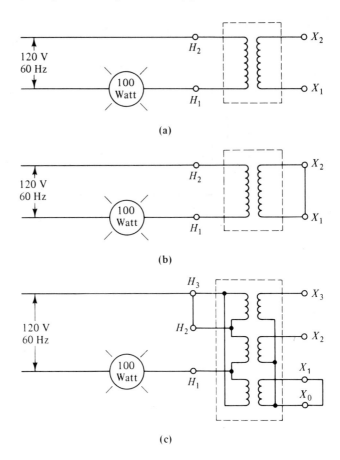

FIGURE 5–4.
(a) Continuity check for transformer winding; (b) continuity check for transformer winding; (c) continuity and phase check for three-winding transformer.

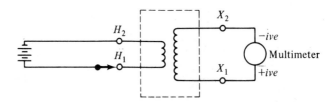

FIGURE 5–5.
Polarity check using the kick method.

time being. The multimeter positive terminal is connected to the transformer secondary terminal X_1 and negative terminal to X_2. To conduct the test, touch the positive side battery jumper to transformer terminal H_1 and notice the multimeter scale indication. If the multimeter scale kick is up scale, the transformer is connected in subtractive polarity. If the kick is down scale, it is connected in additive polarity.

EXCITATION CURRENT TEST

The excitation current of a transformer is the current the transformer draws when voltage is applied to its primary terminals with the secondary terminals open. Excitation current is also known as the no-load current of the transformer. In this test, rated voltage is applied to the primary windings one at a time with all other windings left open. The power factor test set, such as the Doble®, or a conventional ac hi-pot transformer can be used to obtain the test voltage.

The excitation current test method, when used in routine preventive-maintenance or field acceptance testing of transformers, provides means of detection for short circuited turns, poor joints or contacts, core problems, etc. Doble Engineering Company introduced this technique in 1967 for field measurement of transformer excitation current. This test method in its simplest form can be conducted in the following manner as explained by Doble®.

Figure 5-6(a) depicts the single-phase energization of Phase H_{1-2} of a three-phase Delta-connected unit. Three measurements are routinely made (H_{1-2}, H_{2-3}, and H_{3-1}) at voltages generally below the rated voltage—not exceeding 2.5 or 10 kV, depending upon the test equipment rating. The low-voltage winding, not shown in this figure, is isolated from its source or load and is treated as alive during tests. If Wye-connected, the neutral is left grounded, as in normal service.

Figure 5-6(b) illustrates the same single-phase measurement on Phase H_{1-0} of a three-phase Wye-connected transformer.

Test connections with the hi-pot transformer are shown in Figure 5-7. The excitation current readings for each winding are taken and recorded for comparison with future test results. Any major deviations from bench-mark values are cause for investigation. See Table 5-3 for a sample evaluation of test data.

Phase 1 indicates an abnormal value of excitation current. The probable cause may be a turn-to-turn short in the phase 1 winding. The transformer should be further investigated for the location of the problem.

INDUCED POTENTIAL TEST

The induced potential test is a proof test and performed at higher voltage levels than normal operating voltages. Under this test, turn-to-turn insulation and

®Doble Engineering Co., Watertown, Mass.

phase-to-phase insulation are stressed at 65 percent of factory test voltage at higher frequency than 60 Hz, such as 200 to 300 Hz. The frequency of conducting this test should be 5 years or more for large transformers.

The induced potential test for transformers which receive the full standard applied potential test is made by applying between the terminals of one winding a voltage of twice the normal voltage developed in the windings. It is applied for 7200 cycles, and the duration should not exceed 60 seconds.

As the induced potential test overexcites the transformer, the frequency of the applied potential should be high enough to prevent the exciting current of the transformer under test from exceeding about 30 percent of its rated load

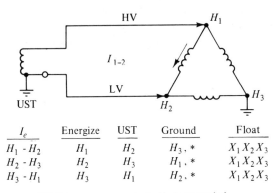

I_e	Energize	UST	Ground	Float
$H_1 - H_2$	H_1	H_2	H_3, *	$X_1 X_2 X_3$
$H_2 - H_3$	H_2	H_3	H_1, *	$X_1 X_2 X_3$
$H_3 - H_1$	H_3	H_1	H_2, *	$X_1 X_2 X_3$

*If X is wye - connected, X_0 is grounded

(a)

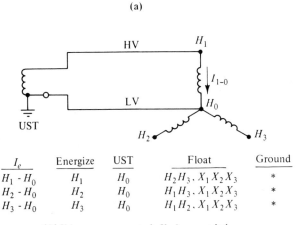

I_e	Energize	UST	Float	Ground
$H_1 - H_0$	H_1	H_0	$H_2 H_3, X_1 X_2 X_3$	*
$H_2 - H_0$	H_2	H_0	$H_1 H_3, X_1 X_2 X_3$	*
$H_3 - H_0$	H_3	H_0	$H_1 H_2, X_1 X_2 X_3$	*

*If X is wye - connected, X_0 is grounded

(b)

FIGURE 5–6.

Excitation current test method connections.

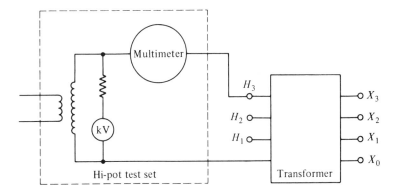

FIGURE 5–7.
Excitation current test connection using the hi-pot test set.

current. Ordinarily this requirement necessitates the use of a frequency of 120 Hz or more, when testing 60-Hz units.

When frequencies higher than 120 Hz are used, the severity of the test is abnormally increased and for this reason the duration of the test should be reduced as shown in Table 5–4.

The voltage should be started at one-quarter or less of the full value and be brought up gradually to full value in not more than 15 seconds. After being held for the time specified in Table 5–4, it should be reduced slowly (in not more than 5 seconds) to one-quarter of the maximum value or less, and the circuit opened.

When transformers have one winding grounded for operation on a grounded-neutral system, special care should be taken to avoid high electrostatic stresses between the other windings and ground.

In the case of transformers having one end of the high-voltage winding grounded during the induced potential test, the ground on each winding may be made at a selected point of the winding itself or of the winding of a step-up transformer which is used to supply the voltage or which is merely connected for the purpose of furnishing the ground.

TABLE 5–3.
TRANSFORMER EXCITATION TEST DATA EVALUATION

Test Conducted	Excitation Current (A)			Evaluation	
	Phase 1	Phase 2	Phase 3	Good	Investigate
Acceptance test (first year)	0.085	0.075	0.085	×	
Maintenance test (2 years later)	0.108	0.075	0.085		×

TABLE 5–4.
FREQUENCY VERSUS DURATION OF TEST

Frequency (Hz)	Duration (sec)
120 and less	60
180	40
240	30
300	20
400	18

Three-phase transformers may be tested with single-phase voltage. The specified test voltage is induced, successively, from each line terminal to ground and to adjacent line terminals. The neutrals of the windings may or may not be held at ground potential during these tests.

When the induced test on a winding results in a voltage between terminals of other windings in excess of the low frequency test voltage specified, the other windings may be sectionalized and grounded. Additional induced tests should then be made to give the required test voltage between terminals of windings that were sectionalized.

5-3   INSULATING LIQUID TESTING

Insulating liquids, such as mineral oil, silicone, etc., are used in transformers, circuit breakers, and capacitors. Because these fluids deteriorate during use, it is essential to monitor and test them in order to maintain their dielectric properties. This section describes the ac voltage and power factor tests for determining the condition of the new and used liquids. The purpose of these tests is to chart the gradual deterioration in order to take preventive measures before liquid failure occurs. The routine dielectric, power factor, and sampling procedures that are conducted on insulating liquids are discussed next.

LIQUID DIELECTRIC TEST (CUP TESTS)

This is an ac overvoltage test applied to the insulating liquids to detect their breakdown strength. A typical test set with cups is shown in Figure 5–8. The American Society for Testing and Materials (ASTM) has established test standards for these liquids, which are listed in Table 1–1. The dielectric test simply consists of placing a liquid sample from the transformer (or circuit breaker) in a cup containing two electrodes of specified gap. High voltage is then applied to the sample. The test is repeated for at least five different samples to determine the average dielectric strength. The minimum accepted values for the various liquids are listed in Table 5–5.

FIGURE 5–8.

Oil dielectric test set-up and cups—60 kilovolts. (Courtesy of Hipo-tronics, Brewster, N.Y.)

TABLE 5–5.

DIELECTRIC TEST VALUES FOR TRANSFORMER INSULATING FLUIDS

Types of Liquids	Dielectric Strength (kV)	
	Satisfactory	Needs Reconditioning
Oil	23	Less than 23
Askarel	26	Less than 25
Silicone	26	Less than 26
RTemp	26	Less than 26
R-113 (G.E.)	26	Less than 26
Wecosol	26	Less than 26

Two different electrodes are used in these tests, one for mineral-based oils and the other for mineral-based oils and synthetic liquids. The VDE *(Verband Dentschev Elektrotechniker)* cup is used for mineral-based oils; it has a gap of 0.04 to 0.08 in. with a rate of voltage rise of 500 V/second(s). The disc cup is used for mineral-based oils and synthetic liquids such as askarel, silicone, and others. It has a gap of 0.1 in. with rate of rise of 3,000 V/s. The step-by-step procedures for conducting these tests are described next.

Dielectric Test ASTM D-877 (Disc Electrodes)

Portable oil dielectric testers are usually used for making dielectric tests on oils in the field. Units with a variable high voltage of 40 kV or greater between the electrodes and which have Bakelite test cups are considered satisfactory. Instructions and procedures are as follows:

- The electrodes and the test cup should be wiped clean with dry, calendered tissue paper or with a clean, dry chamois. The spacing of the electrodes should be checked with a standard round gauge having a diameter of 0.1 in. or with flat steel go and no-go gauges having thicknesses of 0.0995 and 0.1005 in., respectively; the electrodes should be locked in position. It is important to avoid touching the electrodes or the cleaned gauge with the fingers or with portions of the tissue paper or chamois that have been in contact with the hands.

- The electrodes and test cup should be rinsed with dry, lead-free gasoline or other suitable solvent until they are entirely clean. To avoid any possible contamination, care should be taken to avoid touching the electrodes or the inside of the cup after cleaning.

- After a thorough cleaning, the test cup is filled with a sample of the cleaning fluid; voltage is applied and uniformly increased at a rate of approximately 3 kV/s (rms value) until breakdown occurs. If the breakdown is not less than the established value of the oil being tested, the test cup should be considered in suitable condition for testing. If a lower value is obtained, the cup should again be thoroughly cleaned and the test repeated. A cleaning fluid whose breakdown is not less than the established value of the oil being tested must be used.

- At the beginning of each test, the electrodes should be examined for pitting and carbon accumulation, and the electrode spacing should be checked. The test cup should be thoroughly cleaned and tested as described previously. It should then be flushed with a portion of the sample to be tested before it is filled for the test.

- If the test of a sample is below the breakdown value being used by the operator as a minimum satisfactory value, the cup should be cleaned and prepared before testing the next sample. Evaporation of the cleaning fluid from the electrodes may chill them sufficiently to cause moisture to condense on their surfaces. For this reason, after the final rinsing with cleaning fluid, the cup must immediately be flushed with the oil to be tested and then filled for the test.

- The dielectric strength of liquid dielectrics may be markedly altered by the migration of impurities through the liquid. To obtain representative test specimens, the sample container should be gently tilted or inverted and the oil swirled several times before each filling of the test cup, in such a way that any impurities present will be thoroughly mixed with the liquid dielectric. Too rapid agitation is undesirable, since it introduces an excessive amount of air into the liquid. Immediately after agitating, the test cup should be filled with oil to a height of not less than 20 mm (0.787 in.) above the top of the electrodes. To permit the escape of entrapped air, the container should be gently rocked a few times and the oil allowed to stand in the cup for 3 min before voltage is applied.

- The temperature of the sample when tested should be the same as that of the room, but not less than 20°C (68°F). Testing of oil at a temperature lower than that of the room is likely to give variable results, which may be misleading.

- Voltage should be applied and increased at a uniform rate of 3 kV/s from zero until breakdown occurs, as indicated by a continuous discharge across the gap. Occasional momentary discharges that do not result in a permanent arc may occur; they should be disregarded.

- When it is desired to determine the dielectric breakdown voltage of a new liquid for referee purposes, one breakdown should be made on each of five successive fillings of the test cup. If the five values meet the minimum dielectric values, the average should be reported as the dielectric breakdown voltage of the sample. If they do not meet the minimum dielectric values, one breakdown on each of five additional cup fillings should be made and the average of the ten breakdowns reported as the dielectric breakdown voltage of the sample. No breakdown should be discarded.

- When it is desired to determine the dielectric breakdown voltage of a liquid on a routine basis, one breakdown may be made on each of two fillings of the test cup. If no value is below the specified acceptance value, the oil may be considered satisfactory, and no further tests are required. If either of the values is less than the specified value, a breakdown should be made on each of three additional cup fillings, and the test results analyzed.

- *Alternative method:* When it is desired to determine the dielectric breakdown voltage of a liquid on a routine basis, five breakdowns may be made on one cup filling with 1-min intervals between breakdowns.

The average of the five breakdowns should be considered the dielectric breakdown voltage of the sample, provided the breakdown values meet the criterion for statistical consistency. If the breakdown voltages do not meet this criterion, the contents of the cup should be discarded, the sample container again gently inverted and swirled, the cup again filled, and five breakdowns made on this second cup filling. The average of the ten breakdowns should be considered as the dielectric breakdown voltage of the sample. No breakdown should be discarded.

- Compute the range of the five breakdowns (maximum breakdown voltage minus minimum breakdown voltage), and multiply this range by 3. If the value obtained is greater than the next to the lowest breakdown voltage, it is probable that the standard deviation of the five breakdowns is excessive, and therefore the probable error of their average is also excessive.

Dielectric Test ASTM D-1816 (VDE Electrode)

The present ASTM D-877 gap consists of 1-in.-diameter disc, square-edged electrodes spaced at 0.1 in. Use of this test gap results in a uniform electrostatic field at the center line of the test discs and a highly nonuniform field at the edges of the disc. To attain a uniform field strength at all points, spherical electrodes (Figure 5-8(c)) would have to be used. Between these extremes of a highly distorted field and an ideal uniform field, a third gap configuration, designated as VDE, has been used. The VDE gap specifications call for a sector diameter of 36 mm and a 25-mm radius of curvature for the spherically capped electrodes. A gap of about 0.08 in. between electrodes has been found to give about the same breakdown voltage relationships in the 25- to 30-kV range as the ASTM D-877 configuration. Tests have shown the following:

- The VDE configuration depicts more accurately the average electric strength and scatter of the oil as the transformer sees it.
- The VDE gap is relatively sensitive to oil quality.
- The ASTM D-877 is less sensitive.
- The point electrodes are almost completely insensitive to oil quality.

The VDE cell, in which a quart of oil is tested between VDE electrodes, while being mildly circulated, realistically measures changes in oil strength, which determine the electrical strength of typical transformer construction. This test method (ASTM D-1816) is similar to ASTM D-877. The procedure for the VDE (ASTM D-1816) test is the same as for the disc electrodes (ASTM D-877).

INSULATING LIQUID SAMPLING PROCEDURES

The validity of the test results is dependent upon the sampler being certain that the oil sample is truly representative of the oil in the equipment. Glass bottles are recommended as containers for samples, because they can be easily inspected for cleanliness. The glass bottles may be either cork or glass stoppered or fitted with screwcaps having cork or aluminum liners (inserts). Corks should be of good quality. Do *not* use rubber stoppers. Clean, new, rectangular-shaped, 1-quart (qt) cans with screwcaps have been found to be satisfactory containers for shipping samples.

Containers should be rinsed in lead-free gasoline, (which is flammable and should be used out-of-doors only) or Chlorothene (a nonflammable solvent), dried, and washed in strong soapsuds. Then they should be thoroughly rinsed with water, dried in an oven at about 105°C for several hours, and removed from the oven. Cork while still warm. As the bottles cool, they should be sealed by dipping the necks in wax, and then stored for future use. These bottles should be opened only when the bottle temperature and the ambient temperature are the same or nearly so.

Sampling Oil from Transformers

General sampling instructions are as follows:

- At least 2 qt of oil should be taken as a sample for dielectric, acidity, and intrafacial tension (IFT) tests. Allow space at the top of the container for expansion. If two 1-qt bottles are used for a sample, label the bottles "1 of 2" and "2 of 2."

- Samples from outdoor apparatus should be taken on clear days when the humidity is near normal and the oil is at least as warm or warmer than the surrounding air. Cold oil may condense enough moisture from a humid atmosphere to seriously affect its insulating properties. Therefore, this precaution must be observed in sampling spare transformers.

- Samples should never be drawn in rain or when the relative humidity of the atmosphere exceeds 70 percent.

- Guard against wind and dust.

- When taking samples from an opening, such as a valve, clean the valve thoroughly and allow enough liquid to run out (about 1 qt) to remove any moisture or foreign material.

- In a sealed transformer, which has a vacuum, be sure to vent the transformer before drawing the sample.

- Place the sample in the freezing compartment of a refrigerator overnight. If the sample is cloudy when viewed the next day, it contains free water. Since free water is undesirable, take another sample to determine whether water is in the oil or was in the sample container.

Sampling Oil from Drums or Shipping Containers

The oil drum should remain undisturbed for several hours before drawing the sample.

- A glass or Pyrex thief is recommended for sampling, because it can be easily inspected for cleanliness. A glass tube approximately 36 in. long, 1 in. in diameter, and tapered at both ends is recommended for the sampling thief.
- The thief should be cleaned before and after sampling in the same manner as for cleaning sample containers. When not being used, the thief should be corked at both ends.
- Discard the first full thief of oil.
- Draw the sample in the following manner:

    With the top end covered with the thumb, lower the tube to within approximately ⅛ in. from the bottom of the drum.

    Remove the thumb from the top opening until the thief is filled with oil.

    Replace thumb over top of thief and remove thief full of oil to the sample container. Release thumb to permit oil to run into the container.

POWER FACTOR TEST

The power factor of an insulating liquid is the cosine of the phase angle between applied sinusoidal voltage and resulting current. The power factor indicates the dielectric loss of the liquid and thus its dielectric heating. The power factor test is widely used as an acceptance and preventive maintenance test for insulating liquid. Liquid power factor testing in the field is usually done with portable, direct-reading power factor measuring test equipment, which is available from several companies who provide this service. Power factor tests on oil and transformer liquids are commonly made with an ASTM D-924 test cell (Figure 5–9). A typical test set manufactured by Beckman® is shown in Figure 5–10.

The power factor of new askarel should not exceed 0.05 percent at 20°C. A high power factor in used liquid indicates deterioration and/or contamination with moisture, carbon, varnish, Glyptal, sodium soaps, or deteriorated products. Used oil with a power factor in excess of 0.5 percent should be further analyzed in a laboratory to determine the cause of the high power factor. Askarel with a power factor in excess of 2.0 percent should be investigated and either reconditioned or replaced.

Good new oil has a power factor of 0.05 percent or less at 20°C. Higher power factors indicate deterioration and/or contamination with moisture, carbon or other conducting matter, varnish, Glyptal, sodium soaps, asphalt com-

® Beckman Instrument, Inc., Cedar Grove N.J.

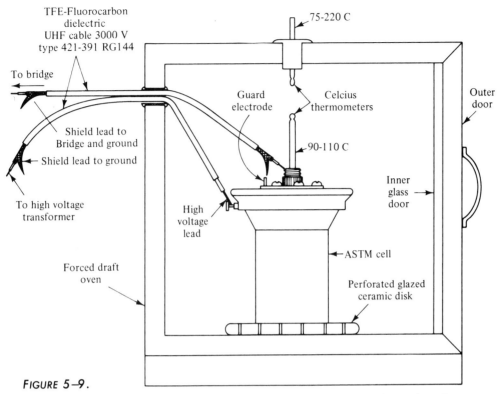

FIGURE 5–9.

Three electrode test cell used for measurement of power factor of insulating liquid per ASTM D–924–76 (Courtesy of ASTM, Philadelphia, Pa.)

pounds, or deterioration products. Carbon or asphalt in oil can cause discoloration. Carbon in oil will not necessarily increase the power factor of the oil unless moisture is also present. It is suggested that the following serve as guides for grading oil by power factor tests.

- Oil having a power factor of less than 0.5 percent at 20°C is usually considered satisfactory for service.
- Oil having a power factor between 0.5 and 2 percent at 20°C should be considered as being in doubtful condition, and at least some type of investigation should be made.
- Oil having a power factor of over 2 percent at 20°C should be investigated and should be reconditioned or replaced.

The preceding guides may be elaborated on by saying that good new oil has a power factor of approximately 0.05 percent or less at 20°C and that the power factor can gradually increase in service to a value as high as 0.5 percent

FIGURE 5–10.

Liquid power factor tester—Model No. PF-2A with JPF-50 test cell.
(Courtesy of Beckman Instruments, Inc., Cedar Grove, N.J.)

at 20°C without, in most cases, indicating deterioration. When the power factor exceeds 0.5 percent, an investigation is indicated. The question of what decision to make regarding disposition of the oil depends on what is causing the high power factor. Dielectric strength tests should be made to determine the presence of moisture. The necessity for further tests will depend to a large extent on the magnitude of the power factor, the importance of the apparatus in which the oil is used, its rating, and the quantity of oil involved. Table 5–6 lists various liquid power factor values.

5-4   CABLES AND ACCESSORIES

Cables and accessories may be field tested with ac voltage, although this is normally not done. The most common field test on cables involves dc voltage tests. However, ac high-potential acceptance and maintenance tests may be conducted on cables and cable accessories. Before a successful test can be carried out the ac test set should have adequate volt-ampere capacity to supply the required cable charging current requirement. The VA capacity of the test set may be determined by the formula

$$VA = 2\pi f c E^2 \quad \text{or} \quad kVA = 2\pi f c E^2 10^{-3}$$

where c is capacitance in microfarad per mile, f is the frequency in hertz, and E is the test voltage in kilovolts of the test set. The test voltage values recommended for acceptance and maintenance tests are 80 and 60 percent, respectively, of the final factory test voltage. The test connections are similar to the test connections indicated in Chapter 4 for dc testing of cables.

The power factor test may also be conducted for cables and accessories. The power factor for each conductor with respect to ground should be made. The evaluation should be based upon comparative analysis with previous test results or correlated with test results of similar types of cables.

5-5   ELECTRICAL SWITCHGEAR

The design of the insulation system for metal-enclosed switchgear is based upon life expectancy of about 30 years. However, environmental conditions such as dirt, moisture, and corrosive atmosphere can shorten the design life. Moisture combined with dirt is the greatest deteriorating factor for insulation systems because of leakage and tracking, which will result in eventual failure. Therefore, it is important to maintain the switchgear insulation and to chart the condition of the primary insulation system by routine testing. Some of the common insulation tests that are used for switchgear are (1) high-potential testing and (2) power factor testing.

HIGH POTENTIAL TESTING

This test should be conducted separately for circuit breakers and switchgear buses (stationary gear). It should be made only after the dc insulation resistance measurement test has passed satisfactorily and all clean up has been finished. The ac test will stress the switchgear insulation similarly to the stresses found

TABLE 5–6.
INSULATING LIQUID POWER FACTOR VALUES

Insulating Fluid Type	Power Factor Values		
	Satisfactory	Needs Reconditioning	Needs Replacement
Oil	Up to 0.5% max.	Above 0.5%	Above 2%
Askarel	Up to 0.5% max.	0.6 to 2.0%	Above 2%
Silicone	1×10^{-4} max.	1×10^{-3} max.	Above 1×10^{-3}
RTemp	Below 1×10^{-3}	1×10^{-3}	Above 1×10^{-3}
Wecosol	Up to 12%	Above 12%	—

during operating conditions. The maintenance test voltages should be 75 percent of final factory test voltage. These values are shown in Table 5–7.

High-potential tests are made with the circuit breaker in both open and closed positions. The high-potential test should be the last test conducted after all repairs have been made, clean up is finished, and the insulation resistance test has been successfully passed. Procedures for the high-potential test of the circuit breaker are as follows:

- The test connection for the high-potential test is as shown in Figure 5–11.
- *Circuit breaker in open position:* Connect high-voltage (HV) lead to pole 6. Ground all other poles. Repeat for poles 1 through 5, in turn, with all other poles grounded. Apply the desired high voltage in each case in accordance with Table 5–6.
- *Circuit breaker in closed position:* Connect high voltage (HV) lead to pole 1 or 2 or phase 1 as convenient with either pole of phases 2 and 3 grounded. Repeat for test for phases 2 and 3 with other phases grounded.
- *Stationary gear (buses):* Connect high-voltage (HV) lead to phase 1 as convenient with phases 2 and 3 grounded. Apply the recommended voltage. Repeat the test for phases 2 and 3 with other phases grounded.

POWER FACTOR TESTING

The power factor testing of an insulation system is useful in finding signs of insulation deterioration. The absolute values of power factor measured have little significance. However, comparative analysis of values from year to year

TABLE 5–7.
HIGH-POTENTIAL TEST VALUES

Rated Operating Voltage (V)	A-C Factory Proof Test (V)	A-C Test Maintenance Values (V)
240	1,500	1,130
480	2,000	1,500
600	2,200	1,650
2,400	15,000	11,300
4,160	19,000	14,250
7,200	26,000	19,500
13,800	36,000	27,000
14,400	50,000	37,500
23,000	60,000	45,000
34,500	80,000	60,000

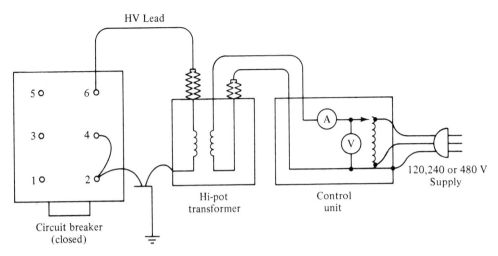

FIGURE 5-11.

Typical connection for high-potential test for circuit breaker in closed position.

may very well show insulation deterioration. Therefore, when a power factor test is made, it should be made under the same conditions of temperature and humidity. If differences exist in the temperature and humidity from year to year, this should be taken into consideration when evaluating the test data. Generally, higher temperature and humidity result in higher power factor values. As a general rule, only the air circuit breaker bushing should be power factored, and the arc chutes, operating rods, and so on, should be disconnected when conducting this test.

The measurement of the power factor of an insulation system is similar to the measurement of the power factor in a power system. It is the ratio of watts (W) to volt-amperes. An insulation system with terminals can be represented as a capacitance in parallel with resistance. When insulation is tested by applying voltage to it, a small current will flow. The current that flows in the capacitance is known as the watt-loss current (reactive current), and the current that flows in the resistance of the insulation is known as pure loss current, that is, the in-phase component (real) current.

In an insulation system, the power factor is very small owing to a very small pure loss current component. Because of large charging current component, the total current is nearly 90° out of phase with the applied voltage. The power factor value (i.e., cosine of the phase angle θ) is nearly equal to the tangent of the loss angle. The loss angle is the complement angle of the phase angle (i.e., $90 - \theta$) and is known as delta. The tangent of $(90 - \theta)$ or delta is known as the dissipation factor. Perfect insulation can be represented as pure capacitance, and therefore its power factor (i.e., cos 90°) should be equal to zero. However, perfect insulation, that is capacitance, has some resistance and therefore exhibits a low watts loss.

A significant change, especially an increase in watts loss or percent of power factor indicates deterioration, which should be monitored. As a general rule, a power factor below 1 percent indicates good insulation. Any value above 1 percent warrants investigation.

To perform a power factor test, a power factor test set is required. Voltage from a 120-V grounded (three terminal) outlet is stepped up to a desired controlled voltage, usually from 2.5 to 10 kV. Applied voltage is held below the apparatus line voltage rating. Current in milliamperes or microamperes will flow through the insulation of the specimen under test. This provides the measured watts loss. The test set, depending on the manufacturer, provides multipliers for converting to percent of power factor values. The power factor values calculated should be converted to 20°C for base comparison purposes. The accepted values for good oil circuit breaker tank loss is between 0 and 0.14 W. The accepted values of power factor for each pole with circuit breaker open and for each phase in the closed position should be below 1 percent, respectively.

5-6 MOTORS AND GENERATORS

Present-day machines are subjected to extremely high electrical and mechanical stresses and therefore have shorter life spans as compared to yesterday's bulky machines. Furthermore, unfavorable operating conditions may lead to unexpected troubles, which can have harmful effects on machine life. The insulation system is extremely important and therefore should be checked on a regular basis. The state of the insulation can be checked by means of the following ac voltage dielectric tests:

- AC high potential test.
- Power factor test.
- Dissipation factor tan δ test.
- Partial discharge test.

HIGH-POTENTIAL TEST

The high-potential test of the armature (stator) winding of a large motor or generator is preceded by a visual inspection and insulation resistance measurements. It provides the "moment of truth" concerning the condition of insulation.

High-potential tests may be performed with the rotor in place or with it removed. It is advantageous to consult and follow the manufacturer's recommendations and schedules, taking into account the operating history of a machine. For example, for a 355-MW, 20-kV generator unit, General Electric recommends removing the rotor every 5 years and performing high-potential tests every 2 ½ years.

To prepare the tests, the machine terminals are disconnected from the busbars, the neutral connection is broken so that each phase winding may be subjected to test voltage with the other two phase windings, and the rotor (if in place) is grounded. Protective ground cables should be connected to all disconnected busbars and the neutral conductor. Each phase winding is short-circuited so that uniform test voltage will be applied to each end. A test lead is attached to each phase winding and secured and terminated so that a convenient connection to the high-voltage test lead and to ground can be made. Temporary insulation, plastic bags over sharp points, and tie offs must be arranged to give proper clearance for the test voltage. A minimum clearance of 7 in. per 10 kV, 60 Hz, is recommended for base conductor clearance.

The 60-Hz ac high-potential test applies stresses to machine winding as near as possible to those that normally exist under operating conditions. Even though the 60-Hz test is preferred over dc or 0.1-Hz tests, there are few ac sets of adequate size (kVA) available to perform this test on large machines. The size of the test set may be calculated from the following formula: $kVA = 0.377 CE^2$, where C is the machine winding capacitance in microfarads and E is the maximum test voltage in kilovolts. For example, in service operation on a 13.8-kV machine, each phase winding is stressed at $13.8/\sqrt{3}$ or approximately 8 kV to ground with mid-point only at 4 kV to ground. The ends of windings T4, T5, and T6 (Figure 5-12(a)) are nearly at zero stress. The insulation toward the ends T4, T5, and T6 could be worn and still not fail in service unless damage to the winding becomes severe. During the high-voltage test the windings are short-circuited. The high-voltage lead is connected to both T1 and T4 and later to T2 and T5 and T3 and T6. Both ends of the winding are subjected to the same potential, full-test voltage. Weak points of any part of the winding that might not fail in service would now fail under test. This is desirable since worn-out coils should be repaired or replaced to avoid unexpected and sudden failure.

Protection against accidental application of overvoltage can be provided by connecting an air gap voltmeter with an appropriate series resistor between the high-voltage test lead and ground. A setting of 2 to 5 kV above the high-voltage test value will provide necessary protection. The test connection is shown in Figure 5–12(b).

High-potential tests are used in connection with manufacture, repair or reconditioning, and routine testing of machines. The following test procedures and safety precautions are important while conducting these tests:

- Keep everyone from coming in contact with any part of the circuit or apparatus while the test is being conducted.

- After the test has been made, never touch the winding tested until it has been properly connected to ground to remove any static charge it may have retained.
- All leads to the circuit being tested should be connected to one terminal of the source of the test voltage. All leads to all other circuits and all metal parts should be connected to ground. No leads are to be left unconnected for high-potential tests as this may cause an extremely severe strain at some point of the winding.

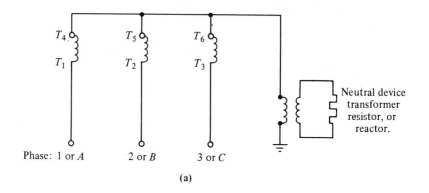

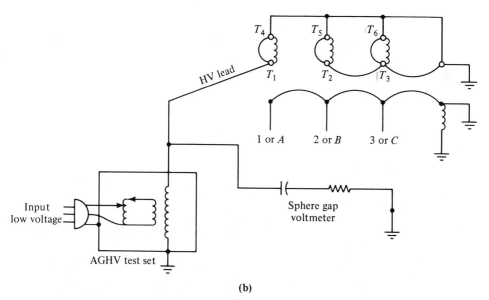

FIGURE 5–12.

AC high-potential test connections: (a) Typical in-service generator stator connections; (b) ac high-potential test connection for generator connection.

- The ac potential test voltage shall be 60 Hz. When making a test, the voltage should be increased to full voltage as rapidly as consistent with its value. This voltage should be maintained for 1 min. After completion of the test, the voltage should be reduced at a rate that will bring it to one-quarter value or less in not more than 15 s.
- The effective voltages to apply to motors and generators are listed in Table 5–8.

POWER FACTOR TEST

This method allows successful ground-insulation tests on machine individual stator phase windings. This test is usually conducted up to and including 100 percent line to ground voltage. The power factor is the ratio of the stator insulation loss and volt-amperes at a specified test voltage. This can be represented by the equation

$$PF = \frac{W_s}{V_a I_a}$$

where W_s = watts loss
I_a = charging current in milliamperes
V_a = test voltage in kilovolts

This test is performed with a power factor test set which is similar to the PF test sets shown under transformer section. The evaluation of the test data is best interpreted by comparing with previous test results or by comparing test results among phases or with those test results obtained on units of similar manufacture and rating. It is generally found that machines up to 24 kV will have a power factor of 3 percent or less, depending upon the insulation system. The power factor tip-up test may also be performed to further evaluate the insulation system. The tip-up test is defined as the increase in power factor as voltage is increased from 2 kV to operating voltage.

DISSIPATION FACTOR TAN δ TEST

The machine winding may be considered as consisting of capacitance and resistance and can be represented by the equivalent circuit shown in Figure 5–13.

The active (resistive) power and reactive (capacitive) power can be represented by the following equations:

$$P_R = I^2R = \frac{E^2R}{R^2} = \frac{E^2}{R}$$

TABLE 5–8.
ALTERNATING HIGH-VOLTAGE TEST VALUES FOR MOTORS AND GENERATORS

Type of Motor and Generator	Motors and Generators Reconditioned but Not Rewound or Restored to Original Condition		Motors and Generators Rewound and Restored to Original Condition (Acceptance)	
	Armature	Field	Armature	Field
Above 250 V and above ½ hp	0.67 (2E + 1,000) V	7 times the excitation voltage but not less than 1,000 V or more than 2,300 V	(2E + 1,000) V	10 times the excitation voltage but not less than 1,500 V or more than 3,500 V
Below 250 V and below ½ hp	600 V	600 V	900 V	900 V

$$P_C = I^2 X_C = \frac{E^2}{X_C{}^2} X_C = \frac{E^2}{X_C} = wCE^2$$

where P_R = active power
P_C = reactive power
C = capacitance in microfarads
R = resistance in ohms
X_C = capacitive reactance in ohms
I_R = resistive current
I_C = capacitive current
w = radian frequency

The active power of the resistance in this equivalent circuit represents all capacitor losses. These losses occur on the surface and in the interior of the dielectric. The power P determines the losses of the capacitor. The dissipation factor tan δ measuring bridge (Schering bridge) is designed to simulate the capacitor (the machine winding) shown in Figure 5–13 by a series connection of

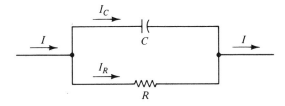

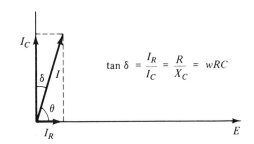

$$\tan \delta = \frac{I_R}{I_C} = \frac{R}{X_C} = wRC$$

FIGURE 5–13.
Machine winding equivalent circuit and vector diagram.

resistance R_s and capacitance C_s. The corresponding values for the series connection for a given frequency can be converted by the following formula:

$$R_s = R \left(\frac{\tan^2 \delta}{1 + \tan^2 \delta} \right)$$

$$C_s = C \left(1 + \tan^2 \delta \right)$$

The losses measured by the Schering bridge and the tan δ can be represented as the following:

$$P = EI_R$$

$$\tan \delta = \frac{I_R}{I_C}$$

or $\quad\quad\quad P = EI_C \tan \delta = wE^2 C \tan \delta$

Substituting the value of C_s in the preceding equation, we have

$$P = wC_s E^2 \, \frac{\tan \delta}{1 + \tan^2 \delta}$$

For small values of tan δ (i.e., less than 1) we can neglect $\tan^2 \delta$; we have

$$P = wC_s E^2 \tan \delta$$

The value of C_s is measured as C_x by the Schering bridge. The resistance and the inductance of the leads have to be considered for high capacitances and resistances; otherwise they are negligible.

PARTIAL DISCHARGE TEST

The measurement of partial discharges is a modern, highly sensitive method. Small charge fluctuations (in coulombs) are measured by testing the corresponding current variations. By this method the weak points of the insulation are measured directly. However, this method does not provide information on those points of insulation where partial discharge has not occurred.

CHAPTER 6

MISCELLANEOUS TESTS FOR ELECTRICAL EQUIPMENT

6-1 INTRODUCTION

This chapter covers miscellaneous tests for electrical equipment and apparatus. For purposes of this text, these tests are defined as those that cannot be categorized under direct current or alternating current. Moreover, these tests are special field tests that are conducted to assess equipment and insulation system integrity, to locate faults, or to determine if the equipment can safely operate during its intended life.

Miscellaneous tests consist of detection of combustible gases in transformers, acidity and interfacial tests for insulating liquids, cable fault locating methods, infrared inspection, resonant testing, and others. Even though some of these tests may use dc or ac power, they have been categorized separately as miscellaneous tests. They are not normally conducted as dc or ac tests for preventive maintenance. They may be conducted on electrical equipment as desired, in addition to the tests discussed under dc and ac tests in Chapters 4 and 5, respectively. The purpose of this chapter is to explain the test methods briefly and their application to electrical equipment. It is recommended that the reader consult the manufacturer of the electrical equipment under test for detailed instructions for carrying out these tests in the field. There may be some tests that can only be performed at the factory or repair shop facilities.

6-2 TRANSFORMERS

The transformers dielectric system consists of insulating liquids and cellulose materials. Under normal use, insulating liquids such as oil deteriorate and liberate certain combustible gases. The detection, analysis, and identification of these gases can be very helpful in determining the condition of the transformer. There are two basic methods of detecting these gases: (1) combustible gas analysis, and (2) gas chromatography (gas in oil).

297

COMBUSTIBLE GAS ANALYSIS

Combustible gas analyzers can be used to test periodically for indication of internal conditions in power transformers with a nitrogen seal or conservator system. In several cases, incipient problems can be detected and corrective action taken in an economical and timely manner. This section gives guidelines for periodic maintenance by gas analysis test.

The combustible gas test has proved to be a particularly valuable means of detecting incipient low-energy faults in transformers, since such faults normally cannot be detected by electrical tests. Early detection of faults is particularly important because it allows time for planned corrective action to be taken and, therefore, minimizes the chances of damage to the units and emergency outages.

It has been established that electrical faults in transformers are invariably accompanied by the generation of a variety of combustible gases as a result of the local decomposition of the surrounding insulated materials. On large units having conservator tanks, protective relays are triggered by gas evolution, but such devices are relatively insensitive indicators of incipient malfunction because they are designed so they will not operate on relatively large accumulations of atmospheric gases, which may normally evolve from transformer oil when heated.

To utilize fault gas generation as an indicator of incipient malfunction, the detector should be specifically designed for combustible gas detection. Quantitative tests can be satisfactorily made using portable gas detectors. Total combustible gas (TCG) can be determined in the field or analyzed in the laboratory.

The recommended program for the performance of quantitative testing for combustible gas on power transformers and regulators with nitrogen seal or conservator system is as shown in Table 6–1. A new transformer should be tested within a week after energization. If it is not gassing and does not start gassing, subsequent tests should be made at progressively increasing intervals until the 12-month normal interval is reached.

To facilitate the combustible gas testing program, all equipment having conservator systems should have a gas sampling line installed from its gas accumulation relay to a ground-level sampling valve. All equipment having a nitrogen blanket should have a gas sampling line installed from the upper portion of the tank to a ground-level sampling valve.

GAS CHROMATOGRAPHY

The gas chromatography method provides analysis of the dissolved gases in the transformer oil. This method identifies the individual gases present in the oil and their relative quantities as a percentage or part per million (ppm) of the total gas present. This analysis of each gas present provides a useful tool in determining

TABLE 6–1.
TRANSFORMER GAS EVALUATION

Percent Combustible Gas	Evaluation
0–1	Check each transformer or regulator every 12 months; after three successive 0 to 1% range tests, the testing interval may be extended to 2 years
1–2	Some indication of comtamination or slight incipient fault; take readings at 3- to 6-month intervals to establish a trend
2–5	Take readings at monthly intervals; if trend continues upward, prepare to investigate cause, preferably by internal inspection; gas samples should be sent to the laboratory for quantitative analysis on the gas chromatograph, which may reveal the cause of the gassing
Greater than 5	Remove equipment from service as soon as possible; investigate by internal inspection; prepare to move equipment to service shop

the condition of the transformer. The interpretation of the analysis result has not yet been perfected to a science and is subject to question.

The oils in transformers break down due to the heat generated by the electrical discharges in the transformers. The gases produced are hydrogen, ethane, ethylene, acetylene, carbon dioxide, and carbon monoxide. Carbon dioxide and carbon monoxide are formed when air and water are present. The formation of gases such as hydrogen, ethane, and ethylene requires low-energy input, whereas acetylene requires high-energy input. Therefore, when electrical arcing (high-energy input) takes place, formation of acetylene may be expected.

The gas chromatography method is a laboratory test. However, a new prototype instrument for field application has recently been developed by Westinghouse for the evaluation of the "dissolved gases in oil" detection. This instrument contains two modules—one module extracts the gas from the oil and the other performs a chromatographic analysis on the extracted gas. Full-scale production of these units is being held up until further large-scale field testing is accomplished.

Taking Oil Samples for Gas-in-Oil Analysis

This procedure has been developed to maintain uniformity of all oil samples taken in the field for a laboratory gas-in-oil analysis. Special stainless-steel containers are used for collecting samples of oil for gas-in-oil analysis using the gas chromatograph. These stainless-steel containers are *not* to be used for any other purpose and should be kept clean to eliminate all contaminants and purged with dry air for shipment to the field.

- Use a can to catch overflow oil from the stainless steel container.
- Obtain two lengths of Tygon clear plastic tubing and attach one to each end of the stainless-steel container. Make certain that the tubing between transformer and container is as short as possible.
- Attach the tubing from one end of the stainless-steel container to the sample valve cock on the transformer.
- Hold the stainless-steel container in a vertical position with the length of tubing on the outlet end in the can to catch the overflow oil.
- Open the sampling valve on the transformer.
- Open valve on the inlet side of container.
- Open valve on the outlet side of container and allow the stainless-steel container to fill and overflow into can. At least 1 pint should overflow to assure removal of all bubbles in the sampling system.
- Close top valve (outlet side) first to ensure a contamination-free sample.
- Close bottom valve (inlet side) and then close sampling valve on the transformer.
- Do not wrap any kind of tape around valves or nozzles of the stainless-steel container.
- Forward the sample to the laboratory.

6-3   INSULATING LIQUIDS

Special tests for insulating liquids are discussed next.

ACIDITY TEST

New transformer liquids contain practically no acids if properly refined. The acidity test measures the content of acids formed by oxidation. The acids are directly responsible for sludge formation. These acids precipitate out, as their concentration increases, and become sludge. They also react with metals to form another form of sludge in the transformer.

The acid number of the neutralization number is the milligrams (mg) of potassium hydroxide (KOH) required to neutralize the acid contained in 1 gram (g) of transformer liquid. Test data indicate that the acidity is proportional to the amount of oxygen absorbed by the liquid. Therefore, different transformers would take different periods of time before sledge would begin to appear. Transformers with free air access would have formation of sludge before transformers with conservators; and transformers with conservators would have sludge before transformers bolted tight; and transformers bolted tight would have sludge before transformers with nitrogen over oil. Refer to Table 6–2 for acceptable values of the neturalization number for the various transformer liquids.

Following is a brief description of the Gervin method for the neutralization number test: Pour the oil sample into a glass cylinder furnished with the Gervin test kit. Single doses of potassium hydroxide (KOH) are furnished in sealed ampules with the dosage indicated on the ampules. For example, if the oil level in the glass cylinder is up to mark ten, then number 3 ampules equals 0.3 mg of KOH/gram of oil; a number 6 ampules equals 0.6 mg of KOH, and a number 15 equals 1.5 mg of KOH.

TABLE 6–2.
TRANSFORMER ACCEPTANCE VALUES FOR NEUTRALIZATION
NUMBER, INTERFACIAL TENSION, AND COLOR TESTS

Liquid Type	Test	Satisfactory	Needs Reconditioning
Oil	Neutralization no. (acidity)	0.4	0.4 to 1.0
	IFT	40 dyn/cm	Below 40 dyn/cm
	Color	3.5	Above 3.5
Askarel	Neutralization no. (acidity)	0.05	Above .05
	IFT	40 dyn/cm	Below 40 dyn/cm
	Color	2.0	Above 2.0
Silicone	Neutralization no. (acidity)	0.01	Above 0.01
	IFT	20.8 dyn/cm	
	Color	15 max	Above 15
RTemp	Neutralization no. (acidity)	0.5	Above 0.5
	IFT	30 dyn/cm	Below 30 dyn/cm
R113 (GE)	Neutralization no. (acidity)	0.2 max	Above 0.2
Wecosol	Neutralization no. (acidity)	.25 or less	Above .25

The pint bottles contain neutral solution to be put in the measured sample before adding the KOH. This solution "washes" the oil, and the KOH can then act on the acids more readily. The netural solution contains a color-changing indicator. If any KOH is left after the acids are neutralized, the indicator is pink. But if the KOH is all used up, the indicator is colorless like water.

INTERFACIAL TENSION (IFT)

It should be recognized that the acidity test alone determines conditions under which sludge may form, but does not necessarily indicate that actual sludging conditions exist. The IFT (interfacial tension) test is employed as an indication of the sludging characteristics of power transformer insulating liquid. It is a test of interfacial tension of water against liquid, which is different from surface tension in that the surface of the water is in contact with liquid instead of air. The attraction between the water molecules at the interface is influenced by the presence of polar molecules in the liquid in such a way that the presence of more polar compounds causes lower interfacial tension. The polar compounds are sludge particles or their predecessors.

The test measures the concentration of polar molecules in suspension and in solution in the liquid, and thus gives an accurate measurement of dissolved sludge components in the liquid long before any sludge is precipitated. It has been established that an interfacial tension of less than 15 dynes per centimeter (dyn/cm) almost invariably shows sludging. An IFT of 15 to 22 dyn/cm is generally indicative of no sludging. For maintenance purposes IFT values are shown in Table 6–2 for transformer liquids.

COLOR TEST

This test consists of transmitting light through oil samples and comparing the color observed with a standard color chart. The color chart ranges from 0.5 to 8, with the color number 1 used for new oil. The accepted color number for used oil is 4, and for askarel it is 2. Color test values are listed in Table 6–2.

6-4   CABLES AND ACCESSORIES

The special tests conducted on cables and accessories are classified as (1) cable fault locating methods, and (2) phasing and identification. These test methods may involve dc and ac voltages and are conducted for a specific purpose.

CABLE FAULT LOCATING METHODS

This section describes the existing methods and techniques used for fault location. Faults may vary widely, and similar faults may exhibit different symptoms depending upon the cable type, operating voltage, soil condition, and so on. Basically, faults can be considered to be shorts, opens, or nonlinear. A *short* is defined as a fault when the conductor is shorted to ground, neutral, or another phase with a low impedance path. An *open* fault is defined as when the conductor is physically broken and no current flows at or beyond the point of break. The *nonlinear* type of fault exhibits the characteristics of an unfaulted conductor at low voltages but shows a short at operating or higher voltages.

Fault-location methods can be divided into two general catagories: terminal techniques and tracing techniques.

Terminal Techniques

These involve measuring some electrical characteristics of the faulted conductor from one of the cable terminals and comparing it with unfaulted conductor characteristics in terms of the distance of the fault. The effectiveness of this method is a function of the accuracy of installation records. The terminal techniques category can be further subdivided in terms of the actual methods employed, which are bridge, radar, and resonance methods.

BRIDGE METHODS
Various types of bridge configurations may be used to locate faults. The most common are the Murry loop and the capacitance bridge. The Murry loop bridge uses a proportional measure so that it is not necessary to know the actual cable resistance. Its principle of operation involves a continuous loop of cable to form the two arms of the bridge. It is necessary to have an unfaulted conductor available to form such a loop. Also, it requires a low-resistance jumper to be installed at the far end of the cable. The Murry loop bridge connections are shown in Figure 6–1. When the bridge is balanced, the distance to the fault can be found by the following expression:

$$X = 2 \times L \left(\frac{A}{A + B} \right)$$

The capacitance bridge technique simply measures the capacitance from one end of the faulted cable to ground and compares it in terms of the distance with the capacitance of the unfaulted conductor in the same cable. The connection diagram for a capacitance bridge is shown in Figure 6–2.

In lieu of a bridge, the charging current of faulted cable and unfaulted cable can be compared, using several hundred volts or several thousand volts of 60-hertz (Hz) supply voltage. The connection diagram is shown in Figure 6–3. The distance L_1 to the fault is given by the expression $L_1 = L_2 (I_1/I_2)$, where I_1 is the current in the faulted conductor, I_2 is the current in the unfaulted conductor, and L_2 is the length of the unfaulted conductor.

The application of bridge methods can be used on all types of cables. The Murry loop bridge is effective where the parallel fault resistance is low or the bridge voltage is high. It is ineffective on open faults. Open faults can be located with the capacitance bridge. The major drawbacks of the bridge method are the following:

- Requires access to both ends of the cable.
- Connection must be of low resistance.
- All lead lengths must be accounted for.
- Cables must be of the same size.

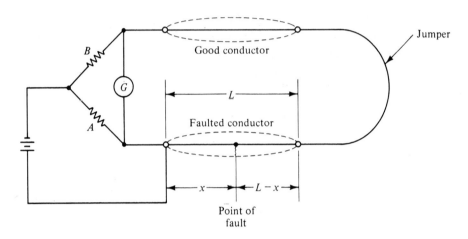

FIGURE 6–1.
Murry loop bridge method.

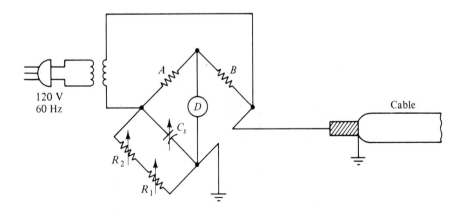

FIGURE 6–2.
Capacitance bridge measurement method.

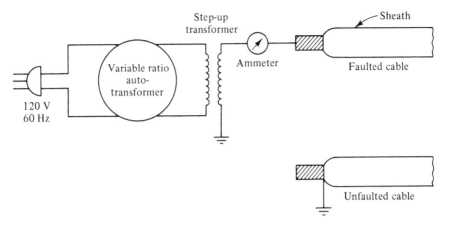

FIGURE 6–3.
Charging current method for fault location.

- Requires considerable operator skill.
- Difficult to use on branched systems.

RADAR METHOD

The radar (reflection or pulse-echo) method is based upon the measurement of the time that it takes the pulse to reach a fault and reflect back. The distance d of the fault for uniform cable can be obtained from the expression $d = vt/2$, where v is propagation velocity and t is the time it takes for the pulse to travel to the fault and back. There are two types of output pulse duration employed in radar methods.

The short-duration pulse type is most commonly used in radar test sets for testing power cables. The pulse duration is short in comparison to propagation time to the fault. The width of the pulse is usually wide enough to be able to be observed on the oscilloscope. Practically, the pulse width must be greater than 1 percent of the transit time for the entire cable length under test. Most commercial equipment has provisions for changing the pulse width depending on cable length. The pulse magnitudes are very small, usually on the order of few volts. The short pulse does not lend itself well to the interpretation of data because of reflections from splices or the nonuniformity of cable size.

The long-pulse system employs long step pulses as compared to the transit time of signal from one end of the cable to the fault and back. Any discontinuities in cable are seen as changes in the voltage level of the step pulse. It is easier to interpret the data in a long-pulse system; that is, the faults can be differentiated from splices, and changes in cable size can be easily observed.

In radar systems the scope trace shows the transmitted and reflected signal. The separation of the two signals is measured and multiplied by the scope calibration factor to give the transit time. The reflected wave can be expressed in terms of the transmitted wave and circuit constants as follows:

$$l_r = \frac{R - Z}{R + Z} l_t$$

where l_r = reflected wave
l_t = transmitted wave
R = resistance at the end of the line
Z = impedance of the line

If the line is open-circuited, then $R = \infty$ and the reflected wave is $l_r = l_t$. Therefore, the reflected wave is of the same magnitude and same polarity as the transmitted wave. If the line is short-circuited, $R = 0$ and the reflected wave is $l_r = -l_t$. Therefore, the reflected wave in this case is of equal magnitude to the transmitted wave but 180° out of phase. These two conditions are shown in Figure 6–4.

The radar can be applied to all types of cable systems provided the propagation velocity is constant along the length of the cable. The radar system does not work very well with nonlinear faults. However, it can be used when the nonlinear fault impedance is burned to a low resistance value. To provide this flexibility, three major variations of radar system are available: the arc-

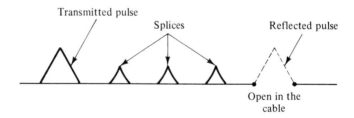

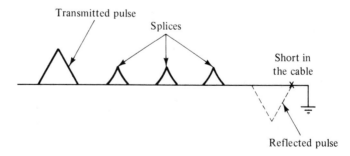

FIGURE 6–4.

Typical wave forms for open- and short-circuit conditions in cable.

radar system, the free oscillation system, and the differential radar system. The arc radar uses a high-voltage pulse system so that the high-impedance (non-linear) faults can be burned down until they appear as shorts and the radar pulse can be reflected from the arc short. The free oscillation system is also used for high-impedance faults in which the breakdown of the arc causes a pulse to be transmitted down the cable. In this method the cable end at which measurements are made is terminated in a high impedance (i.e., open) so that the pulse formed at the arc is reflected from the open end to the short at the arc and back to the open end. This reflection back and forth continues until the energy is completely absorbed by the cable. The period of signal is four times the transit time of the pulse as it travels the distance of the fault. Therefore, the distance to the fault is one-fourth the product of the propagation velocity and transit time. Differential radar is applicable for fault location on branched systems. It is based on the fact that a faulted cable phase is almost always paralleled by an identical unfaulted phase. The radar prints of two phases will be identical, except that part of the print associated with the fault itself. The differential radar signal is applied to both phases simultaneously and the return signals are subtracted. The radar pulse input shows at the point of the fault.

RESONANCE METHOD

The resonance technique is based on the principle of wave reflection. The resonance method for fault location measures the frequency at which the length of the cable between the terminal and the fault resonate. The resonant frequency is inversely proportional to the wavelength. The distance d of the fault can be determined by the following expression:

$$d = \frac{V}{f_r N}$$

where V = propagation velocity
f_r = resonant frequency
N = number of quarter- or half-wavelengths

Normally, quarter-wave resonance is used for locating shorts, in which case $N = 4$, and half-wave resonance is used for locating opens, in which case $N = 2$. The resonance technique uses a frequency generator (or oscillator), which is connected to the end of the faulted cable. The frequency is varied until resonance is reached. At resonance, the voltage changes rapidly from voltage at nonresonance frequency. The voltage will increase for shorts and decrease for opens, respectively.

The minimum frequency required is determined by the cable length, and the maximum frequency is determined by the distance to the nearest point at which a fault may occur. For insulated cable the phase shift governs the speed of the transmitted and reflected wave to the fault and back. The phase shift is a function of the dielectric constant of the insulating material. Usually, the velocity of propagation for insulated cables varies between one-third to one-forth of the velocity of propagation of bare conductors, which is 984 feet per microsecond (ft/μs). Therefore, the velocity for cable will be somewhere between 328 to 246 ft/μs. Therefore, for each insulating medium its dielectric constant must be known for fault location. The relationship between frequency and distance to the fault is given by the following expression:

$$d = \frac{466N}{f_r K}$$

where N = number of quarter- or half-wavelengths
f_r = resonance frequency in megahertz
K = dielectric constant of cable
d = distance to the fault

This method can be used on all types of cables and works well on branched systems. It does not work very well with nonlinear faults.

Tracer Techniques

Trace techniques are those which involve placing an electrical signal on the faulted feeder from one or both ends, which can be traced along the cable length and detected at the fault by a change in signal characteristics. The following methods are available under this classification:

- Tracing current.
- Audio frequency (tone tracing).
- Impulse (thumper) voltage.
- Earth gradient.

TRACING CURRENT METHOD
In this application both dc and ac methods are employed. This method can be used for fault location on a branched system as well as on a straight uniform cable system. The fault current is injected into the circuit formed by the faulted conductor and the ground, and a detector is then used to measure the cable current at selected manhole locations. This technique is applicable where fault resistance is low or the voltage of the test set is high enough to send sufficient current through the faulted conductor. This method is mostly applicable for duct line installations, because it is sufficient to know the fault between manholes, since the entire section of cable between manholes must be replaced when faulted.

The major consideration for use of this method is to assure that substantial amounts of return current is via the ground path rather than the neutral. If all the current flows through the neutral, current seen by the detector is canceled for three-conductor cables, and there is no output from detector. This is very important for insulated neutral cables, such as paper insulated lead covered (PILC), where it is necessary to assure neutral to ground contact between the point of the measurement and the fault.

The tracing dc method uses a modulated dc power supply ranging from 500 volts (V) to 20 kilovolts (kV) and current ranging from 0.25 to 12.5 amperes (A). The detector can be either an electromagnetically coupled circuit using a pickup coil and a galvanometer to detect directional signal, or test prods may be used on the cable sheath, using a drop-of-potential circuit with a galvanometer for signal-direction detection.

The tracing ac method uses a 25- or 60-Hz modulated transmitter consisting of 100 percent induction regulation or a constant-current transformer. The detectors can consist of either a split core current transformer and an ammeter or a sheath drop detection circuit consisting of test prods and a millivolt meter. The test-set range is from 15 to 450 kVA, and audio amplifiers are available with output meters, headsets, or speakers.

This method applies to direct buried, insulated cable for a short to ground fault. It is not very effective for other types of faults or cable configurations. Audio frequency (tone tracing) can be used to locate phase to ground faults (or to neutral) in concentric neutral cables if the neutral can be isolated from the ground so that the fault return current flows through the ground. If the neutral cannot be isolated, substantial fault return current may flow through the neutral, canceling the magnetic fields and thus reducing the pickup sensitivity. This technique can be used equally well to locate and identify cables. Because of its application to insulated cable, audio frequency is most commonly used for finding secondary faults. This method is very effective for faults that are near zero resistance. It is not as effective for resistance faults above a few ohms. This method is particularly applicable to low-voltage class systems.

AUDIO FREQUENCY (TONE TRACING) METHOD
In this method, audio frequency is injected in the fault circuit formed by the faulted cable and the ground. The flow of current through the conductor causes a magnetic field, which exists both in air and ground. The magnetic field can be sensed by using a simple magnetic loop antenna. Moreover, the magnetic field can be resolved into horizontal and vertical components for predicting antenna orientation. The loop antenna that responds to the horizontal component of magnetic field has maximum excitation directly above the cable, whereas the loop antenna that responds to the vertical component of the magnetic field has minimum excitation. Also, the magnetic field varies in the vicinity of the fault. The magnetic field characteristics change beyond the fault because of no current flow, and therefore the horizontally polarized antenna output falls off rapidly. The change in characteristics of the vertical component of the magnetic field is not as pronounced when moving beyond the point of the fault location. The magnetic fields are a function of the current in the cable and therefore essentially constant along the cable route.

The receiver sensitivity is a function of antenna gain to obtain maximum output. The receiver employs high-gain amplifiers for the same purpose. The detectors are usually made of exploring coils.

IMPULSE (THUMPER) METHOD
This method consists of using a charge capacitor to transmit a high-energy pulse between the faulted conductor and ground. The pulse creates an arc at the fault, which in turn heats the surrounding air, and the energy is released as an audible thump. The fault location can be found by listening to the acoustical thump or by tracing the magnetic field generated by the arc. A functional diagram of fault location using the impulse method is shown in Figure 6–5.

The impulse source is a capacitive discharge circuit consisting of power supply, capacitor bank and high-voltage switch. A typical capacitor discharge (thumper) test set is shown in Figure 6–6. The impulse signal can be detected by means of a magnetic loop antenna, a microphone, an earth gradient detector, or a seismic transducer. The relationship between signal loudness and duration depends on the physical situation. The tendency is for the loudness to increase with the duration; however, beyond a certain point the impact on the loudness is negligible. This method has been applied to both secondary and high-voltage systems. The major application of the impulse method is to faults where an arc is readily formed. This method can be made effective for faults down to zero resistance (dead shorts), depending upon the source of surge tracing methods,

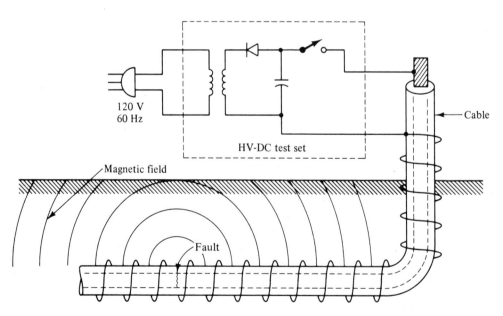

FIGURE 6–5.
Impulse (thumper) method for fault location.

FIGURE 6–6.
Capacitor discharge (thumper) test set, 60 kilovolts with 100-multi-ampere burn capacity. (Courtesy of Hipotronics, Brewster, N.Y.)

because a dead short fault does not produce a thump. Signal detection can be divided into the following methods:

- *Acoustic signal pickup:* In this case the fault of high resistance is arcing over due to the periodic voltage pulses, which makes a very loud thumping sound. Detection can be very simply accomplished by patrolling the line and listening to the noise of the voltage discharge. Audio amplifiers with suitable pickup of electronic type, headphones, or a stethoscope can be used.

- *Electromagnetic pickup:* When a fault of zero resistance (i.e., fault impedance is low compared to surge impedance) is being located, then of course there will be no noise. Also, even faults of high resistance when surrounded by mud and water will not give off loud noise. Faults of line to line or conductor to sheath, where the outer sheath is not broken, will not give off any loud noise. For these cases, a detector that traces the impulse signal to the fault by electromagnetic coupling can be used. It consists of pickup coil and a detector. The detector amplifies the signal, and detection can then be made by galvanometer. It is effective for duct lay and nonlead buried cable.

- *Impulse current pickup:* In this method impulse current signals are derived from a linear coupler, which can be incorporated in the surge generator, or an external linear coupler can be used with any surge generator or high-voltage dc test set. The linear coupler in both cases is in the earth return (cable sheath) circuit to the surge generator or high-voltage dc test set. High-resistance, flashing, and intermittent flashing faults are located using the external pulses generated by the high-voltage surge generator. The signals generated are stored digitally in the memory of the test set. The stored wave form can be extracted continuously from the digital memory and displayed on a low-speed oscilloscope. Measurements of fault position can be directly measured digitally in microseconds, thus calculating an accurate estimate of the distance of the fault location by the following formula:

$$\text{Distance to fault } L = \frac{T \times V_p}{2}$$

where T is in microseconds, L is in feet, and V_p is the velocity of propagation of electromagnetic waves for the cable dielectric.

EARTH GRADIENT METHOD

This method locates faults by injecting a fault current into the faulted circuit formed by the conductor and earth return. The current spreads into the ground, and potential is developed in the ground between the fault and current injection point. The voltage drop between any two points on the ground surface can be measured. Usually, the direction of the voltage drop points toward the fault location. As the fault is approached by moving along the cable length, the voltmeter deflection decreases until the null point is achieved directly over the fault location. However, when the fault location is passed, the voltmeter deflection increases again. In this method precise location of the cable is necessary for pinpointing the fault location.

Where precise routing of cable is not known, a dc or pulsed fault current source may be used to locate the fault using the earth gradient technique. In this case the meter direction will always be toward the fault location. To minimize difficulties and make judicious use of time in locating the fault, a simple procedure is usually followed; the negative probe is always inserted first and the positive probe is moved to obtain maximum positive deflection of the voltmeter. By following this procedure the deflection will then always be in the general direction of the fault, and fault tracing can proceed in sequence until the fault is located. This method at best is time consuming, and at worst it will not work at all, especially when cable lay is not known. The limitation of this method is the measurement sensitivity, because ground potential is a function of both cable depth and fault distance.

The fault current source can be an ac tone, a pulse, or dc voltage. With an ac tone, the voltmeter will show an amplitude of large magnitude on either side of the fault, whereas the amplitude will fall off as the fault location is passed. Also, care must be taken to minimize 60-Hz interference. The dc source is most commonly used, which provides sufficient current flow through non-linear faults. The pulse source is also similar to the dc source, except that it offers higher fault currents. The earth gradient technique is used to locate conductor to ground faults. This method may not be applicable to concentric neutral cables because much of the current returns through the neutral rather than the ground, making measurements rather difficult. Therefore, the earth gradient method is most applicable to insulated wire cables, which are usually found in secondary distribution systems.

A special application of the earth gradient method is the dc sheath potential difference method. In this method a direct current from a 6-V battery is passed through a short length of a faulted lead sheath cable. A voltage drop appears between the faulted conductor and the lead sheath, which can be measured at one of the cable terminals. This connection is shown in Figure 6–7. If the fault resistance is low enough or the internal resistance of the voltmeter is high enough, a voltage will be measured on the unfaulted side of the battery. Therefore, to locate the fault the battery contacts can be moved in the fault direction until fault is located.

Application Guide for Cable Fault Locating

Cable fault locating in the past has been more of an art than a science. The tools used were megohmmeter, shovels, and hacksaws. The common technique for locating faults was the "halving" technique, which can be described as follows: "Cut cable at halfway point after excavation of a hole, check resistance with a megohmmeter. If the value of resistance is acceptable, move to one-quarter the length of the line, then to one-eighth length, and so on. Repeat the same procedure on the second half of the remaining length of cable until the precise point of fault is found." The halving technique is time consuming and costly compared to the modern methods that are now available for fault location. Instruments are available today to, first, find the fault, second, localize the fault, and, third, pinpoint the fault. To achieve these objectives, the following

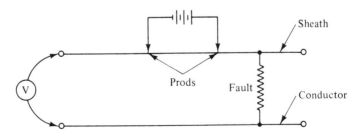

FIGURE 6–7.
DC sheath potential difference method.

practical application guide is offered for fault locating using the terminal and tracer methods on transmission and distribution circuits. A summary is given in Table 6–3.

PRIMARY CABLE SYSTEM
Sheathed Cable: The faults occurring in this cable may be between phases or between phase and sheath. The fault may have minimum resistance (direct short), or may have high resistance (shunt resistance). Because of the resistance of the fault, wave characteristics are different when using reflection methods. When the fault has minimum resistance, the reflected wave will appear as a negative pulse; that is, all energy will be reflected at the short, giving a maximum amplitude. If either of these conditions is measured between the faulted phase and the good phase or sheath, a negative pulse of lesser amplitude may

TABLE 6–3.
SUMMARY OF CABLE FAULT LOCATING METHODS

Method	Criteria	Parallel Fault (Shorts)	Series Fault (Open)
TERMINAL MEASUREMENT TECHNIQUES			
Bridge:			
Murry loop	Uses cable length sensitivity	Low resistance	—
Capacitance bridge	Uses capacitance from conductor to sheath	High resistance	High resistance
Radar:			
Pulse	Produces a short-duration pulse	Low resistance	High resistance
Resonance	Produces a standing wave	Low resistance	High resistance
TRACER TECHNIQUES			
Tracing current	DC current AC current	Low resistance Low resistance	— —
Audio frequency	Transmitting audio tones	Low resistance	—
Impulse (thumper)	Transmission of high-energy pulse	Low resistance	High resistance
Earth gradient	Drop at potential	Low resistance	—

at times be observed. For fault values of 10 ohms (Ω) or less, the wave does not reflect past the fault point.

High-resistance faults occur in parallels, with surge impedance. The negative reflected wave amplitude of these types of faults is a function of impedance rather than resistance alone. Typical faults in the range of 500- to 1,500-Ω resistance can be measured readily with a 1,000-V or above megohm tester. Faults that are within a few percent of the surge impedance must then be observed by means of a pulse amplifier.

Concentric Neutral: The faults in the concentric neutral may be an open conductor or a series resistance fault. The characteristics of an open conductor fault are marked by a positive pulse when observing between the conductor and the concentric neutral. An open in the concentric neutral when observing with a good phase will also appear as a positive pulse similar to the open conductor reflected wave. The series-type fault is characteristic of water penetration through pinholes in the polyethylene insulation system. The reflection of the pulse wave will appear as an open condition (i.e., positive pulse), but its amplitude will depend upon the state of deterioration of the cable system. In general, the resistance necessary to reflect full wave energy decreases as the wire size increases.

SECONDARY CABLE SYSTEM

The types of cables found in the secondary distribution system are usually concentric neutral, duplex and triplex cables using direct buried installations. They are subject to the same type of faults as discussed for the primary cable system. The dc resistance is typically high, in the range of 1,000 to 2,000 Ω to the ground. Therefore, reflection between conductors and the ground usually provides very little useful information, thus rendering reflection methods ineffective.

SPLICES

Splices in cables represent a decrease in capacitance and an increase in inductance. The reflected wave will appear as a small, rounded positive pulse followed by a pointed overshoot whose amplitude is characteristic of the splice.

LINE TAPS

A tap appears as a negative pulse with a small positive overshoot having an amplitude proportional to its length. The end of the tap is indicated by the positive pulse that follows the negative pulse. The far terminal of the line will be observed on the same trace, depending upon whether it is open or shorted. The distance of these terminals (i.e., line tap and line far end) will overlap, and to positively locate the fault, it will be necessary to take readings from a number of terminals.

CAPACITORS

A power factor connection capacitor provides a low impedance path to radar frequencies. When observed between two phases, it will appear as a negative pulse (direct short) with a positive overshoot.

CHANGE IN WIRE SIZE

A change in wire size affects the reflected wave. When wire size increases, its resistance decreases, giving a negative pulse. The amplitude of this pulse is less than the line tap pulse amplitude.

CHANGE IN DIELECTRIC MATERIAL

A change in dielectric material affects the propagation velocity constant (PCV) inversely by the square root of the dielectric constant of the insulation material. It can be expressed as $PVC = 1/\sqrt{e}$, where e is the dielectric constant of the insulation material. An increase in PVC will produce a decrease in surge impedance, thus yielding a negative pulse. Again, the amplitudes are smaller than the line-tap pulse amplitude.

LOAD COILS

High resistance values, such as in series resistors and load coils, appear as open to short-duration pulses. When testing for locating faults, it may become necessary to disconnect such loads, or it is possible to troubleshoot loaded circuits by testing from alternate load locations.

MULTIPLE FAULTS

Multiple faults in series may or may not be located, depending on the characteristics of the various faults involved. If the resistance of the first fault is low (direct short), all the pulse energy will be dissipated into this fault, thereby not allowing any other faults to be observed downstream. If the fault resistance is relatively high, two or more faults may be seen simultaneously. However, the amplitude of each fault pulse will be progressively smaller. Test the cable in sections to locate where multiple faults are expected.

PHASING AND IDENTIFICATION

Phasing methods can be classified as follows:

- Voltage to ground method.
- Current indication method.
- Phase markers.
- Color coding of conductors.
- Phasing procedures for closing loops.
- Phasing procedures for making splices.

Voltage to Ground Method

This method consists of a voltage with current limiter and voltage-indicating device. These devices can consist of the following:

- Battery with bell, buzzer, or lamp.
- Test lamp with an existing grounded secondary.
- Coded phasing set.
- Phasing sets with separate source and indicator.

When the voltage source and indicating device are in the same housing unit, phasing can be done by placing a ground on one conductor at the terminal point and picking up the ground at the work point. When the source voltage and indicating device are separate, the voltage can be applied at the terminal point and the indicating device used at the work point to identify the conductor. The requirement for the voltage source is that it should be high enough to overcome contact resistance usually in the range of 45 V.

The indicating device should be such that it draws sufficient current to prevent false indication through leakage resistance or cable capacitance. Phasing sets are no different than components already described. The phasing set source is usually connected between phase and ground at the terminal point and the indicator used at the work point. The source is moved to the second phase, and then to the third, and so on, until all phases are identified. One method of identifying three phases is to apply source voltage, say, to phase A and ground, and a ground to phase B, and nothing to phase C. At the work location, phase A will show voltage to ground, phase B will show voltage from B to A, and phase C will show no voltage at all. This method is not as reliable when transformers remain connected to the cable system being identified.

Another extension of the phasing set is the coded phasing transmitter. The coded transmitter phasing set is a motor-driven drum switch that has three or four contacts. Each contact is coded to close separately once, twice, and so on, respectively, through the drum switch. The source voltage is usually 14 V, and the indicator is a 6- to 8-V flash lamp or buzzer equipped with leads and contact prods. The transmitter is connected at the terminal between phase and ground, and the contact leads are connected to the cable being tested as code 1 to phase A, code 2 to phase B, and so on. Phase identification is made by counting the flashes or buzzes of the indicator, when it is held between each conductor and ground.

Current Indication Methods

In this method the cable being tested is short-circuited to ground beyond the test point. The source is ungrounded. The methods used in the category are (1) modulated direct current, and (2) condenser discharge.

The modulated dc method uses exploring coils and a galvanometer. The transmitter operates from a 120-V source ungrounded. A motor-driven mercury switch device transmits series of single pulses on phase A, and a series of double pulses on phase B during alternate minutes. The pulses of phases A and B return through phase C. The position of each conductor in three-conductor cable may be determined by positioning the detectors around the cable and counting the pulses.

The condenser discharge method uses a split core, which is applied around phase ground leads that are connected to the cable leads at the work location. The charged condenser is discharged into phases A and B through a phase transmitter. Phase C is left unconnected. The detection is made in phases A and B by positioning the split core phase receiver with a diode and ammeter. The indication in phases A and B is caused by half-cycles of one polarity due to leading and trailing sides of condenser discharge current.

Phase Marker

Phase markers can be used to identify single-conductor cables in three-phase systems after phases have been established. On three-conductor shielded cable, the phases can be stamped on the sheath or metal tag wired to show rotation of the phases within the sheath. To be useful for phase identification, it is important to maintain these phase markers.

Color Coding of Conductors

Color coding of a conductor's insulation is another method used to identify single-conductor cables. Usually, this method is commonly used in low-voltage (i.e., secondary) service to identify phases. The National Electrical Code has recognized this method of phase identification for systems below 600 V.

Phasing Procedures for Closing Parallel Loops

To show how phasing procedures may be accomplished, consider the following typical section of a power system shown in Figure 6–8. The phasing procedures are the following:

- At substation X, phases A, B, C, are traceable to the generator phases A, B, and C and are known.

- At substation Y on circuit 1, the transformer T1 high-voltage terminal H1 is connected to phase A, H2 to phase B, and H3 to phase C. On the low-voltage side, transformer T1 terminal X1 is connected to phase A, X2 to phase B, and X3 to phase C.

- When circuit 1 is placed in service, phase sequence or rotation is checked with phase meter for phase rotation A-B-C.

- To connect circuit 2 and place it in service, repeat the steps indicated for circuit 1, using transformer T2.

- Before circuit 2 can operate in parallel with circuit 1, live phasing must be performed to ensure proper phases. To do live phasing, the following steps are carried out.

Circuit 1: CB-1, CB-1H, and CB-1X are closed. Circuit 2: CB-2, CB-2H, and CB-2X are open.

Close CB-2 for cable potential tests. If phases check out, proceed to next step.

Close CB-2H to energize transformer. Measure its voltage and perform live phasing check on CB-2H. If phasing check is satisfactory on CB-2H, proceed to next step.

Close CB-2X to pick up load and cause circuit 2 to operate in parallel with circuit 1.

Live phasing could be done across CB-2H and CB-2. As a precaution, the parallel loop should not be closed until phasing has been performed.

Check phases of both bus sections of substation Y, and if they are the same, proceed to next step.

Check voltages of both bus sections, and if they are the same, close the tie breaker 2T to operate circuits 1 and 2 in parallel.

The proceding steps are shown schematically in Figure 6–9.

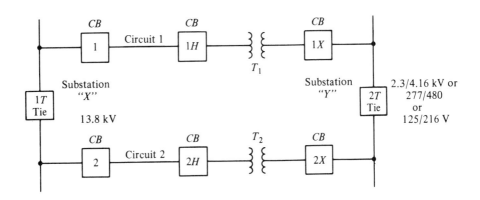

FIGURE 6–8.
Typical section of power system.

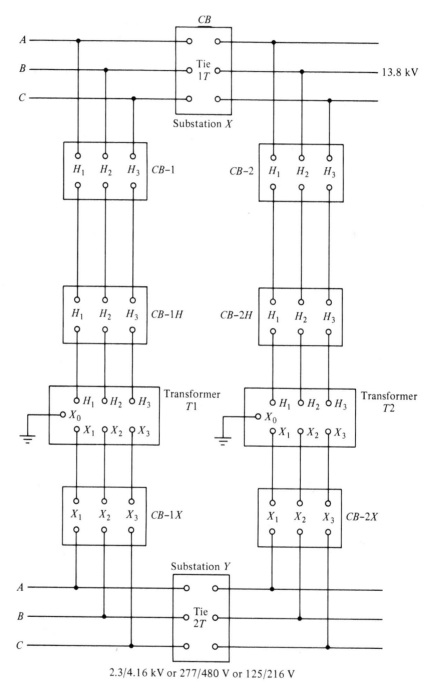

FIGURE 6–9.
Typical phasing arrangement.

Phasing Procedures for Making Splices

To show how phasing can be done for making splices, consider the circuit in Figure 6–10. Assume that the circuit is to be connected and spliced at some point between CB-2 and CB-2H. The following steps need to be taken for making the splices.

- Identify cables from substation X and mark each conductor as follows:

  Phase A with single-band tape.

  Phase B with two-band tape.

  Phase C, no bands at all.

- Identify cables from substation Y and mark each conductor as for substation X.

- After the ends are placed together for phases A, B and C, check continuity from substation X to substation Y for the following:

  Phase A from substation X agrees with phase A from substation Y.

  Phase B from substation X agrees with phase B from substation Y.

  Phase C from substation X agrees with phase C from substation Y.

- Once the three phases are verified, complete the splice.

The tape markings are shown for circuit 1 in Figure 6–9.

6-5   ELECTRICAL SWITCHGEAR

Direct-current and alternating-current voltage tests for electrical switchgear have been discussed in general in Chapters 4 and 5, respectively. This section covers those parts of electrical switchgear that need special consideration.

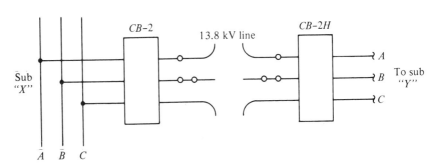

FIGURE 6–10.
Phasing marking for splicing.

INFRARED SCANNING

The infrared scanner is an instrument that provides a real-time televisionlike image on the natural infrared energy being emitted from objects within its field of view. This is in contrast to infrared thermometer-type devices, which view a point or single line. Infrared scanners are not cameras; they do not use infrared film. They work because any object at a temperature above absolute zero is radiating energy proportional to its temperature, and these scanners contain detector material sensitive to infrared energy. Applied to electrical power distribution systems, infrared scanning is one of the few tests that can be performed while the system is energized and under load to determine if weaknesses exist that could lead to power failures and "surprise" electrical outages.

Generally, two specific pieces of equipment are involved when portable, real-time imaging infrared scanners are being considered. These are the Probeye®, manufactured by the Hughes Aircraft Company, Carlsbad, California, and the AGA Thermovision made in Sweden. Both of these are excellent pieces of equipment, the AGA being somewhat more sophisticated and, correspondingly, considerably more expensive. The major difference functionally between the two units is that the AGA Thermovision can provide quantitative information concerning temperature differences between objects in the field of view. This is accomplished by proper operation of controls on the control unit to set isotherms, which can be converted to tempearture differences with accompanying data that are provided with the equipment. The Hughes Probeye does not provide quantitative information. To obtain temperature information on a particular object identified by the Probeye to be overheated, other means are used. These include infrared thermometers for inaccessible objects or those which cannot be touched and contact thermometers.

LIGHTNING ARRESTERS

The maintenance tests that may be made on lightning arresters are insulation resistance measurement, ac high-potential test, and power factor test. These tests have been discussed in detail in Chapters 4 and 5 for various electrical equipment and apparatus. Following are generalized maintenance procedures for lightning arresters for conducting these tests:

- Apply (usually) 2,500 V to line terminal with base grounded with an insulation resistance tester as shown in Figure 6–11. Readings are characteristic of each type of arrester. Some may be as high as 10,000 MΩ; others may be much lower, such as 500 MΩ. The evaluation

® Registered trademark.

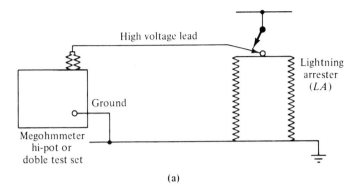

(a)

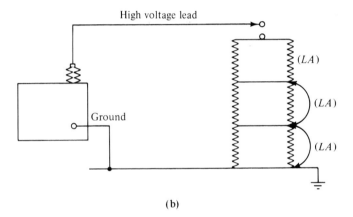

(b)

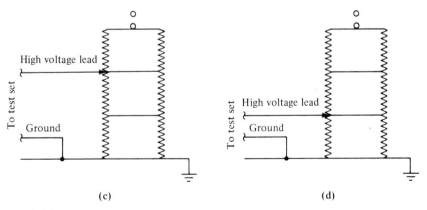

(c)   (d)

FIGURE 6–11.
Lightning arrester test connections: (a) basic test connection for light-ning arrester; (b) to test top arrester in stack; (c) to test middle arrester; (d) to test bottom arrester.

should be based on comparing readings with previous test results or test values of similar equipment.

- Apply ac high-potential test using rated voltage or apply dc high-potential test using 1.7 times rated voltage of lightning arrester.

- The field testing of station-class arresters may be accomplished during normal operation by measuring the leakage current through the arrester. Because of the high impedance to ground characteristics of arresters, an increase in leakage current above normal usually indicates a defective arrester. The evaluation of test data should be based upon comparing the leakage current values with previous values or measurements obtained on similar units or comparative values of the three single-pole arresters in the single installation. It is also recommended that oscillographic measurements be made, if possible, because this will provide the most complete information, which allows for the best comparison.

- Lightning arresters may be tested by applying a power factor test. Again, evaluation of the test data should be based upon comparative analysis with previous test data on the units being tested or similar lightning arresters.

CAPACITORS

Several different tests may be performed on power-factor correction capacitors to determine their suitability for service. From these, users may select tests that they deem practical and necessary. Factors that influence the selection of tests may be the type of banks, such as substation banks or distribution lines, electrical arrangements, failure rate experiences, and others. NEMA Standards Publication CPI-1976, Section 6.06, amended March 1977, "Field Test on Capacitor Units," lists the following options.

Tests to Check the Condition of New Capacitor Units

Before placing in service, perform the following tests:

- Terminal-to-terminal ac or dc high-voltage test at 75 percent of factory routine (production) test voltage.

- Short-circuited terminal-to-case (two-terminal units only) impulse and dc high-voltage test according to voltage rating table. (See Table 6–4.) This section states, "Experience has shown that these tests are not necessary on all capacitor units."

Tests to Check the Condition of a Capacitor Unit after It Has Been in Service

Serviceability of a capacitor unit may be determined by one or more of the following tests in case of trouble or after exposure to possible damage.

- Insulation strength line-to-line and line-to-case high-voltage tests, as described under tests for new capacitors.
- Capacitance measurements by current measurement at known voltage and rated frequency.
- Line-to-line insulation resistance measurement.
- Line-to-case insulation resistance measurement.
- Liquid tightness at 75%C.
- Line-to-case and line-to-line insulation power factor.

NEMA Standard CPI-1976, amended March 1977, provides options that enable a user to develop a test program suitable to its needs. The discharge resistor measurements and calculations from current measurements at low voltage can be compared readily with manufacturers' values and serve as a reference for future comparison.

TABLE 6–4.

CAPACITOR AC TO DC HIGH-VOLTAGE FIELD TESTS, REFERENCE NEMA CPI-6.06 AND CPI-5.10

Line to Line
　AC and dc test voltage = 75% of factory routine (production) test
　　AC: 0.75 × 2E volts = 1.5E volts (E = nameplate rating); ac volts should be sinusoidal, 20-70 Hz and 10-s withstand; energize and deenergize capacitor at voltage not to exceed E.
　　DC: 0.75 × 4.3E volts = 3.2E volts; duration of test including time to charge capacitor should not exceed 15 s to avoid possibility of damaging built-in discharge resistors
Line to Case
　Apply dc volts according to following tabulation (ac volts not listed in this tabulation, CPI-6.06 A)

Capacitor Rating (V)	DC Field Test (V)
216– 1,199	15,000[a]
1,200– 5,000	28,500
5,001–15,000	39,000
13,200–22,000	45,000

[a]For indoor units, only 7,500 should be used.

Current measurements at low voltage have proven value for two other purposes:

- Detection of short-circuited sections in a capacitor.
- Predetermination and correction of unbalanced current in split-wye banks during installation.

The test programs for substation and distribution lines have proved to be realistic during installation and in service situations. Table 6–4 references NEMA recommended test values.

6-6 MOTORS AND GENERATORS

In testing large generators, several tests may have to be performed to evaluate the insulation condition. The tests involving dc and ac high potential have been discussed in Chapters 4 and 5, respectively. The following additional tests are made on motors and generators, which form the basis of a composite maintenance program.

SLOT DISCHARGE TEST

This test is performed to evaluate the coil surface grounding in the slot portion. The stator coil outer surfaces are painted with conducting varnish in order to make good electrical contact with the machine frame to prevent voids. However, at higher voltages, ionization can take place in the voids, resulting in insulation damage. The slot discharge test consists of applying approximately 7 kV ac and observing the wave form on an oscilloscope. This wave form is compared to a wave form of one coil side arcing to the slot at a single point. The slot discharge phenomena usually consist of high frequencies, such as 2,500 Hz/s. The line disturbances are usually filtered out in order to obtain an accurate slot discharge phenomena.

CONDUCTOR INSULATION TESTS

The insulation failure between conductors of motors and generators depends upon the machine insulation design. Failure between conductors can be as likely as the failure of ground insulation. Coils are tested during manufacture well above the minimum sparking voltage to ensure that the coils do not fail owing to thermal effects, vibrations, and the like. Where a high level of reliability is needed, maintenance testing of conductor insulation should be performed to the level of new coil test values. Normally, this test should be performed at the factory or repair shop facilities. The following test methods are in common use:

- Surge comparison test.
- Induced surge voltage test.
- Rotating spark-gap-type high-frequency oscillator.

MOTOR AND GENERATOR COMPONENT TESTS

These tests include insulation resistance tests on components of motors and generators such as resistance temperature detectors (RTD), exciter windings, stator insulated through bolts, rotor windings, and so on. The reader should consult the equipment manufacturer for recommendations for conducting these tests.

VOLTAGE SURGE COMPARISON TEST

The surge comparison tester is used to simultaneously test turn-to-turn, coil-to-coil, and coil-to-ground insulation. The surge tester is an electronic device which applies surge voltage stress between turns of a coil, between phases, from winding to ground, and it can detect short-circuited turns in windings under test. The surge voltage is of very short duration and therefore will not damage the windings. However, the surge voltage can be increased high enough so that insulation breakdown and arcing can be observed. The surge comparison test can be used as a go or no-go test. This test is a very useful diagnostic test for quality-control shop testing when reconditioning or rewinding wound components. Rewound and reconditioned motors and generators should be given a surge comparison test before varnishing so that winding faults, such as shorted turns or coils, reversed coil groups or phases, and incorrect number of turns in a coil, can be corrected before the windings are treated with varnish.

The voltage surge comparison tester stresses the turn and phase insulation by application of a repetitive surge voltage to the winding in opposite directions. A mid-potential is displayed on an oscilloscope. If a short-circuit occurs in one-half of the winding and does not exist in the other, the difference in the impedance of the windings causes two traces to be observed on the oscilloscope, indicating a fault. If the winding is good, only one trace appears. The tester surge voltage comparison tester should be able to vary voltage from zero up to the maximum required. A maximum voltage of not less than 5,000 V is usually recommended for motors and generators of 600 V and below. For machines above 600 V, a tester of 10,000 V is recommended.

Three-phase motors and generators of various sizes can be tested as shown in the connection diagram of Figure 6–12.

Detection of one-turn shorts or grounded coil is possible in all windings of few parallel circuits. Often only a small trace separation may be detectable with a one-turn short in a very large motor that has several parallel paths per phase. However, the winding connections can be broken to reduce the parallel paths in order to obtain a larger trace.

It may be difficult to indicate the type of fault from the wave shape observed on the oscilloscope; however, a double trace indicates that a definite fault exists, which should be investigated. Double lines at the top of the trace and at the horizontal center line for formed and wound stators are typical and do not indicate faults.

6-7   OTHER INSULATION TEST METHODS

Direct-current voltage testing has been used extensively for high-capacitance current load such as machine windings and high-voltage cables. However, the stress distribution imposed by dc voltage does not stress the insulation system

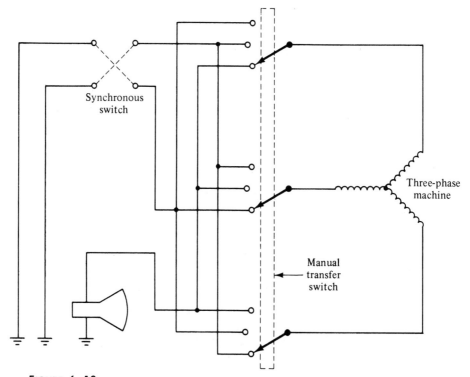

FIGURE 6–12.
Typical voltage surge comparison test connection for three-phase machines.

as does the ac voltage system. Field testing with ac voltage would require substantially large test equipment (because of the capacitive charing requirements), which is impractical. Therefore, the need for new test methods has led to the development of the one-tenth hertz test and resonant test methods. These two methods are described briefly next.

ONE-TENTH HERTZ TESTING

This test is a variation of the 60-Hz ac high-potential test. It utilizes 0.1-Hz voltage for searching flaws in the insulation system similar to that of 60-Hz test voltage equipment. The equipment, however, is considerably lighter and easier to handle. This is because the frequency is 0.1 Hz instead of 60 Hz, resulting in a kVA size reduction in the ratio of 1:600 in the test equipment. The recommended test value for maintenance and acceptance testing is 1.15 times the 60-Hz test value to achieve an equal searching effect, that is, $1.15(1.3E + 1,000)$ and $1.15(1.5E + 1,000)$ volts, respectively, where E is the rated line-to-line rms voltage of the equipment under test. The 1.3 and 1.5 factors correspond to 65 and 75 percent multipliers used for maintenance and acceptance testing.

SERIES RESONANT TESTING

Series resonant testing is comparatively a new method. A series resonant test set is shown in Figure 6–13. It has been used for field testing of large generators, sulfur hexafluoride (SF_6) bus systems and switchgear. It can also be used for power factor, dielectric loss, cable fault location, and corona with some modifications to the test equipment. At series resonance, the energy supplied to the test specimen is dissipated energy (I^2R) in the insulation system. Energy stored in the tuned circuit (i.e., at resonance) transfers back and forth between capacitance and inductance each half-cycle. The ratio of energy stored to energy dissipated per half-cycle is known as the *quality factor*. A higher value of Q gives a low-loss circuit, where as a low value of Q gives a lossy circuit. Q can be represented by the following equations:

$$Q = \frac{\text{maximum energy stored in } L \text{ (or } C \text{) during a cycle}}{\text{energy loss per half-cycle in } R}$$

$$= \frac{1}{WRC} \quad \text{or} \quad \frac{WL}{R}$$

At resonance $X_L = X_c$, and in a series resonance circuit of RLC, the voltage across the capacitor is given by

$$V_c = \frac{-jX_cV}{R + j(X_L - X_c)} = \frac{-jX_L}{R} V$$

FIGURE 6–13.
Series resonant test set, 500 kilovolts, 2,250 kilovolt-amperes capacity.
(Courtesy of Hipotronics, Brewster, N.Y.)

or $|V_c| = QV$, where V is the applied voltage. The Q of typical winding systems is 40 to 80 for high-quality capacitance loads. At resonance the current in the circuit is in phase with the voltage, V. Therefore, input power is $P = VI$, and the reactive power available to the capacitive load is

$$kVA = QVI = QP$$

Therefore,

$$P = \frac{(kVA)}{Q} = \frac{\text{reactive output power}}{Q}$$

The power required from the mains is reduced to $1/Q$ of the reactive load requirements. This results in a very substantial reduction in input requirements.

The series resonant method consists of low kVA source input during a *LC* series circuit. If breakdown in the capacitive load should occur, the fault current is limited to a low value by the high inductance value in series with the fault. Furthermore, the output wave form is purely sinusoidal because the harmonics of tuned frequency are attenuated. The attentuation of power frequency harmonics makes series resonance testing very attractive for dielectric loss and partial discharge testing. Consult the manufacturer's instructions on the operation and use of the series resonance test set.

CHAPTER 7

MAINTENANCE AND TESTING OF PROTECTIVE RELAYS AND OVERCURRENT DEVICES

7-1 INTRODUCTION

This chapter outlines a maintenance program for protective relays and overcurrent devices for medium- and low-voltage systems. It also covers auxiliary devices, such as instrument transformers and control power equipment, which are associated with the protective devices. The frequency of testing of these devices may be dependent upon many factors; however, an annual schedule of maintenance is recommended. Before a successful maintenance program can be implemented, it is essential that the personnel performing or evaluating maintenance should be thoroughly familiar with the types of protective devices and auxiliary equipment. Therefore, in this chapter a brief overview of protective relays and trips, instrument transformers, and control power is given for the reader to become familiar with the system equipment. The maintenance and testing of protective relays and overcurrent trips involves inspection, mechanical adjustment, and electrical tests. Since the protective equipment plays such an important role for the safety of personnel and property, they should be given special attention. Moreover, since these devices operate during abnormal conditions on the power system, the only way to assure correct operation is by a comprehensive inspection, maintenance, and testing program.

7-2 INSTRUMENT TRANSFORMERS

Instrument transformers are essential parts of many electrical metering and relaying systems. The quality of instrument transformers will affect directly the overall accuracy and performance of these systems. Instrument transformer performance is critical in protective relaying, since the relays can only be as good as the instrument transformers. They serve two basic functions:

- To change the magnitude (but not the nature) of primary voltage and current to secondary values to 120 volts (V) or 5 amperes (A) where relays, meters, or other devices can be applied.

- To provide insulation between primary and secondary circuits for equipment and personnel safety.

When relays compare the sum or difference of two or more currents or the interaction of voltages and currents, the relative direction of the current must be known. The direction of current flow can be determined by knowing the instrument transformer polarity. Polarity markings are normally shown on instrument transformers; however, they can be determined in the field if necessary. Several aspects of current and potential instrument transformers are discussed next.

CURRENT TRANSFORMERS

Current transformers are designed for connection in series with the line. The secondary current of the transformer bears a known relationship with the primary current. Any change in the primary current is reflected in the secondary circuit. Relays, meters, and other devices are connected in series with the secondary terminals of the transformer. Current transformers are made in many different current ratios, different voltage insulation systems, and for different environmental conditions such as indoor or outdoor use. Generally, the following types of construction are used for current transformers.

- *Wound type:* In this type more than one primary turn is frequently used to obtain low exciting current and high accuracy. The usual current ratings for this type of transformer are 800 A and below.
- *Bar-primary type:* In this type, the primary consists of a single bar extending through the core, which is connected in series with the circuit conductor. This type of construction is suited to withstand the stresses of heavy overcurrent. The usual current rating for this type of transformer is 1,200 A or above in order to provide sufficient ampere-turns for good accuracy.
- *Window type:* The window-type current transformer contains no primary winding. The current transformer has an insulated hole through the core and secondary winding. The circuit conductor is inserted through the window of the current transformer, and thus this conductor then becomes the primary of the current transformer.
- *Bushing type:* The bushing-type current transformer is similar to the window-type. It has a circular core that is designed to fit on the bushing of a power transformer, circuit breaker, or other device. The secondary windings are wound on the circular core and can be tapped to give multiple ratios. This transformer is mostly used for relaying purposes where high accuracy at normal current value is not extremely important.

- *Double-secondary type:* A double-secondary transformer is actually two transformers, each transformer having its own core. This type of transformer occupies less space than two single-secondary winding transformers. The double-secondary winding transformer permits instruments, relays or other devices to be separated if required.

- *Split-core type:* This is a window-type current transformer with hinged cores, which permit them to be installed on buses or other circuits.

- *Air-core type:* The air-core current transformer is used where saturation of the iron core due to high fault currents is a problem. The air-core transformer has relative constant error over a wide range of overcurrent and transient conditions.

- *Tripping transformers:* Several types of small and inexpensive transformers are available for protective control functions. These transformers are not made with the same accuracy as instrument transformers.

- *Auxiliary transformers:* Auxiliary transformers are used to adjust the difference in ratio between different current transformers. These transformers are connected in the secondary circuits of main transformers.

Current Transformer Accuracy Standards

Current transformers can be divided into two categories for purposes of establishing accuracy standards: (1) accuracy standard for metering current transformers, and (2) accuracy standard for relaying current transformers. Since accuracy is a function of the burden on the current transformer, standard burdens have been established. Accuracy has been established at various burden values. The standard burdens established by ANSI C57.13-1968 are shown in Table 7–1. The performance rating is based on 5-A secondary current unless otherwise specified.

ACCURACY CLASSES FOR METERING
The ANSI accuracy classes for metering state that the transformer correction factor (TCF) should be within specified limits when the power factor of the metered load is from 0.6 to 1.0 lagging for a specified standard burden, at 100 percent of rated primary current. Current transformers for metering service have accuracy classes of 0.3, 0.6, and 1.2 percent.

ACCURACY CLASSES FOR RELAYING
The ANSI has standardized on the accuracy classes and the conditions under which they apply. The ANSI standard C57.13 was revised in 1968 and hence is different than the older standard of 1954. Because many older current transformers are still in use, it is appropriate to discuss the older standard. In general the accuracy ratings are on the basis of the standard secondary terminal voltage a transformer will deliver without exceeding a standard percent ratio error.

Old Standard (ANSI C57.13-1954): The classification of current transformer performance is based on the ratio error at 5 to 20 times secondary current. Therefore, the current transformers are divided into classes, H and L. Class H has a nearly constant percentage ratio error when delivering a fixed secondary voltage over a wide range of secondary current. Class L has a nearly constant magnitude error (variable percentage error) when delivering a fixed secondary voltage over a wide range of secondary current. Standard percent ratio error classes are 2.5 and 10 percent. Secondary voltages are 10, 20, 50, 100, 200, 400, 800 V. For example, transformer classification may be as 2.5H 200 or 10L 200. The first term describes the maximum percent ratio error, the second term (H or L) describes the transformer performance characteristic, and the third term describes the secondary voltage. The class H transformer can deliver a secondary voltage equal to its voltage class at 5 to 20 times secondary rated current. A class L current transformer, on the other hand, can only deliver a secondary voltage within its voltage class at 5 to 20 times secondary rated current at fixed burden. In other words, class L cannot be used with proportionately higher burdens at lower secondary current without exceeding its classified ratio error.

New Standard (ANSI 57.13-1968): A relaying accuracy under the new standard has been designated by symbols C and T.

- C means that transformer ratio error can be calculated, and T means that the ratio error must be determined by test.
- The secondary terminal voltage rating is the voltage which the transformer will deliver to a standard burden (as listed in Table 7–1) at 20 times normal secondary current.
- The transformer ratio error must be limited to 10 percent for all currents from 5 to 20 times normal current for burdens not to exceed those listed in Table 7–1.

TABLE 7–1.
STANDARD BURDENS FOR CURRENT TRANSFORMERS,
ANSI C57.13-1968

Standard Burden Designation	Characteristics for 60 Hertz and 5 Amperes		
	Impedance (Ω)	Volt-Amperes	Power Factor
B-0.1	0.1	2.5	0.9
B-0.2	0.2	5.0	0.9
B-0.5	0.5	12.5	0.9
B-1	1.0	25.0	0.5
B-2	2.0	50.0	0.5
B-4	4.0	100.0	0.5
B-8	8.0	200.0	0.5

- The C classification covers bushing transformers, and the T classification covers any other transformer.
- The secondary voltage values are 10, 20, 50, 100, 200, 400, 800 V based on 5 to 20 times the normal current standard burdens listed in Table 7–1.

To specify a current transformer under the new standards, one needs only to select either a class C or T transformer and then specify the burden.

POTENTIAL TRANSFORMERS

Potential transformers are designed for connecting line to line or line to neutral. The purpose of the potential transformer is to provide an isolated secondary voltage that is an exact proportionate representation of primary voltage. However, transformers draw core-magnetizing current from the primary line, and a constant error results independent of the burden connected to it. Also, variable error results due to load or burden current flowing through the effective impedance of the transformer. The total error is the sum of these two errors under any burden condition. The ANSI standard C57.13-1968 lists the classification of potential transformers encountered in service as W, X, Y, Z, and ZZ. The standard burden designations are shown in Table 7–2 for these transformers.

Accuracy classes are based on the requirement that the transformer ratio correction factor (TCF) be within specified limits when the power factor of the metered load is between 0.6 to 1.0 lagging for a specified burden and at voltages from 90 to 110 percent of rated transformer voltage. The ANSI accuracy classes for potential transformers are shown in Table 7–3.

The ratings of potential transformers encompass the following:

- Insulation class and basic impulse level.
- Rated primary voltage and ratio.
- Accuracy ratings at standard burdens.

TABLE 7–2.
ANSI STANDARD BURDENS FOR POTENTIAL TRANSFORMERS

Burden	Volt-Amperes at 120 V	Burden Power Factor
W	12.5	0.70
X	25.0	0.70
Y	75.0	0.85
Z	200.0	0.85
ZZ	400.0	0.85

TABLE 7–3.
ANSI ACCURACY CLASSES FOR POTENTIAL TRANSFORMERS

Accuracy Class (%)	Limits of Transformer Ratio Correction Factor	Limits of Power Factor of Metered Load
1.2	1.012–0.998	0.6–1.0
0.6	1.006–0.994	0.6–1.0
0.3	1.003–0.997	0.6–1.0

- Thermal burden, that is, the maximum burden the transformer can carry at rated secondary voltage without exceeding its temperature rise, above 30°C ambient.

POLARITY OF INSTRUMENT TRANSFORMERS

Instrument transformers are marked to indicate the instantaneous direction of primary and secondary currents. Usually, one primary and one secondary terminal are marked with a cross (**X**) or a dot (●) or a square (■) to indicate the polarity. The following conventions apply to either current or potential transformers with subtractive or additive polarity.

- The current flowing out at the polarity marked terminal on the secondary side is nearly in phase with the current flowing in at the polarity marked terminal on the primary. This is shown in Figure 7–1
- The voltage drop from the polarity to the nonpolarity marked terminals on the primary side is nearly in phase with the voltage drop from the polarity to the nonpolarity marked terminals on the secondary side.

TESTING FOR POLARITY OF INSTRUMENT TRANSFORMERS

The polarity of instrument transformers can be determined by dc or ac tests.

Direct-Current Test

Connect a dc permanent magnet ammeter of 5-A capacity or less (depending on the transformer ratio) across the current transformer secondary terminal. The marked secondary terminal of the transformer should be connected to the plus (+) ammeter terminal. Then connect a 7.5-V battery to the primary side such that the negative terminal is connected to the unmarked primary terminal of the transformer. Make an instantaneous contact with the positive battery terminal to the marked terminal of the transformer. A kick or deflection will be noticed on the ammeter. If the kick is in the positive direction (i.e., upscale) upon making the contact, the transformer leads are correctly marked. If the initial kick is in the negative direction (i.e., downscale), the polarity markings are not correct. See Figure 7–11 for connections for this test.

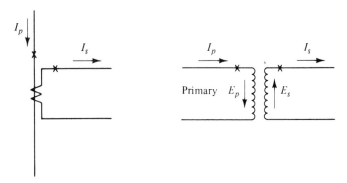

I_p = primary current, I_s = secondary current

FIGURE 7–1.
Polarity marking of transformers.

Potential transformers can be tested by using a dc permanent magnet moving-coil-type voltmeter having a 150-V scale. The test is performed in a manner similar to the test for current transformers, except that the voltmeter is connected across the high-voltage terminals of the transformer first, and then the battery voltage is applied to the low-voltage terminals.

Alternating-Current Tests

The following ac methods are used for determining polarity.

EXCITATION TEST
This test consists of exciting the transformer high-voltage winding with low voltage and comparing the voltage across the winding with voltage across both windings in series. This method is not very practical with transformers with high ratios such as 100:1, because the difference between the two voltages is very small, which cannot be measured with ordinary instruments. Moreover, there is always a danger of exciting the low-voltage winding instead of the high-voltage winding, thereby producing dangerous voltages on the transformer.

SUBSTITUTION METHOD
This method involves using a transformer with known polarity. Make connections as for the "known polarity" transformer, as shown in Figure 7–2(a) and (b), and then connect the transformer whose polarity is to be determined. If the wattmeter deflects in the same direction in both cases, the polarities of two transformers are the same. By knowing the polarity of the first transformer, the polarity of the second transformer is then determined.

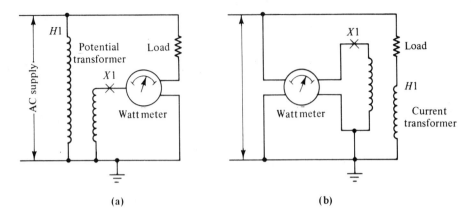

FIGURE 7–2.
Connection for substitution method.

DIFFERENTIAL METHOD

The differential method involves exciting the primaries of both transformers (known and unknown polarities) and making a differential measurement with an ammeter or voltmeter. When the secondaries of two potential transformers are connected in series, the readings should be the sum of the voltages of two transformers. Similarly, when the two current secondaries of the transformers are connected in parallel, the ammeter should read the sum of the currents in two transformers. The connections are shown in Figure 7–3(a) and (b).

MAINTENANCE AND TESTING OF INSTRUMENT TRANSFORMERS

The following general recommendations are offered to supplement the manufacturers' instructions.

General Maintenance

- If instrument transformers are allowed to remain out of service for a long period of time, they should be dried before being put into service.
- Instrument transformers containing oil or synthetic dielectrics should be tested periodically to maintain the breakdown voltage at 22 kV or more.
- The secondaries of current transformers that are not connected to relays, meters, and the like, should have their secondaries shorted and grounded.
- The secondary circuits and cases of all instrument transformers should be grounded with at least number 12 conductor.

Testing

Routine testing as described next should be performed on instrument transformers.

GENERAL-PURPOSE INSTRUMENT TRANSFORMERS

■ Ratio and phase angle tests should be made on current transformers for metering at 100 and 10 percent of rated primary current, when energized at rated frequency with maximum standard burden for which the transformer is rated.

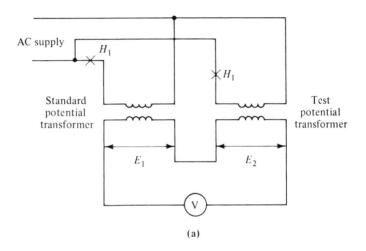

(a)

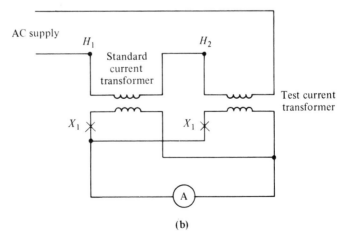

(b)

FIGURE 7–3.
Connection for differential method.

- The turns ratio test should be made on current transformers for relaying to ensure that they have the correct turns ratio and relaying accuracy.
- Routine accuracy tests should be made on each potential transformer. These tests consist of ratio and phase angle tests at 100 percent rated primary voltage at rated frequency with zero burden accuracy.

REVENUE METERING AND TRANSFORMER

- Calibrate all meters at 10, 50, and 90 percent of full scale. Instruments used for calibration of test equipment should have precision of no more than 50 percent of the instrument being tested.
- Calibrate watt-hour meters to ½ percent.
- Verify all instrument multipliers.

7-3 PROTECTIVE RELAYS

Protective relays are used in power systems to assure maximum continuity of service. They are constantly monitoring the power system to detect unwanted conditions that can cause damage to property and life. They can be considered as a form of insurance designed to provide protection against property and personnel loss and continued service. Protective relays are found throughout small and large power systems from generation through transmission, distribution, and utilization. A better understanding of their application, operation, and maintenance is essential for the operating and maintenance personnel in order to understand how they fit into modern power systems.

CLASSIFICATION AND CONSTRUCTION PRINCIPLES OF RELAYS

The American National Standards Institute (ANSI) C37.90 classifies relays associated with power apparatus into the following categories:

- Protective relays
- Auxiliary (slave) relays
- Programming relays
- Verification relays
- Monitoring relays

In addition to these generalized categories, relays can be further divided by input, operating principles, and performance characteristics. The input can consist of current, voltage, pressure, temperature, frequency, and so on; the operating principles can consist of thermal, electromagnetic, product of voltage and current, percentage, restraint, and so on; and the performance characteristics can consist of time delay, directional, differential, distance, phase or ground, comparison of operating quantities, and so on.

Protective relay construction principles are based upon basic fault-detecting units, which are called basic relay units. These can be classified into instantaneous (magnetic attraction) and time-delay (torque controlled) units.

Instantaneous Units

This type of relay unit consists of the plunger, solenoid, hinged armature, and balance-beam types in which by magnetic attraction the armature is attracted into a coil or to a pole face of an electromagnet. Relays of this construction type can be applied in either ac or dc power systems. The plunger-type construction is shown in Figure 7–4.

Time-Delay Units

This type of delay unit consists of the induction-disc and induction-cup type in which, owing to magnetic induction, a torque is produced in a movable rotor (i.e., disc or cup), which rotates between two poles faces of an electromagnet. Obviously, this type of relay can only be applied in ac power systems. The induction-disc type of construction is shown in Figure 7–5.

The preceding types of basic relay units are the electromagnetic type, but can also be obtained in the solid-state (static) type. Solid-state relays are extremely fast in their operation because they have no moving parts. Basic relay

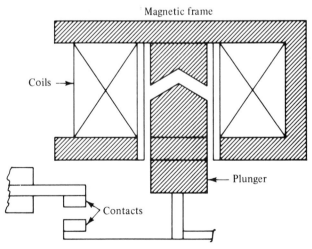

FIGURE 7–4.
Plunger-type relay.

circuits (units) can be obtained to provide various functions of level detection, measurement of phase angle, timing functions, and so on. In solid-state relays, the basic circuits use power system inputs (i.e., voltage, current, frequency, phase angle) to provide the conventional output functions similar to electromagnetic relays. Solid-state relays are rack mounted, consisting of many printed circuit boards, as compared to electromagnetic types, which are permanently mounted on a switchboard. However, in both types the solid relay printed card or the electromagnetic relay chassis can be removed from the case for testing and maintenance.

RELAY APPLICATION AND OPERATION PRINCIPLES

The application of protective relays involves factors such as reliability, selectivity, speed of operation, complexity, and economy. Obviously, compromises need to be made among these factors to achieve a protection system that offers the most protection at minimum cost. The information needed to evaluate the application factors is the following:

- One-line system diagram.
- Degree of protection required.
- Short-circuit study.

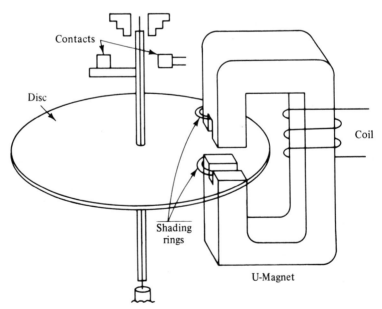

FIGURE 7–5.
Induction-disc type of relay.

- Load currents.
- Transformer and motor data.
- Impedance data for the system equipment.
- Operating procedures.
- Existing protection and/or difficulties.
- Ratios of current and potential transformers.

The function of protective relaying can be classified as *primary* or *back-up* relay protection. Primary relaying is the first line of defense when trouble occurs on the power system. When the primary relaying fails, then back-up relaying takes over to provide the protection. Primary relaying should operate as fast as is technically and economically feasible. Prompt removal of faults minimizes equipment damage and helps maintain system stability. Primary relaying may fail because of the following:

- Control power for tripping failure.
- Protective relay malfunction.
- Breaker failure to open.
- Relay and control wiring failure.
- Current and/or potential transformer failure.

Therefore, back-up relaying should be arranged so that anything that causes primary relaying to fail will not cause the back-up relaying to fail. Back-up relaying should be as completely separated from primary relaying as is possible, including control power, control circuits, and instrument transformers.

The relay operation is a function of the input quantities, such as current, voltage, and/or phase angle. The relay can be made to respond to either a single quantity or combination of two or all input quantities. When the relay is operated by a single quantity, its response is strictly a function of time, whereas when the relay is operated upon by two or more quantities, its operation is a function of the relative magnitude and phase angle difference of those quantities. Each relay then can be made to respond to its input quantities, known as the *operating* or *relay characteristics*. Relay characteristics are very useful in determining the relay setting, which in turn will determine relay speed, sensitivity, and selectivity for protection from power system short-circuits.

Relay application practices can be classified according to relay characteristics and the special requirements of various elements. They are discussed next.

Overcurrent Relays

When excessive current flows in a circuit, it is necessary to trip the circuit breaker protecting that circuit. This type of protection is usually provided by either time-delay or instantaneous overcurrent relays. The instantaneous relay, although inherently fast, requires a short time to operate, whereas time-delay relays have intentional time delay built into them to provide coordination with other overcurrent relays for selectivity. The selectivity is obtained by adjustment of current setting (sensitivity) and time, using the most applicable of several time-characteristics. The relay time characteristics differ by the rate at which the time of operation of the relay decreases as the current increases. The time characteristics for each family of overcurrent relay consist of inverse, very inverse, extremely inverse, definite time, short time, and long time. These curves are shown in Figure 7–6. The application of overcurrent relay is generally more difficult and less permanent than that of other types of relaying. This is because the operation of overcurrent relays is affected by variations of short-circuit current magnitudes. These magnitude variations in short-circuit current are caused by changes in system operation and system configuration.

Over-Under Voltage Relays

The over-under voltage relays have characteristics similar to the overcurrent relays. The actuating quality in the operating element is voltage instead of current. Voltage relays often combine the under-over voltage elements in one relay, with contacts for either an undervoltage or overvoltage condition. These

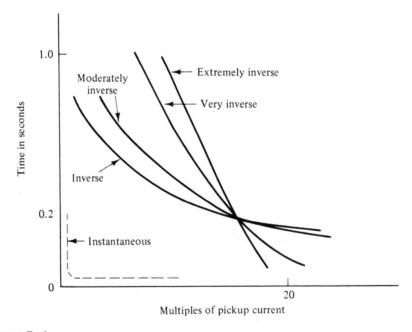

FIGURE 7–6.
Time-current characteristics of various families of overcurrent relays.

relays may be used to trip the breaker or sound an alarm in case of the voltage exceeding a predetermined limit or falling below a predetermined value.

Directional Relays

Directional relays are used where it is desirable to trip the circuit breaker for current flow in one direction. That is, the direction is made responsive to the directional flow of power. This is achieved by making the relay distinguish certain differences in phase angle between current and reference voltage or current. The directional relay has a current winding and directional winding. The current winding is connected to the current transformer, whereas the directional winding is connected to the potential transformers to provide the circuit voltage for polarizing the unit. Therefore, the pickup of the relay is dependent on the magnitude of current and voltage and the phase relationship between them. The directional relay thus establishes one boundary of the protected zone; that is, it protects the circuit only in one direction. Directional relaying is often used where coordination becomes a problem, such as in tie lines between two supply substations or to provide protection against the motoring of a generator.

Current- or Voltage-Balance Relays

Current-balance relays compare the magnitudes of current (or voltage) in two circuits (where these quantities vary within restricted limits) to detect an abnormal condition. The current-balance relay has two torque-producing elements actuated by currents (or voltage) from two different circuits or phases. Current-balance relaying between the phases of a motor is used to protect the machine against overheating in case phase currents become unbalanced owing to short-circuits or fuse blowing. Current balance can be set with sufficient time delay to provide coordination with other relaying.

Distance Relaying

The principal application of distance relaying is for transmission lines. A distance relay operates by comparing the voltage with the current at its location, that is, measuring the impedance of the line. The relay is designed to operate whenever the impedance under an abnormal condition becomes less than a predetermined value. Since the impedance is a function of line length, the relay operates when a short-circuit occurs within the given length of line that the relay is set to protect. Distance relays are built in three different types: (1) impedance, (2) admittance (MHO), and (3) reactance.

Differential Relaying

Differential relaying provides selectivity by providing a zone of protection by proper connection of the current transformers. Current transformers having the same ratio are installed in all the connections to the component to be protected, and the secondaries of the current transformers are connected in parallel to the relay restrain and operating coil. A typical one-phase differential connection is shown in Figure 7–7. As long as the current flow through the protected component is unchanged in magnitude and phase, the relay does not pick up. Such a condition would occur for a short-circuit fault outside the zone of relay protection. However, should a fault occur inside the zone of relay protection (that is, between the current transformers), the differential relay would receive current in the operating coil. To obtain differential protection, almost any relay type can be used. However, differential relays are constructed to provide very sophisticated, fast short-circuit protection. A differential relay has two restrain coils and an operating coil. The restrain coils prevent the undesired relay operation for fault outside the differential zone, as well as current transformer errors. Maximum restrain is produced if the current is in the same direction in the two restrain coils, and minimum restrain is produced if currents are in opposite directions in the two restrain coils. The current flowing through the operating coils (i.e., $I_1 - I_2$) must exceed a certain percentage of the through current (I_2) before the relay will operate. Because it is inherently selective, differential relaying is used as primary relaying on power system components and equipment.

Pilot-Wire Relaying

Pilot-wire relaying is a form of differential relaying for line protection. The pilot-wire employs a wire channel to compare currents entering and leaving the

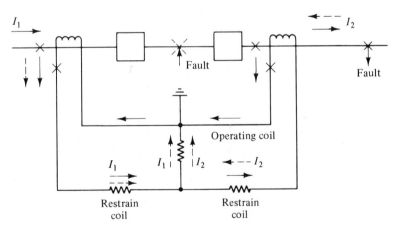

FIGURE 7–7.
Typical differential relay connection.

protected line between two terminals. The wire pilot channel can consist of the following:

- *Wire pilot,* consisting of a two-wire circuit between the ends of the line.
- *Carrier-current pilot,* wherein one conductor of the line and the earth comprise a pilot circuit for superimposed high-frequency currents.
- *Microwave pilot,* which is an ultra-high-frequency radio channel between the ends of the line.

For external faults the currents are balanced at the two terminals of the line, whereas for internal faults the currents are not balanced and therefore relay pickup would occur.

7-4 CONTROL POWER FOR SWITCHGEAR

This section covers the requirements, selection, and maintenance of control power for medium-voltage switchgear.

CONTROL POWER REQUIREMENTS

The requirements for any control power equipment are that it have sufficient capacity to deliver maximum power at rated voltage under all operating conditions. The most important requirement of a control source is that it must provide tripping power to circuit breakers. In addition to tripping power, it should also provide closing power. It is not uncommon to include other loads, such as indicating lamps, emergency lights, excitation power to synchronous motors, space heaters, fans, and remote lights, in the control power requirements. All these requirements must be considered when selecting a control power system.

Two main types of control voltages are used for medium-voltage switchgear: (1) direct-current (dc) control and (2) alternating-current (ac) control. The source of dc control is storage batteries, whereas transformers are used for ac control. When ac control is used for closing, the tripping power is obtained from a capacitor trip device or a separate "tripping" battery. The choice between ac and dc control power depends on the following factors:

- Number of circuit breakers in the switchgear.
- Number of breakers operating simultaneously.
- Number of auxiliary equipment connected.
- Degree of reliability required.
- Future expansion requirements.

- Environmental conditions.
- Maintenance of system.
- Cost of the system.

National Electrical Manufacturers Association (NEMA) standards have established standard voltages and operating ranges for the switchgear circuit breakers, which are shown in Table 7–4.

Circuit Breaker Tripping

Power circuit breakers are equipped for manual tripping (pistol-grip handle or push button) and for electrically actuated tripping via a trip coil. The trip coil opens the breaker automatically when energized by a protective relay or manually by an operator via the manual handle. Tripping devices used for power circuit breakers are discussed next.

DC BATTERY TRIP
The battery is probably the most reliable source of control power when it is properly maintained and serviced. It uses single contact protective relays to energize the breaker trip coil. It is unaffected by voltages and current during fault conditions. Generally a 125- or 250-V battery is recommended for medium-voltage switchgear when both closing and tripping is required. When such is not available, a 48-V battery may be used for tripping only. However, it must be sized to meet the required load of the switchgear. The battery trip is shown in Figure 7–8(a). Long service can be obtained from batteries when they are serviced regularly, fully charged, and the electrolyte level maintained at the proper level.

TABLE 7–4.
NEMA STANDARD VOLTAGES AND OPERATING RANGES FOR
POWER CIRCUIT BREAKERS

	Operating Ranges (V)			
	Stored Energy Mechanism		Solenoid Mechanism	
Nominal Control Voltage (V)	Spring Motor and Closing Spring Release Coil	Tripping Coil	Closing Coil	Tripping Coil
DC 24	—	14–30	—	14–30
48	36–52	28–60	—	28–60
125	90–130	70–140	90–130	70–140
250	180–260	140–280	180–260	140–280
AC 115	95–125	95–125	—	95–125
230	190–250	190–250	190–250	190–250

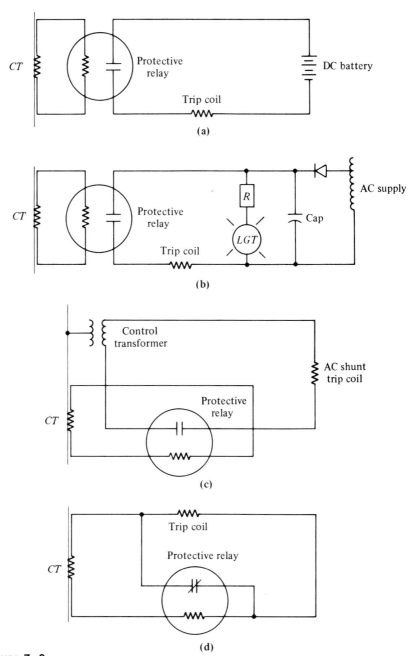

FIGURE 7–8.
*Various methods of tripping for circuit breakers: (a) battery trip;
(b) capacitor trip device; (c) ac shunt trip coil; (d) circuit opening
relays.*

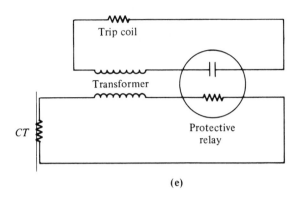

(e)

FIGURE 7–8 (continued).
(e) tripping transformer relay.

CAPACITOR TRIP
The capacitor trip device is commonly used where a dc battery source is not available or uneconomical, such as in outdoor switchgear or where only few circuit breakers are installed. The capacitor device simply consists of a capacitor and half-wave rectifier charged from an ac control power transformer. When using a capacitor trip device, a separate capacitor trip unit is required for each breaker.

The capacitor trip device comes in two types: nonautocharge and autocharge. The nonautocharge retains adequate charge for a short time (about 30 s) after the ac supply is lost. The autocharge consists of a regulated charge. It contains a voltage amplifier, a battery, and a battery charger. In case of loss of ac supply, the voltage amplifier steps up the battery voltage to maintain an adequate charge on the capacitor for several days. The simple capacitor trip device is shown in Figure 7–8(b).

AC METHODS OF TRIPPING
The ac methods of tripping are used when sufficient current is always available during fault conditions. The tripping energy is obtained from the faulted circuit via the current transformers. This tripping is always associated with overcurrent protection. A potential trip coil is provided for each breaker for normal switching operations through a breaker control switch. The following ac trips are used in switchgear:

- AC shunt trip.
- Circuit opening relays.
- Tripping transformers.

In the ac tripping schemes, three ac current trip coils are used, one in each phase to ensure that under all fault conditions the breaker will have adequate current to trip. The ac trips are shown in Figure 7–8(c) through (e).

Circuit Breaker Closing

The closing power for a circuit breaker can be either dc or ac voltage. However, it is desirable to have closing power independent of voltage conditions on the power system. For this reason the dc battery is a preferable source of closing power. The choice may be dependent on economics, particularly where the switchgear consists of only a few circuit breakers or the investment in battery power could not be justified. The factors that influence the choice of closing power are the following:

- Need to close breakers with power system deenergized.
- Maintenance of the closing power.
- Availability of space to house the control power equipment.
- Degree of reliability required.
- Expansion plans.

All these factors must be considered in the evaluation of the closing power before a final decision is made on what equipment is best suited for a particular installation. The following basic methods for closing power are available for switchgear applications:

- *Stored-energy mechanism*
  DC battery
  230-Volt control power transformer.
  230-Volt lighting or power panel.
- *Solenoid-operated mechanism*
  Manually (stored-energy close).
  DC battery close.
  230-Volt ac rectifier close.

The basic methods of closing circuit breakers are shown in Figure 7–9(a) through (f). The current required for closing of stored-energy-mechanism breakers can be either direct or alternating current. The power required for the next close operation is stored in the springs with the preceding close operation of the breaker. The ac power must be present to initiate the control circuit to the spring-release solenoid for automatic close operation of the breaker. For nonautomatic operation, the spring release can be initiated manually. If needed, the store-energy breaker close mechanism can be manually charged. The ac source for solenoid breakers requires a separate closing rectifier for each breaker.

When selecting a control source power for breaker closing, the maximum closing load must be calculated. The number of breakers required for simultaneous closing must be known so that the system can provide the required energy. In addition, any other loads that are connected to the system must be known.

SELECTION OF CONTROL POWER

The selection of control power involves the sizing and selection of dc battery and ac control power transformer equipment.

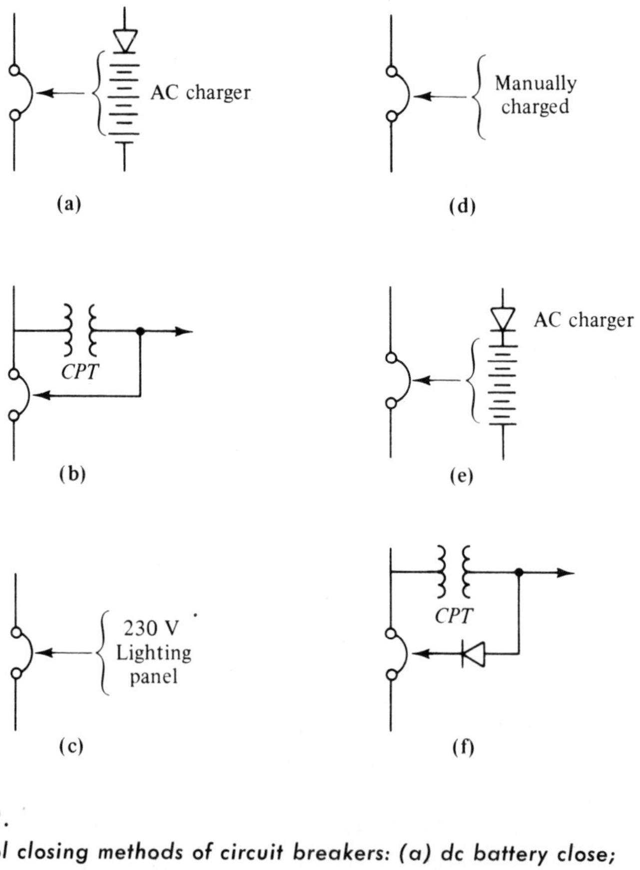

FIGURE 7–9.

Basic control closing methods of circuit breakers: (a) dc battery close; (b) 230-volt close; (c) 230-volt close; (d) manually close; (e) dc battery close; (f) ac rectifier close.

DC (Battery) Control Power Equipment

The following is offered as a general guide for the selection and application of dc battery equipment for switchgear.

SIZING

To size a control power source, each type of load must be known. For batteries, the steady-state and short-time loads must be converted to a common rate base. Also, the long-time loads must have specified time periods, since the battery is not a continuous source when the charger is off. After all the loads have been totaled, the next higher size of control power source should be selected.

The capacity of the battery is usually expressed in ampere-hours, that is, the product of discharge current and time in hours. The basic rate is normally expressed for 8 hours; however, many other rates are used to express battery capacity. In switchgear application, the short-time rates, such as 1-min rate per cell, is frequently used to express the terminal voltage drop early in the discharge period. The manufacturer's data are usually given for cells at 25°C (77°F), and when the battery is at a lower temperature than the stated temperature, the battery rating must be reduced. The voltage drop due to discharge current specified in terms of 1-min rate per cell for a nickel cadmium battery is 1.14 V, and 1.75 V for the lead-acid battery, at 25°C.

To convert the 1-min rate loads to the equivalent ampere-hours rate, the battery or switchgear manufacturer should be consulted. For sizing the capacity of a battery for switchgear, the worst case should be assumed. The worst case occurs when the battery has carried steady-state load for 8 hours and then is subjected to maximum load involving 1-min rate. For indoor locations, the battery temperature is assumed to be 25°C, and for outdoor applications, $-10°C$.

TYPES OF BATTERIES

For switchgear applications, two types of batteries are used: lead acid batteries and nickel-cadmium batteries. Lead acid batteries are made in several types:

- *Pasted plate with lead antimony grids:* This is a basic lead-acid battery, similar to the common automobile battery. However, for switchgear control work thicker plates and lower gravity of acid provide longer life. It also is suitable for long-time float charging. The expected life of this battery is from 6 to 14 years depending upon the plate thickness. It is also the lowest-cost battery.

- *Lead-calcium:* This is basically pasted-plate construction, with antimony replaced by calcium for additional grid strength. It has an expected life of about 25 years. Because of pure lead electrochemical characteristics, it requires slightly different charging voltages.

- *Tubular positive:* This is also known as an iron-clad battery. These batteries are suitable for large stations and long-time load applications.

- *Plante:* This is a long-life battery, with expected life of 20 to 25 years. In this battery the positive plate is formed from pure lead. Its short time rates are somewhat higher and ampere hours slightly less as compared to pasted-plate types. This is the most expensive lead-acid battery.

The nickel-cadmium battery is constructed with pocket-plate cells for switchgear applications. The battery plates have three different construction thicknesses. Medium or thin plate construction is used for switchgear applications. The maintenance of this battery is less than for lead acid. Its low-temperature discharge currents are higher, and it can be charged more rapidly than lead-acid batteries. The cost of the nickel-cadmium battery is higher than the lead-acid battery.

BATTERY CHARGERS

Two types of battery chargers are available. One is known as the "trickle-charge," which is the unregulated type, and the other is the regulated type. The regulated charger provides longer life, especially for lead-acid batteries. The regulated charger is recommended for switchgear applications. The selection of charger equipment should satisfy the following functions simultaneously:

- Steady-state loads on the battery.
- Self-discharge losses of the battery.
- Equalizing charges.

Steady-state loads are those that require power continuously. Self-discharge losses are due to trickle current, which starts at about 0.25 percent of the 8-hour rate for lead-acid batteries. Self-discharge losses increase with the age of the battery. The equalizing charge is an extended normal charge and is given periodically to ensure that the cells are restored to the maximum specific gravity. All lead-acid batteries require a monthly equalizing charge except the lead-calcium type. Nickel-cadmium batteries do not require the equalizing charge; however, it is recommended that they be given this charge for occasional boosting. In the sizing of charger equipment, the steady-state loads, equalizing charge current, and self-discharge current should be added to arrive at the capacity of the charger. Select a charger with ratings that exceed or equal the sum of currents required.

AC Control Power Equipment

The following is a general guide for the selection and application of ac control power equipment.

SIZING

For sizing the capacity of an ac control potential transformer, all the loads should be totaled. These loads may be steady-state, breaker closing, and tripping loads. If the tripping is provided by a capacitor-trip device, the tripping demand may not be included. The closing demand of breakers that require simultaneous closing should be totaled and included in sizing the control transformer. The total load should then be compared to the available sizes of control power transformers, and the next larger size should be selected.

APPLICATION

It is recommended that the control power be supplied from a separate transformer strictly used for control purposes. This will minimize inadvertent loss of control power. The transformer should be connected to the bus or the line side of the circuit to minimize control power interruption. For multiple services, each service should have its own control power source. Circuits that are not exclusively associated with either source should be supplied control power automatically from either of the control power transformers in case of loss of one control source.

MAINTENANCE AND CARE OF CONTROL POWER EQUIPMENT

The monitoring and maintenance of control power equipment is very important from the point of view of service reliability. The consequences of electrical failures are catastrophic in cases where no control power is available for tripping the circuit breakers. Proper maintenance is the key to dependable battery operation. The following battery maintenance procedures are offered as a guide to ensure long life and dependable service.

Charging

The station batteries are sized in terms of their discharge capacity, which is usually stated in ampere-hours. The ampere-hours are based on supply current during an 8- or 3-hour period with electrolyte temperature at 25°C. To maintain a constant voltage at the battery terminals, the charger is connected in parallel with the battery and the load circuits. The purpose of the float charge voltage is to prevent the internal discharge of the battery. The practical float voltages are listed in terms of volts per cell (VPC). Following are the VPC values for the various types of batteries:

- Nickel-cadmium: 1.4 to 1.42 VPC.
- Lead-calcium: 2.17 to 2.25 VPC.
- Lead-antimony: 2.15 to 2.17 VPC.
- Plante: 2.17 to 2.19 VPC.

When the battery is equipped with a constant voltage charger, it is automatically charged after an emergency discharge. In the case of lead-acid batteries, a periodic equalizing charge is required when the specific gravity falls below its full-charge value of 0.001 or the average floating voltages of a cell is below its average value by 0.04 V. The frequency for equalizing charging varies, but is usually from a minimum of 3 months to 1 year. Also, an equalizing charge should be given to a battery after the addition of water to the battery. Different types of batteries require different lengths of time for the equalizing charge. The length of time is a function of cell temperatures. A normal electrolyte value for specific gravity based on a temperature of 77°F is taken to be 1.215 for a fully charged lead-acid battery. Battery performance is affected by electrolyte temperature. Generally, for every 3° below 77°F, the battery performance can be evaluated by subtracting 0.001 from the specific gravity. Similarly, for every 3° above 77°F, add 0.001 to the specific gravity.

Addition of Water

Due to charging, the battery will normally lose water through evaporation and chemical action. Distilled water must be added to the battery, preferably before the equalizing charge is applied.

Acid Spillage

When acid is spilled on the battery exterior, it should be wiped clean with a cloth dampened in baking soda solution. Furthermore, the battery exterior should be wiped dry after wiping with a water-dampened cloth following the initial cleaning.

Loose Connections

Battery terminal connections and intercell connections should be checked periodically.

Corrosion

All corrosion on battery terminals should be removed by applying baking soda solution and the terminals cleaned by using a brass brush. Antioxidant coating should be applied before reconnecting.

Other Maintenance Hints

- Do not ground the electric storage battery, because a second accidental ground on the ungrounded polarity of any circuit fed by the battery would cause the control circuit fuse to blow.
- New batteries after initial charge should be kept on float charge for a week.
- Take weekly readings of the voltage of selected cells and total battery voltage.

- Take monthly readings of electrolyte level, cell voltage, specific gravity, and temperature.
- Every 3 months to 1 year, take a complete set of cell readings.

7-5 MAINTENANCE AND TESTING OF SWITCHGEAR PROTECTIVE RELAYS

The reliability of protective relays in isolating faulted equipment is dependent on proper installation and maintenance. After protective relays are properly installed and tested, the maintenance testing objective should be to achieve maximum performance with minimum testing. Relays usually operate for an extremely short time during their long life. Therefore, the question arises as to whether the relay will operate under fault conditions. The answer is to routinely test all protective relays. However, overtesting should be avoided, because testing can potentially add more trouble than is corrected. All relay test programs should include tests that simulate normal operating conditions. The test program should include acceptance, installation, routine, and repair. Before meaningful tests can be conducted, advance preparation should be undertaken in order that the testing personnel become familiar with the relays or relay systems.

PROTECTIVE RELAY INSPECTION AND TESTS

General

The installation, maintenance, and small repair testing are done in the field, whereas acceptance and major repair testing are conducted in the laboratory. To minimize the potential liability of adding trouble to the relays or relay system, the following general procedures are recommended.

ADVANCE PREPARATION

- Study the protection scheme (station prints, relay instruction manuals).
- Obtain and review results of previous tests and other pertinent information.
- Arrange for test equipment to perform all tests.
- Make outage request and switching arrangements.
- Schedule remote tripping and load tests, when required.

DAILY PREPARATION

- Set up test equipment. Observe precautions in selection and connection to low-voltage service.

- Operating or test personnel perform switching, as arranged, according to approved outage requests.

  Open and isolate, TEST DEAD, and ground if reuired; place "Keep Out" tag, and report "On" the circuit; complete operating log entries.

  If test personnel are not present when switching is performed, verify the isolation, grounding, tag placement, and TEST DEAD before reporting "On" the circuit.

- Isolate control circuits; that is, remove control fuses, open test switches, and/or operate selector controls as required. *Caution:* Be aware of overlapping and interconnecting protective circuits associated with operating equipment. Take measures necessary to keep such schemes in operation. Isolate control, current, and potential transformer secondary circuits to protect against an unintentional operation from tests on the "tagged" circuit.

TESTS AND INSPECTIONS

- Perform and record results of "as found" tests. Confirm calibrations and settings with a system protection study or relay setting and manufacturer's instructions. Record any defects found; discrepancies should be reported promptly to a supervisor or person in charge and resolved, if necessary.

- Verify printed information on the routine inspection sheet (RIS) test forms from previous tests. Prepare other RIS forms, if required.

- Perform visual and mechanical inspections.

  Check tightness, clearance of exposed lugs, and condition of wiring on panels and switchboards. Check clips of fuse holders for tightness and alignment.

  Inspect and perform minor repairs on relays and auxiliary devices. Observe clearances, mechanical freedom, condition of contacts and control springs, condition of internal insulation, and tightness of internal connections. Clean magnets. Check targets and reset mechanisms. Wash and clean glass covers and inspect and replace cover gaskets as needed.

- Inspect and test current and potential transformers (CT and PT), related auxiliaries, and associated wiring.

  Inspect for evidence of corona.

  Check nameplate information with test forms and other data sources available on the equipment.

  Perform CT secondary winding impedance and continuity ("back-feed" test).

Electrical tests on PT secondary windings normally are not necessary. PT performance is assured by in-service observations and primary fuse monitoring schemes.

- Perform "as left" relay tests. Record results on test forms. Make necessary electrical and mechanical adjustments to achieve desired results.

- Calibrate local indicating and recording instruments, and adjust as necessary. Record results on instrument test forms. Calibrate and adjust supervisory telemetering transducers.

- Perform complete tripping and operational tests to verify all control and protective functions and alarms. Include supervisory, remote tripping, and bus differential trip circuits.

- Complete test forms. Make necessary corrections for circuit designation changes and other changes that may have occurred but were not previously recorded. Include manhours required to make the tests.

AFTER COMPLETION

- Replace covers, switchgear plates, remove test leads, jumpers, and separators, close test switches, replace fuses, inspect circuit equipment, and set up control and selector switches preparatory to switching.

- Make inventory of tools, jumpers, separators, instruments, and other equipment used. When completed, instruct crew members to consider the circuit as energized and the tag holder to advise that he is ready to report "Off" the circuit.

- Report "Off" the circuit and arrange for circuit restoration.

- Operating or testing personnel, remove protective grounds and perform switching to restore the circuit to service.

- Perform desired tests under load. Replace covers when completed.

- Restore all station controls to normal, complete station operating log and "Keep Out" tag entries.

AFTER TESTS COMPLETED ON ALL CIRCUITS
Most of the following items may be performed progressively during the total test period.

- Make necessary field corrections to station prints. Arrange for follow-up in order that corrections are made in permanent records.

- Arrange for necessary changes or additions to panel or other circuit designations.

- Complete entry of the relay test records in station ledger if such a ledger is available.
- Prepare a list of items that were not complete or tests not performed. Include items that may need to be referred to other groups. Submit this list along with completed test forms to your supervisor or persons in charge.
- Inspect station to confirm that prints and records are secured and various equipment accessories and spare parts are properly stored.

PROTECTIVE RELAY TEST PROCEDURES AND CIRCUITS

The testing of protective relays and associated circuitry can be carried out by following recommendations outlined in manufacturer's bulletins or the user's own test procedures. These procedures should always be updated based upon a review of past relay performance, test equipment evaluation, and testing methods.

The test interval can be adjusted based upon experience. Otherwise, testing of relays on a yearly basis is recommended. The test methods used for relay testing consist of relay functional tests (i.e., relay equipment is separated from power equipment) and only secondary tests are made. The following general guidelines are recommended for electrical testing of protective relays, associated instrument transformers, and wiring.

General Protective Relay Calibration and Checklist

- Perform insulation resistance test on each branch circuit to frame. Do not perform this test on solid-state relays. Check manufacturer's instructions to verify if any other precautions are required.
- Perform the following tests on the nominal settings specified.

  Pickup parameters on each operating element.

  Timing tests should be performed at three points on the time dial curve.

  Pickup target and seal-in units.

  Special tests as required to check operation of restraint, directional, and other elements per manufacturer's instruction manual.
- Perform phase angle and magnitude contribution tests on all differential- and directional-type relays after energization to vectorially prove proper polarity and connection.

Relay Test Points and Test Circuits

TIME OVERCURRENT RELAYS

Overcurrent relays are checked for minimum pickup. Check a minimum of three timing points at $2 \times$ tap, $4.5 \times$ tap, and $6 \times$ tap settings. The periodic inspection pickup tolerance is ± 5 percent of tap value for nongeared relays and ± 7 percent for geared relays. For new relay the tolerance is ± 1 percent of tap value. Pickup is defined as that value of current which will just close the relay contacts. Check the instantaneous unit pickup by gradually applying the current. Also check the target seal-in unit by blocking the main overcurrent contacts. The testing of overcurrent relay is done one phase at a time. The ground relay is tested similarly to the phase relays.

DIRECTIONAL OVERCURRENT RELAYS

The overcurrent unit of directional relay should be checked similar to the overcurrent relay, with the directional unit blocked closed. The directional relay should be tested for minimum pickup, maximum torque angle, contact gap, and clutch pressure. If the phase power supply is not available, the directional unit can be tested by applying single-phase voltage and current in phase. Usually, this test will give large variations in in-phase pickup, because of in-phase angle being far different from maximum torque angle.

DIFFERENTIAL RELAYS

The test conducted on differential relays is to check minimum pickup values using operating and differential currents. The slope (differential characteristic) and harmonic restraint should also be checked. It may also be desirable to trip all circuit breakers from differential relays as a regular testing procedure.

DISTANCE RELAYS

The distance characteristics of the relay are checked near the fault and load angles. Similar to the directional overcurrent relays, the pickup, maximum torque angle, clutch pressure, and contact gap tests should be made.

PILOT WIRE RELAYS

The pilot wire relay schemes should be tested for shorts, continuity, and grounds in the pilot wires. The operating values are checked along with supervisory and alarm relays used in pilot wire schemes.

PLUNGER-TYPE RELAYS

In this type, relays such as PJC, SC, and HFA, are included. These relays are tested for operating pickup and dropout values by gradually increasing or decreasing the operating current or voltage.

CURRENT BALANCE RELAYS

Check pickup of each coil as explained under section on overcurrent relays. Check for no-trip condition by applying equal amounts of current to opposing coils. Also check operation of the target indicator coil similar to overcurrent relay.

OVERVOLTAGE RELAY

Check minimum pickup of overvoltage coil similar to overcurrent relays. Select three timing points on the specified time dial. Pickup and timing points should be within ±1 percent for new installations and within ±5 percent on existing installations. Check the instantaneous (if applicable) pickup and target indicator coil.

UNDERVOLTAGE RELAY

Check dropout of relay and time relay trip when voltage is suddenly reduced from rated voltage to dropout voltage settings or to zero. Dropout and timing points should be within ±1 percent for new installations and within ±5 percent for existing installations. The instantaneous unit should be checked for dropout and target indicator coil.

THERMAL OVERLOAD RELAYS

The thermal overload relays minimum pickup value should be checked using some convenient multiple of tap settings. Because of long time characteristics, the relay pickup point below 200 percent of tap setting may take a considerable time. Therefore, for test purposes, check pickup at about 200 to 400 percent of tap settings. Similar to overcurrent relays, the relay time should be checked for several points on the time dial curve. The acceptable time should be within ±10 percent of specified values. Also check the instantaneous pickup values and target indicator coil.

INSTRUMENT TRANSFORMERS CALIBRATION

Instrument transformers, such as current transformers, potential transformers, and capacitive potential devices, should be given ratio, polarity, and continuity checks.

Ratio Check

The connections for the ratio check test are shown in Figure 7–10. Apply current to the primary to give 1 A in the secondary. For example, in the connection diagram, 120 A is applied to the primary of a 600/5 current transformer. For a proper ratio check, 1 A should be measured in the ammeter connected in the current transformer secondary.

Polarity Check

The connection diagram for polarity check is shown in Figure 7–11. The negative side of the 7½-V battery is connected to the nonpolarity side of the current transformer. Connect a dc voltmeter or low-reading ammeter in the secondary

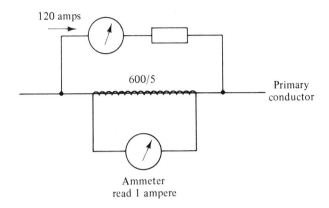

FIGURE 7–10.
Current transformer ratio check.

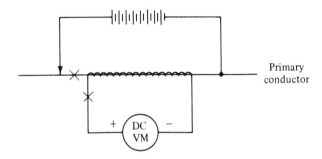

FIGURE 7–11.
Current transformer polarity check.

of the current transformer; the positive side of the battery terminal is left unconnected. To verify polarity connections, momentarily touch the battery positive terminal as shown in the diagram. If the meter needle deflects in the positive direction, polarity is true as connected. If the meter needle deflects in the negative direction, then polarity connections are not as shown connected.

Continuity Check (Backfeed Test)

This test is conducted to check the current transformer windings and the wiring from test switch to current transformer (backfeed) for the three phases. The relay test connection diagram is shown in Figure 7–12. Conduct tests as follows:

- Apply 120-V low current (about 3 A) or a 120-V source with a 100-W lamp at point A. Point A is the test switch location where the protective relay is isolated from current transformers with the relay ground maintained. If the lamp has no glow or no current reading is observed, the current transformer windings are checked.

- Next, jumper to ground the hot side of the current transformer. The lamp will glow brightly (or 3 A will read on low-ampere source). This indicates that relay circuit wiring is continuous without any shorts or open.

- Repeat the preceding test to check all three phases.

- Measure the insulation resistance of transformer secondary windings and CT leads with a 500-V megohmmeter.

- Measure the transformer primary insulation with applicable potential test.

- Verify the connection of the secondary potential transformer leads by applying a low voltage to the leads and checking for this voltage at applicable devices.

- Check for a potential transformer secondary load with secondary voltage and current measurements. Make sure that the load is less than allowable potential transformer burdens.

- Record values on charts of all tests performed on all instruments.

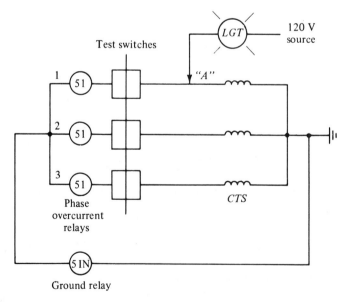

FIGURE 7–12.
Continuity check for current transformers and associated wiring.

7-6 MAINTENANCE AND TESTING OF LOW-VOLTAGE PROTECTIVE DEVICES

Low-voltage protective devices consist of protective devices for low-voltage molded-case circuit breakers, draw-out power circuit breakers, overload relays, and ground fault protective devices. The protective devices are integral parts of the circuit breakers, and motor starters and their maintenance and testing should be coordinated with the maintenance of the circuit breakers, motor starters, and switchgear assemblies. Low-voltage protective devices are classified as low-voltage power circuit breaker trips, molded-case circuit breaker trips, overload relays, and ground fault sensing and relaying equipment.

LOW-VOLTAGE POWER CIRCUIT BREAKER TRIPS

Protective devices for power circuit breakers consist of electromechanical type and solid-state types.

Electromechanical Trips

These are hermetically sealed units that provide time-delay and instantaneous overcurrent protection. The maintenance and testing of these devices involves checking the operation of the trip device and evaluating their trip characteristics. Before any field tests are made, the tester should be thoroughly familiar with the operating and maintenance procedures of these devices. He should also check that the breaker mechanism and trip latch are properly functioning. Ensure that the breaker is deenergized and perform the following maintenance and tests:

MECHANICAL CHECK
Perform a mechanical check on the trip device to assure a successful tripping operation just before the armature reaches its fully closed air gap condition. Consult the manufacturer's information on the unit under test for conducting this check. Also assure that the time-delay escapement is operative. Visually check for missing hardware, evidence of leaking oil, and cracked trip paddles. Use manufacturers' manuals for cleaning methods for trip units.

OVERCURRENT TEST
The purpose of this test is to determine that the trip device will open the circuit breaker to which it is applied. This test can usually be performed by injecting 150 to 300 percent current of the coil rating into the trip coil. The test equipment used should be able to produce the required current and be reasonably sinusoidal. Two low voltage ac test sets are shown in Figures 7–13 and 7–14. The following test procedure is offered as a general guide:

- Connect the test set to the upper and lower studs of one pole of the breaker. Set the long-time-delay (LTD) trip unit at 100 percent setting. Close the breaker and adjust the current of the test set to the desired value (i.e., 150 to 300 percent) required for the particular trip device.

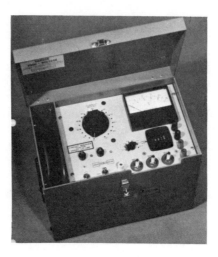

FIGURE 7–13.
Low-voltage alternating-current test set, 400 amperes, used for molded-case breakers. (Courtesy of Hipotronics, Brewster, N.Y.)

Consult the manufacturers' recommendations for exact values of the test current value.

- Shut off the test set and allow the trip device to reset. After the trip device has reset, again apply the current to it until it trips. Record the trip time and trip current.

- If repeat tests are required, allow the device to cool sufficiently between each test.

- Compare the trip time measured at the test current values with the factory trip curve. Make adjustments to bring the trip device within factory trip curve values. However, do not exceed adjustable ranges of the trip unit when making field adjustments.

In view of the wide variation in test conditions between field tests and factory tests, it will be difficult to duplicate the factory trip curves. Judgment should be used when evaluating the test data as to whether the trip unit is functioning within specified limits. The short time delay and instantaneous tripping units may be tested similarly. The setting of these units should not be indiscriminately changed because the protection provided by these units maybe compromised.

Solid-State Trip Units

The field testing and calibration of solid-state units can be performed by a specially designed power supply unit. Most solid-state trip units have terminal blocks that are equipped with test plug terminals for making the calibration test. The test set allows checking of the solid-state trip unit operation without using

FIGURE 7-14.
Low-voltage alternating-current test set, 50,000 amperes, used for
power-circuit breakers. (Courtesy of Hipotronics, Brewster, N.Y.)

primary current. The test set will pass enough current to check any desired calibration point. The breaker must be disconnected from the bus before checking the operation of the solid-state trip units. If the test set shows that the solid-state trip unit is not functioning properly, the trip unit should be replaced and the defective unit returned to the manufacturer for repairs. It is recommended that the reader refer to the instructions of a particular test set for operating procedures.

MOLDED-CASE BREAKER TRIPS

Molded-case circuit breakers are low-voltage protective devices that are available in a wide range of sizes and ratings. They are used widely in the industry to provide a resettable circuit interrupting device. Molded-case circuit breakers have a good record of reliability when they are maintained and calibrated regularly and properly. Following are the field and verification testing of molded-case circuit breakers.

Routine Field Testing

The following tests are listed for molded-case circuit breakers in order to ensure that the circuit breaker will perform its basic protective functions. All tests are to be performed when the circuit breaker is deenergized and disconnected from line and load conductors.

INSULATION RESISTANCE MEASUREMENT TEST

This test is made to verify the condition of the insulation of the circuit breaker. A minimum of 500-V test voltage should be used for making this test. It would be preferable to use a test voltage that is at least 50 percent higher than the voltage of the circuit breaker. Tests should be made between pole to ground, between adjacent poles with circuit breaker contacts closed, and between line to load terminal with breaker in open position. A minimum value of 1 MΩ is considered safe. Resistance values below 1 MΩ should be investigated for possible trouble.

MILLIVOLT DROP TEST

This test consists of applying a direct current across the closed circuit breaker contacts and measuring the voltage drop due to the contact resistance. Excessive voltage drop indicates abnormal conditions such as contact and/or connection erosion and contamination. This test is similar to the microhming test described under medium-voltage switchgear. The manufacturers of molded-case circuit breakers should be consulted in order to find the acceptable millivolt drop values for particular breakers being tested. It is recommended that large breakers be tested with direct current of 50 to 100 A and smaller breakers be tested at rated (or below rated) currents.

MECHANICAL OPERATION

Before making any electrical connections, the circuit breaker should be checked by manually turning the breaker on and off several times. This check is to ensure that all mechanical linkages are operating.

CONNECTION TEST

This is a visual test that is conducted to assure that there is no overheating and/or that arcing is present in the electrical joints. An infrared gun may also be used to spot heated joints instead of visual observation. If signs of arcing or excessive heating are present, the connections should be removed and thoroughly cleaned. Also, during installation, proper attention should be given to electrical connections to minimize damage to the aluminum lugs and conductors.

PROTECTIVE TRIP TESTING

The testing of protective trips involves the calibration of overload (thermal) and magnetic overcurrent trips to verify that the circuit breaker will automatically open. This is important from the viewpoint of protection and system selectivity. The overload trip characteristics (i.e., time-current relationship) can be verified by selecting a certain percentage of breaker current rating, such as 300 percent, and applying this current to each pole of the circuit breaker to determine if the breaker will open in accordance with the manufacturer's specified time. The obvious goal is to see if the circuit breaker will automatically open and, further, to see if it opens within the minimum and maximum range of operating times.

For specific values of operating times, refer to the manufacturer's manual for breakers under test. The evaluation of test results is based upon the following:

- *Minimum trip times:* If the minimum tripping times are lower than indicated by the manufacturer's manual for the breaker under test, the breaker should be retested after it has been cooled to 25°C. If the values obtained are still lower after retest, the breaker manufacturer should be consulted before reenergizing.

- *Maximum tripping time:* If trip time of the breaker exceeds the maximum tripping time as indicated in the manufacturer's manual, recheck the test procedure and conditions (as shown under verification testing), and retest. If the test still indicates higher values than maximum tripping, further check the breaker for "maximum allowable tripping time."

- *Maximum allowable tripping time:* If the breaker does not trip within the allowable maximum time, the breaker should be replaced. However, if the breaker tripping time is below the "maximum allowable" but higher than the maximum tripping time, the breaker should be checked to see if it is below the tripping time for cable damage. If so, the breaker is providing an acceptable level of protection.

The magnetic (instantaneous) trip should be checked by selecting suitable current to ensure that the breaker magnetic feature is working. The difficulty in conducting this test is the availability of obtaining the required high value of test current. Again, to verify the breaker trip characteristics, precise control of test conditions is necessary; otherwise, different test results will be obtained. Moreover, due to large values of test current, the trip characteristics of the breaker can be influenced by stray magnetic fields. Also, the current wave shape can influence the test results. Therefore, when conducting this test, stray magnetic fields should be minimized and true sinusoidal test wave shape should be used. The magnetic trip unit may be tested as follows:

In the *runup method,* one pole of the breaker is connected to the test equipment and approximately 70 percent of the tripping current is injected into the breaker gradually until the breaker trips. The injection of current into the breaker has to be done skillfully so that it is neither too slow nor too fast. If the injection of current is too slow, the breaker may trip owing to the thermal effect and not provide a true value of tripping current. Whereas if the current is injected too quickly, the meter reading will lag the actual current owing to damping of the meter and thus provide an erroneous test result. It is very difficult to obtain true test results from this test.

The *pulse method* requires equipment with a pointer stop ammeter or an image-retaining oscilloscope. This method is generally considered more accurate than the run-up method. The current to the circuit breaker under test is applied in short pulses of 5- to 10-cycle duration until the breaker trips. The current is then reduced just below this value, and the pointer stop on the ammeter is adjusted by repeated pulses until the pointer movement is barely noticeable. The current is then raised slightly and the tripping value of current rechecked. One disadvantage of this test is that it is subject to dc offset when conducted in the field. The dc offset may be as high as 20 percent, and therefore the tripping current indicated by the ammeter may be 20 percent lower.

Because of inherent errors in the field testing of protective trips, test results may vary from the manufacturer's published values. Therefore, the main thrust of any field testing of molded-case breakers should be to ensure, first, that the breaker is functional and, second, that its trip characteristics are within the range of values for that particular type of circuit breaker.

Verification Testing

The verification testing of molded-case circuit breakers in the field is intended to check the circuit breaker performance against manufacturer's published test data. All low-voltage molded-case circuit breakers that are Underwriter's Laboratories (UL) listed are tested in accordance with UL standard 489. The UL testing is conducted in the laboratory and under controlled conditions. It may be very difficult to simulate the same conditions in the field. Therefore, any field verification testing of molded-case circuit breakers must recognize the differences in the test results, because it is not practical to meet all the test conditions specified in UL standard 489. The following is a summary of conditions under which UL calibration and trip-time values are obtained.

- Circuit breakers are tested in open air at 25°C ambient temperature.
- The trip values of circuit breaker are measured from cold start.
- The calibration tests are made with UL specified size conductors connected to line and load terminals.
- The current must be held constant without variation over the entire test period.
- The rated maximum interrupting current for testing magnetic trip is 5,000 A or more.

When performing verification testing in the field, the conditions as stated in UL standard 489 must be simplified. But the simplified testing must recognize the differences in testing results that are obtained for various test setups. If the data measured under the verification tests vary 10 percent for the magnetic trip, the test conditions must be verified or the manufacturer should be consulted before discarding the breaker.

OVERLOAD RELAYS

Overload relays usually found in motor starters or other low-voltage applications require the same attention and calibration as do low-voltage circuit breaker trips. Overload relays should be given an overcurrent test to determine that the overloads will open the starter contacts to provide protection to the motor at its overload pickup value. These test procedures are similar to the test conducted for low-voltage circuit breakers, except that the current injected into the overload relay should be limited to 350 percent or less. The frequency for testing and calibration should be checked to assure that it is selected properly. In addition, the trip setting of the relay should be evaluated to account for any ambient variations between motor location and starter location. Refer to Section 2-2 for adjustment of ambient variations.

TESTING OF GROUND FAULT SENSING AND RELAYING EQUIPMENT

Ground fault sensing and relaying equipment is covered by UL standard 1053. It classifies ground fault protection into class I and class II. Class I ground fault protection is intended to be used with disconnecting devices at high levels of fault current, whereas class II ground fault protection is used with disconnecting devices with limited interrupting current capacity. This testing application guidance is directed toward class I ground fault relaying.

In accordance with NEMA Publication PB1.2-1977 (Application Guide for Ground Fault Protective Device and Equipment), manufacturers are required to perform design and production tests. The design tests include calibration, temperature rise, overvoltage, overload, dielectric withstand, endurance, and the like. The production tests are conducted to determine if calibration settings are within performance limits, control circuits are working properly, and current sensors have correct turns ratio. The field testing of ground fault protective relaying equipment is discussed next.

Preparation for Fielding Testing

- Review the electrical drawings for the power system, as well as the manufacturer equipment drawings, to ensure that ground fault equipment is installed as designed.

- With the power off, remove the disconnect link on the switchboard to isolate the neutral of the wiring system from both supply and ground. Measure the insulation resistance of the neutral to ground with the main disconnect open to ensure that no ground connections exist downstream of the GFP devices being checked. For a dual fed (double-ended) power system, remove all the disconnect links to isolate the neutral from both the supply and ground before measuring the insulation resistance.

- Visually inspect the wiring system to confirm there is an adequate grounding connection at the service equipment upstream of any ground fault sensor, and that the neutral connection is run from the supply transformer to the service equipment in accordance with the National

Electrical Code. Where dual power sources are involved, confirm that the main grounding connection at the service equipment is in accordance with manufacturer's recommendations.

- Once these steps have been accomplished, return all neutral and ground connections to their normal intended operating condition.

Field Testing

- Field testing should be limited to only those tests that are necessary to determine that installation is correct and the ground fault protection system is operational. Because of the many variables involved, field testing cannot be considered as an accurate check of the calibration of any sensing relay. Field test current sources can introduce errors owing to nonsinusodial wave shapes, power source regulation problems, and metering accuracy. In addition, timing measurements often include additional delay times owing to the use of auxiliary relays and timers. Field testing should be limited to a go/no-go type of testing, which confirms the serviceability of the system involved.

- Before field testing is initiated on any ground fault sensing and relaying equipment, the manufacturer's installation and instruction literature should be reviewed and understood. The manufacturer's field test recommendations should be followed.

- Ground fault sensing and relaying equipment utilizing either ground return or vectorial summation sensing methods can be checked in the field by passing a measured test current directly through the sensing transformer or test windings. To confirm the proper functioning of the equipment while it is installed in the switchboard or panelboard, the following tests can be performed.

SIMULATED GROUND FAULT TEST USING SENSORS WITHOUT BUILT-IN TEST WINDINGS

- Turn off all power to the switchboard section or panelboard. Set the relay to its minimum current setting.

- Loop a test coil of wire having sufficient current-carrying capacity through the sensor window. Prefabricated multiturn test cables may be used for convenience.

- Provide control power only and close the disconnect associated with the GFP device being tested.

- Apply sufficient test current so that the ampere turns of the test winding numerically equal or exceed 125 percent of the relay current setting. The relay should trip the disconnect. Immediately return the test current to zero.

- Turn off all power, remove the test winding, and restore all equipment to the operating condition.
- Reset the relay to the predetermined setting, reestablish control power, and turn on main power as needed.

SIMULATED GROUND FAULT TEST USING SENSORS WITH INTEGRAL (BUILT-IN) TEST WINDINGS

A go/no-go test for the proper tripping of the GFP devices and the interconnections between the sensor, the relay, and the disconnect mechanism can be made by following manufacturer's test instructions. The manufacturer usually provides for a test current greater than 125 percent of the maximum current setting, so a test can be made anytime without disturbing the current settings. If there is any question concerning the ability of the GFP device to operate at its minimum setting and for low ground fault currents, a test as described in simulated ground fault tests using sensors without built-in test windings can be made immediately following installation. Periodic tests using the manufacturer's test circuit should be adequate after installation.

EQUIPMENT WITH BUILT-IN TEST CIRCUITRY BUT WITHOUT A BUILT-IN TEST WINDING

Following installation, the GFP devices should be tested in accordance with "Simulated Ground Fault Test Using Sensors without Built-in Test Windings" to confirm that sensors and interconnections to the ground fault relay are functioning. Thereafter, the manufacturer's test circuit can be used to check the operation of the GFP relay and the tripping circuitry.

TEST BUTTONS AND INDICATORS

Operate test buttons to check the functions described in the manufacturer's instructions. Pilot lights and other indicators should signal ground fault tripping or other functions as described in the manufacturer's instructions.

ZONE SELECTIVE INTERLOCKING FUNCTION

The manufacturer should be consulted for specific instructions when this test is to be performed in the field.

CHAPTER 8

ELECTRICAL POWER SYSTEM GROUNDING AND GROUND RESISTANCE TESTING

8-1 INTRODUCTION

System grounding has been used in electrical power systems since its beginning. However, many companies and industrial plants have used system grounding methods differently. The problem of whether a system neutral should be grounded, and how it should be grounded, has many times been misunderstood completely. Therefore, grounding of many systems has been based upon past experience rather than engineering analysis.

This chapter provides applicable information for grounding, such as definitions, reasons for having a system ground, the most desirable grounding method, and so on, and how to measure ground resistance in order to maintain the grounding system.

The definition of grounding is commonly used for both systems, grounding and equipment grounding. The National Electrical Code (NEC) defines system ground as a connection to ground from one of the current-carrying conductors of an electrical power system or of an interior wiring system, whereas an equipment ground is defined as a connection to ground from one or more of the non-current-carrying metal parts of a wiring system or equipment connected to the system.

The Institute of Electrical and Electronic Engineers (IEEE) standard 142-1972 and American National Standard Institute (ANSI) standard C114.1-1973 cover system grounding. The following definitions are taken from these standards.

- *System neutral ground:* a connection to ground from the neutral point or points of a circuit, transformer, motor, generator, or system.
- *Grounded system:* a system of conductors in which at least one conductor or point is intentionally grounded.
- *Ungrounded system:* a system of conductors in which there is no intentional connection to ground.

375

- *Solidly grounded:* a system in which there is no intentional impedance in ground connection; in such a system the line to ground fault currents may equal three-phase fault current.
- *Resistance grounded:* a system grounded through a resistance the value of which can be such as to provide either a low- or high-resistance ground system. The low-resistance ground system can have from 25 to several thousand amperes depending upon the value of the resistance. The high-resistance ground system usually has a value less than 25 a but greater than the value given by $X_{co}/3$, where X_{co} is the charging capacitance of the system.
- *Reactance grounded:* a system grounded through a reactance.
- *Resonant grounded:* the system grounding reactance value is such that the rated frequency fault current flowing through it is substantially equal to the current flowing between the conductors and the earth (charging current of the system).
- *Ground fault neutralizer:* a grounding device that provides an inductive component of current in a ground fault that is substantially equal to, and therefore neutralizes, the rated frequency capacitive component of the ground fault current.

8-2   SELECTION OF GROUNDING METHOD

The selection of a method for power system grounding is very difficult because a large number of factors must be considered before a power system grounding method can be chosen. The following discussion outlines some problems with various grounding methods and explains how and why grounding systems are applied.

UNGROUNDED SYSTEMS

Early electrical systems are almost universally operated ungrounded. On small systems an insulation failure on one phase did not cause an outage. The failure could probably be found and repaired at a convenient time without a forced outage. This worked well as long as the systems were small. However, as systems increased in size and voltage rating, an increasing number of insulation failures produced multiple failures and major faults. At first the reasons for these failures were not understood, and considerable work was done to find why they occurred. Figure 8–1 shows a typical "ungrounded" neutral system. Actually, it is a capacitive grounded neutral system, the capacitance being the conductor capacitance to ground. In normal operation the capacitive current of all three lines is leading the respective line to neutral voltages by 90°, and the vector sum of all three currents is zero. Figure 8–2 shows what happens when

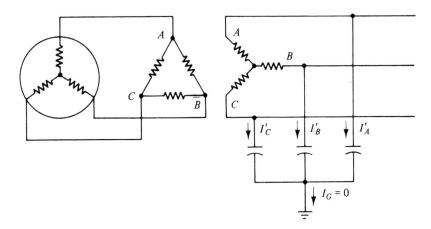

FIGURE 8–1.
Ungrounded system-normal condition.

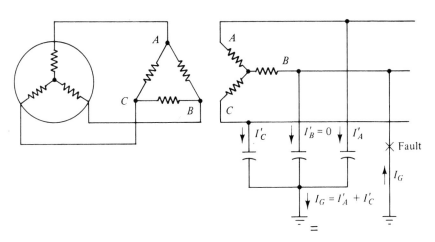

I'_B is 0 since E_B is 0.

Voltage across C_A and C_C now E_{BA} and E_{BC} instead of E_A and E_C.

$I'_A = \sqrt{3} I_A \underline{/+30°}$ and $I'_C = \sqrt{3} I_C \underline{/-30°}$. Assume $I_A = I_B = I_C = 1$ P.U.

Then $I_A = 1 \underline{/+210°}$ and $I_C = 1 \underline{/-30°}$ or

$I'_A = \sqrt{3} \underline{/+30°} \underline{/+210°} = \sqrt{3} \underline{/+240°}$ and $I'_C = \sqrt{3} \underline{/-30°} \underline{/-30°} = \sqrt{3} \underline{/-60°}$.

$I'_A + I'_C = I_G = \sqrt{3} \underline{/-120°} + \sqrt{3} \underline{/-60°} = 3 \underline{/-90°} = -3 I_B$ of Fig. 8.1

FIGURE 8–2.
Ungrounded system, Bϕ fault to ground.

the system of Figure 8–1 is accidentally grounded. The charging current of the faulted phase goes to zero because its voltage to ground is zero. The voltages of the unfaulted phases increase to full line-to-line value with respect to ground, and their charging currents increase proportionally. In addition, because of the 30° shift of the line voltages with respect to ground, the charging currents shift accordingly, and the sum of the charging currents in the unfaulted phases is three times the normal value and appears in the ground, returning to the system through the fault. If the fault can be interrupted, it will most likely be done at a current zero. However, since the current leads by 90° in the capacitive circuit, current zero occurs at the instant of a voltage maximum; thus, if the fault momentarily clears, a high voltage immediately appears across the fault, and restrike of the fault will probably occur.

In the momentary interval of time that the fault has been cleared the excessive voltage charge of the capacitors on the unfaulted lines has been trapped as a dc charge. When the arc restrikes again, the capacitors are again recharged by a line-to-ground voltage added to the trapped charge. Thus a restrike after another current zero clearing is more inevitable, adding another charge. The phenomenon thus probably becomes an oscillating and self-perpetuating buildup in voltage, which eventually will lead to an insulation failure on another phase and a major two-phase fault. While the first failure may have been a tree branch in the line, the second failure may occur at some other location entirely, perhaps involving expensive equipment insulation, such as a transformer. Thus the principal advantage claimed for the ungrounded system actually caused troubles that resulted in its abandonment.

These troubles coupled with other factors led to the adoption of grounded neutral systems in some form. Some of the other factors were as follows:

- Because of greater danger to personnel, code authorities frowned on ungrounded systems.
- Equipment costs were generally lower for equipment rated for grounded neutral systems because of the reduction in insulation permissible; because graded insulation could be used, single-bushing, single-phase transformers could be used.
- At the higher voltages being used today (69 kV and above), material savings in transformer costs can be realized by employing reduced insulation levels (BIL). These savings are in addition to the modest savings above, and may amount to substantial savings in the cost of transformers in the various voltage classes with reduced insulation. The requirements for safely reducing insulation level demand that system neutrals be well grounded. Thus these savings are not available on the ungrounded system.

SOLIDLY GROUNDED SYSTEMS

The simplest and most effective method of grounding is to solidly connect the neutrals of any wye-connected transformers or generators to ground. This method has two major advantages:

- It is simple and inexpensive in that it requires no extra equipment.
- It minimizes the magnitude of the overvoltage that will appear on the unfaulted phases during a ground fault, resulting in a reduction in the stress on insulation as compared with other methods. This is the reason that solidly grounded neutrals are a necessity where reduced BIL insulation is to be used.

In spite of the advantages of the solidly grounded system, there are associated disadvantages such that other grounding methods are often used. These disadvantages all stem from the fact that a solidly grounded system produces the greatest magnitude of ground fault current when a fault to ground occurs. It is realized that with a grounded neutral system perhaps 95 percent or more of all faults start as a single phase to ground fault. If the amount of ground current that flows can be controlled and the fault cleared promptly, the amount of damage at the fault will be reduced and the fault probably restricted so as not to involve more than the one phase. This may result in preventing burn-downs, reduction in the cost of making repairs, and reduction in the frequency or extent of maintenance on the breakers that interrupt the fault. In the case of machines or transformers, the difference in repair cost may be that of replacing a few damaged coils as compared with completely replacing the machine or transformer, which may be necessary where oil fires and explosion follow the transformer fault, or where heavy fault currents melt down coils and burn and weld together expensive areas of laminated electrical steel in the transformer core or machine stator iron. Since the damage done is approximately proportional to I^2t, it is obvious that much more can be done in the reduction of current than by reduction in time. Figure 8-3 shows the relationship of impedances controlling three phase and single phase to ground faults. Under the proper conditions, single phase to ground faults can give rise to short-circuit currents 50% in excess of three phase short-circuit current. Thus breakers whose ratings make them entirely capable of interrupting three-phase faults may be in severe difficulty handling a single phase to ground fault. In view of this, the potential savings in damage and repair costs or avoiding the cost of having to install larger breakers may justify avoiding the simple and inexpensive solidly grounded system in favor of a more complex and expensive system that will provide control of the amount of fault current.

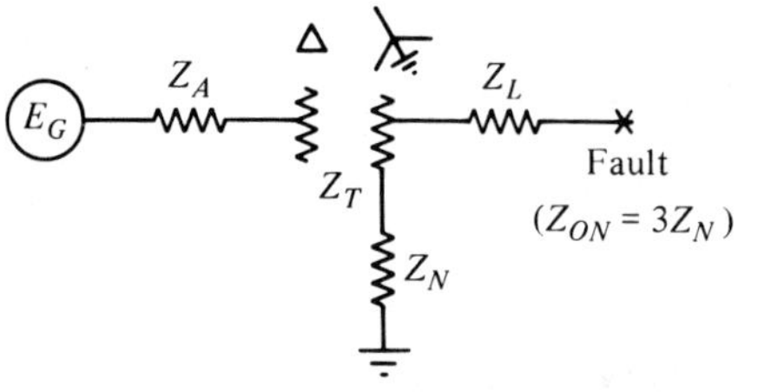

Typical
Grounded Neutral
System

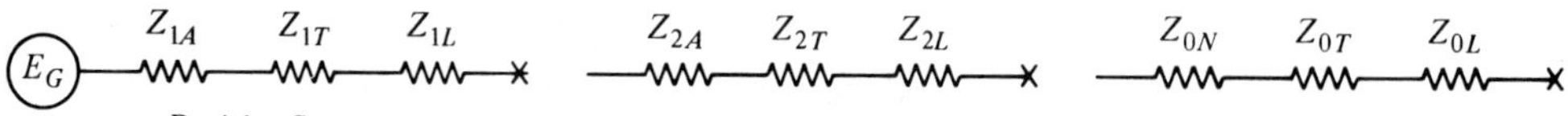

Positive Sequence
Impedance System

Negative Sequence
Impedance System

Zero Sequence
Impedance System

	3φ Fault Current	1 Phase to Ground Fault Current
①	$I_{F3\phi} = \dfrac{E_G}{Z_{1A} + Z_{1T} + Z_{1L}}$	$I_{F1\phi} = \dfrac{3E_G}{Z_{1A} + Z_{2A} + Z_{1T} + Z_{2T} + Z_{1L} + Z_{2L} + Z_{0N} + Z_{0T} + Z_{0L}}$

But $Z_{1A} \cong Z_{2A}$; $Z_{1T} = Z_{2T}$ and $Z_{1L} = Z_{2L}$

②	$I_{F3\phi} = \dfrac{E_G}{Z_{1A} + Z_{1T} + Z_{1L}}$	$I_{F1\phi} \cong \dfrac{3E_G}{2(Z_{1A} + Z_{1T} + Z_{1L}) + Z_{0N} + Z_{0T} + Z_{0L}}$

If we assume fault at transformer secondary, $Z_{1L} = Z_{2L} = Z_{0L} = 0$.

③	$I_{F3\phi} = \dfrac{E_G}{Z_{1A} + Z_{1T}}$	$I_{F1\phi} \cong \dfrac{3E_G}{2(Z_{1A} + Z_{1T}) + Z_{0N} + Z_{0T}}$

But if $Z_{0N} = 0$; $Z_{1T} \cong Z_{0T}$ and Z_{1T} is small compared to Z_{1A}.

④	$I_{F3\phi} = \dfrac{E_G}{Z_{1A}}$	$I_{F1\phi} \cong \dfrac{3E_G}{2Z_{1A}}$ or $I_{F1\phi} = \dfrac{3}{2} I_{F3\phi}$

Going back to equation ③ by changing value of Z_{0N} the 1φ
fault can be varied from a maximum approaching $I_{F1\phi} = \dfrac{3}{2} I_{F3\phi}$
down to $I_{F1\phi} = 0$ for infinite value of Z_{0N}.

If fault is out on line from station: since Z_{0L} varies
from approximately 3 to 10 times value of Z_{1L}, it follows
that $I_{F1\phi}$ value drops off rapidly with respect to $I_{F3\phi}$
as fault location is moved out on line. In a short distance
it will become less than $I_{F3\phi}$ value and on long feeders
may approach rated load current values even where $Z_{0N} = 0$.

FIGURE 8–3.

Relationship of three-phase and single phase to ground faults.

REACTANCE AND RESISTANCE GROUNDED SYSTEMS

Reactors are commonly employed as a neutral impedance for ground-current limitation when the amount of current reduction is small. This is because reactors of low ohmic value to handle large quantities of current can be built quite inexpensively as compared with a resistor for the same current limitation. Reactors to provide current limitation to values less than approximately 30 to 50 percent of three-phase short-circuit value are not practical. This is true partly because the high ohmic values necessary to provide the higher current limitation makes them more expensive than resistors, and partly because high values of reactance grounding approach the conditions of ungrounded systems and give rise to high transient voltages.

Where it is desired to limit fault currents to moderate to small values, resistors are generally used. The directly connected resistor is not practical for extremes of current limitation. Where a small reduction of current is required, reactors are used, because a resistor large enough to handle the large quantities of current remaining would have to have resistor grids of tremendous cross section or many parallel grid paths, and as a result would be very expensive. On the other hand, if extreme limitation of ground current by resistors is desired, the resistor again becomes excessively expensive. This is because there are maximum values of resistance that it is practical to build into a resistor unit before the cross-sectional area of the resistance conductor becomes so small as to make it too susceptible to mechanical failure from shock, rust, corrosion, and the like. Thus, to get very high values of resistance, the resistor must be made up by connecting a tremendous number of moderate resistance units in series and it becomes expensive and bulky.

Where it is desirable and practical to limit ground fault currents to extremely low values, a variation of the directly connected resistor is used to avoid the expense and difficulties of the very high value resistance. A distribution transformer is connected between the neutral to be grounded and ground. A resistor is then connected across the secondary of the transformer, as shown in Figure 8–4. The actual 0.25-Ω resistor in the transformer secondary is stepped up in value as it appears to the generator neutral by the square of the transformer ratio of 13,200/240 or 3,024 times. Thus the $\frac{1}{4}$-Ω secondary resistor appears as a 756-Ω resistor in the generator neutral. This limits the ground fault current to a maximum of 10.5 A. This represents only a small percent of current on the basis of machine full-load current and of the maximum three-phase fault current available. This is representative of the extreme of current limitation. It accomplishes the ultimate in the reduction of fault damage. Further reduction of fault current would be dangerous, because if it were attempted, the capacitance of the generator and step-up transformer windings and the generator lead bus duct would predominate over the higher values of resistance, and the system would approach the characteristics of the original ungrounded system of Figure 8–1 with its dangers of arcing grounds.

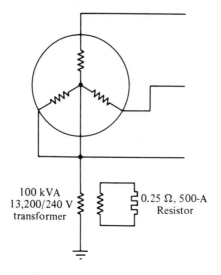

Voltage across transformer primary

on solid ground fault = $\dfrac{13800}{\sqrt{3}}$ = 7970

Resistance of 0.25 Ω resistor to

primary circuit = $0.25 \times \left(\dfrac{13200}{240}\right)^2$ = 756 Ω

$\text{Max } I_{F1\phi} = \dfrac{E}{R} = \dfrac{7970}{756}$ = 10.53 Amps

100 kVA
13,200/240 V
transformer

0.25 Ω, 500-A
Resistor

FIGURE 8—4.
High-resistance grounding method.

RESONANT GROUNDING

One of the earliest methods of attempting to eliminate the faults of the un-grounded system and still retain the claimed advantages for it was by means of resonant grounding using the Peterson coil. This method attempted to eliminate the fault current that could cause the arcing ground condition. Figure 8–5 shows the system of Figures 8–1 and 8–2 with the Peterson coil applied. This is simply a tuneable, iron-cored reactor connected between neutral and ground. It is tuned so that the current it furnishes matches the current furnished by line capacitance under fault conditions. Under normal system conditions, it does not carry current. However, upon the occurrence of a fault it contributes a reactive component of current through the fault matching the capacitive component. Since the two currents are 180° out of phase, they cancel. This leaves no current at the fault, minimizes the chance of restrike, and thus eliminates the cause of voltage buildup.

The ground fault neutralizer is said to be effective in 70 to 80 percent of the faults. It is not in great favor because it is not 100 percent effective, because of its expense, and because of the expense of the equipment necessary to protect it in the 20 to 30 percent of the cases when it does not work. The principal cause of its failure to work is improper tuning. This might seem to be easily corrected, but when it is realized that retuning would be required upon each feeder extension or rearrangement, for each emergency switching condition, or that even if kept properly tuned the system could be detuned by a broken conductor associated with the fault it was to clear, some of the difficul-

ties of its application can be realized. It can work well in a three-phase radial circuit. However, it is not practical in a tie feeder or network system unless it is blocked off by delta transformers or other zero-sequence impedance isolators so that the tuned setting required can be definitely known and is not variable because of system operating conditions. To calculate the reactance value of the neutral reactor, the following equations can be used:
From Figure 8–2

$$I_G = I_A' + I_C' = -3I_B$$

It is desired that $I_L = 3I_B$ so that $I_G + I_L = 0$ at the fault. Voltage across $X_L = -E_B$. Call the capacitive reactance of the line X_c. Then

$$I_L = \frac{-E_B}{X_L} = \frac{-3E_B}{X_c} = 3I_B$$

$$-E_B = 3E_B \quad \text{or} \quad -X_c E_B = 3E_B X_L \quad \text{or} \quad -X_c = 3X_L$$

Therefore, for fault current zero,

$$X_L = \frac{-X_c}{3}$$

GROUNDING UNGROUNDED SYSTEMS

So far our discussion of grounding has assumed we had a wye-connected neutral to ground. This is not always the case, and in some cases it is not a three-phase system that it is desired to ground. For situations of this kind a grounding

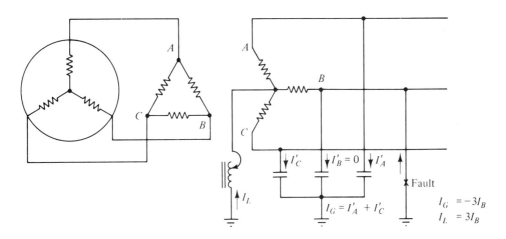

FIGURE 8–5.
Resonant grounded system (Bϕ fault to ground).

transformer is used. This may be a conventional wye-delta transformer of suitable rating or a special zigzag wye unit may be used. Once the neutral is established, any of the grounding methods already discussed may be employed, provided the rating of the grounding transformer is adequate for the amount of current permitted by the grounding method used. Figure 8–6 shows the setup of a zigzag wye transformer used for the grounding.

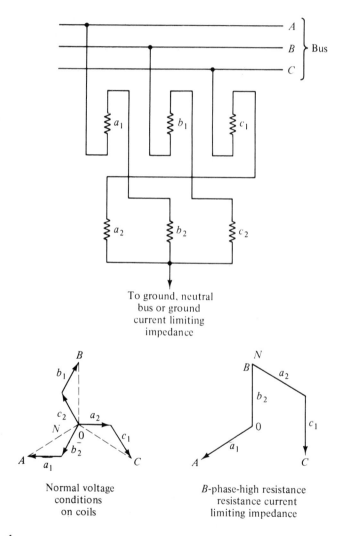

FIGURE 8–6.

Ground source through a wye-zigzag grounding transformer.

In the selection of grounding equipment and methods, many factors must be considered. It is desirable from the reduction of fault damage, repair costs, and switching equipment maintenance to limit ground fault current as much as possible. However, the greater the limitation of current, the higher the possible transient overvoltages that will be encountered. This will determine the equipment insulation levels required and the rating of lightning arresters required to protect the equipment, and will consequently effect costs. Therefore, these factors are in conflict with the desire for maximum fault limitation. Whether resistors or reactors are used will determine the degree of overvoltage expected on a given system for a given degree of current limitation and thus affect the selection of the use of resistors or reactors.

Whenever grounding of any kind is used, it is obvious that fault current will flow when a normally ungrounded conductor becomes grounded. It is necessary that relays fuses or other protective devices sense and operate to clear the fault. Since the degree of current limitation employed may well have a serious effect upon the ability of these devices to operate as desired, it follows that the degree of current limitation that can be employed may well be determined by the sensitivity of protective devices used, or, conversely, the type and sensitivity of the protective devices required may be determined by the degree of current limitation selected. However, since a multiplicity of feeders at generator voltage depends upon ground overcurrent relays for their ground fault protection, ground fault current must be kept up to a value that will give adequate relay operating torque for any and all ground faults on them, with reasonable current transformer ratios and relay current ranges.

Thus the selection of the value to which the ground fault is to be limited becomes the problem of making a selection between minimum ground fault current to limit damage, the minimum ground fault that will give adequate protective device operation, and the maximum ground fault current that the generator windings can tolerate before there is danger of the magnetic forces forcing windings out of the generator armature slots. The extreme ground current limitation can be used only where there are no feeders at generator voltage that must have ground fault protection, and delta-wye transformers isolate the zero-sequence network for which ground fault protection at this very low current level must be provided to a very small number of equipment units. Even then, very special relaying methods must be employed.

In conclusion, several important points with respect to impedance grounding of system neutrals are so obvious that they are often overlooked.

- Since grounding equipment is electrically active in a circuit only during a ground fault, considerable money can be saved by buying equipment rated for short time duty. Grounding equipment for a station with all underground circuits will be expected to be subjected to very infrequent faults, and since cable faults are usually permanent, repeated reclosing attempts will probably not be made. Under these circumstances a short time rating of the grounding equipment of 10 seconds or less may be adequate. However, grounding equipment installed in a station having all overhead circuits will be subjected to the cumulative heating effect of perhaps many closely spaced feeder faults during severe storm conditions, each circuit outage being accompanied by several unsuccessful closing attempts. Under these conditions, equipment having a rating on a 10-minute or more basis may be inadequate.

- Impedance neutral grounding equipment must always be considered hot, since there is no telling when a fault to ground will occur and raise the neutral end of the equipment to full phase to ground voltage. This not only poses a safety problem but also creates the problem of how to maintain the equipment, unless the machine, bus, or station for which the impedance furnishes the ground is shut down.

- Where a multiplicity of grounding units is employed to avoid the preceding difficulties, care must be exercised in switching facilities for their transfer to avoid the danger that someone will get caught operating disconnects for the transfer just as a ground fault occurs. If multiple units are used, care must be exercised that the protective relaying will operate and coordinate properly through the range of conditions possible with the multiple units.

- Where impedance grounding is used, no other neutrals in the same zero sequence system may be grounded except through the same impedance. To do so will shunt or short-circuit the original impedance and raise the ground fault current above the desired design value.

8-3   SELECTION OF GROUNDING SYSTEM

As discussed earlier, the various methods of grounding commonly used are solidly grounded, resistance grounded, reactance grounded, and ground fault neutralizer grounded. The ungrounded system is, in the true sense of the word, grounded, because the charging capacitance from the phase conductor to earth acts as the grounding point. The various grounding methods are shown in Figure 8–7.

The selection of a grounding system should be based upon the following systems factors:

- Magnitude of the fault current.
- Transient overvoltage.
- Lightning protection.
- Application of protective devices for selective ground fault protection.
- Types of load served, such as motors, generators, and on on.

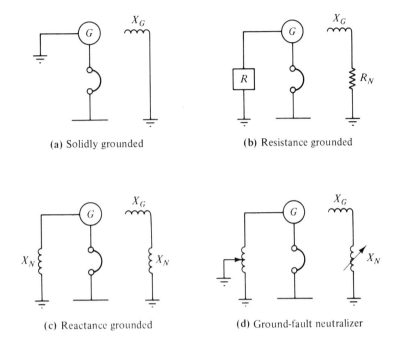

(a) Solidly grounded   (b) Resistance grounded

(c) Reactance grounded   (d) Ground-fault neutralizer

FIGURE 8–7.
Methods of grounding system neutrals.

The application limits and a guide for the various grounding methods for consideration of the above-mentioned factors are shown in Table 8–1 and discussed in the following.

SOLIDLY GROUNDED SYSTEM

A solidly grounded system is one in which a generator, transformer, or grounding transformer neutral is directly grounded to earth or station ground. Because the reactance of source (generator or transformer) impedance is in series with the neutral circuit, this system cannot be considered a zero impedance circuit. In nearly all grounded systems, it is desirable to have the line to ground fault current in the range of 25 to 100 percent of three-phase fault current in order to prevent the development of high transient overvoltage. The higher the ground fault current, the less are the transient overvoltages.

TABLE 8–1.

GROUNDING METHODS FOR LOW- AND MEDIUM-VOLTAGE
SYSTEMS

MEDIUM-VOLTAGE SYSTEM (2,400 TO 13,800 V)

System	Grounding Practice	Comments
Wye-connected generator on the system	Use low-resistance grounding resistor	Allows the use of neutral-type lightning arresters if $X_0/X_1 \leq 3$ $X_0/X_1 \leq 10$ for limiting transient overvoltages
Wye-connected transformer on the system	Use low-resistance transformer with resistor	Does not allow the use of neutral-type lightning arresters To limit transient over-voltage, $R_0/X_0 \geq 2$
System un-grounded (i.e., no wye-connected generators or transformers)	Use grounding trans-former with resistor Zig-zag transformer	Same comments as for wye-connected trans-former

LOW-VOLTAGE SYSTEM (120 TO 600 V)

System	Grounding Practice	Comments
Wye-connected generator on the system	Use low-voltage re-actance to ground generator neutral	Ground fault current should be not less than 25% of three-phase fault current

TABLE 8–1. (continued)

Wye-connected transformer power supply system	Ground transformer neutral solidly to ground	
System ungrounded (i.e., no wye-connected transformer)	Use grounding transformer solidly grounded	Ground fault current to be equal to at least 25% of three-phase fault current

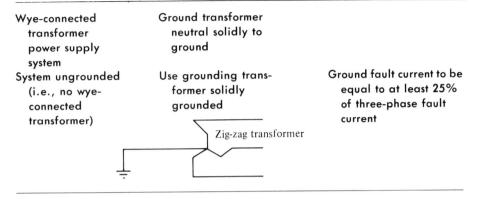

Zig-zag transformer

Ground-neutral-type lightning arresters may be applied on this system provided that the ground fault current is at least 60 percent of three-phase fault current. Another way of expressing this value is to express the reactance and resistance ratios as follows:

$$\frac{X_0}{X_1} \leqq 3$$

and

$$\frac{R_0}{X_1} \leqq 1$$

where

$$X_0 = \text{zero-sequence reactance}$$
$$X_1 = \text{positive-sequence reactance}$$
$$R_0 = \text{zero-sequence resistance}$$

Normally, direct grounding of the generator is not desirable because the ground fault current may exceed three-phase fault current. Since the generator is rated for maximum three-phase fault current, it is not desirable to have higher ground fault currents than three-phase fault current. Therefore, most grounded systems having generators are grounded through low reactance values to keep ground fault currents less than three-phase fault current. Generally, low-voltage systems (i.e., below 600 V) are solidly grounded. Medium-voltage systems may be either solidly or low resistance grounded.

LOW-RESISTANCE GROUNDING

In low-resistance grounding the neutral is grounded through a resistance of low ohmic value. The reasons for using the resistance grounding system are the following:

- To reduce the ground fault current to prevent damage to switchgear, motors, cables, and the like.
- To minimize magnetic and mechanical stresses.
- To minimize stray ground fault currents for personnel safety.
- To reduce the momentary line-voltage dips by clearing of ground faults.

The line-to-ground voltage that may exist during fault conditions can be as high as the voltage present on ungrounded systems. However, the transient overvoltages are not as high. If the system is properly grounded by resistance, there is no danger from destructive overtransient voltages.

HIGH-RESISTANCE GROUNDING

In this system the neutral is grounded through a resistance of high ohmic value. The line-to-ground voltage of unfaulted phases during a ground fault is nearly equal to line-to-line voltage. If the insulation system was selected for a grounded system, it will be subjected to an overvoltage condition during a line-to-ground fault.

The ground fault current available in this type of system is very small, usually 25 A or less. It should be remembered that when using this system the ground fault current should never be less than the charging current. Moreover, the lightning arresters for this system should be the ungrounded type. This type of system is subject to the following types of overvoltage conditions:

- Ferroresonance type, that is, resonance effects of series inductive-capacitive circuits.
- Limited transient overvoltage conditions.
- Overvoltage conditions due to direct connection to higher voltages.

The reasons for using high-resistance grounding are similar to those for low-resistance grounding except that in this system ground fault current is limited to a very small value.

REACTANCE GROUNDING

In a reactance grounded system the neutral circuit is grounded through a reactor. In general, reactance grounding is used for grounding generator neutrals. The value of the reactor chosen is usually such that the ground fault current is not less than 25 percent of three-phase fault current to prevent serious transient overvoltages during ground fault clearance. The value of X_0 must be less or equal to ten times the X_1 value for this type of system.

GROUND-FAULT NEUTRALIZERS (RESONANT GROUNDED)

In this system a reactor having a specially selected high value of reactance is connected in neutral connection to ground. The current that flows through the reactor, during a line-to-ground fault condition, is equal to and 180° out of phase with the charging current that flows in two unfaulted phases. Under this condition the two currents cancel, leaving the faulted current due only to resistance. Because resistive current is in phase with the voltage, the fault current is quenched when both the voltage and fault current pass through zero axis.

A precaution required in this system is that care must be taken to keep the ground fault neutralizer tuned to the system capacitance. If any switching is done to take circuits out, the neutralizer reactance values must be changed by adjusting neutralizer taps. Ground fault neutralizers have been used only to a limited extent and are not as common as the other systems of grounding.

8-4   PERIODIC TESTING OF GROUNDING SYSTEM

As explained in Sections 8-2 and 8-3, electrical systems are grounded to limit transient overvoltages, provide a ground path for induced currents due to lightning strikes, and reduce the shock hazards to personnel. To achieve these objectives, it is essential that the grounding connection to earth have sufficiently low resistance.

The National Electrical Code (NEC) specifies that the resistance value of a ground system shall not exceed 25 Ω. It must be assumed that this is the upper limit value, and lower ground resistance values would be desirable. It is generally recommended that smaller substations have a ground resistance value of 5 Ω and larger substations have a value of 1 Ω or less. The resistivity of earth affects the ground resistance values in direct proportion, because soil resistivity is dependent upon soil material, moisture content, temperature, and seasonal changes.

Grounding resistance is made up of three components; (1) the resistance of the electrode connecting the grounding rods; (2) the contact resistance of the ground rods; (3) the resistance of the earth immediately surrounding the grounding rods, which is the main resistance of the three. When ground fault current flows from a ground rod to earth, it flows in all directions through a series of concentric spheres surrounding the rod. The resistance of the closest sphere to the ground rod is the highest because it is the smallest sphere. As the distance from the ground rod is increased, the resistance becomes less because the spheres become larger. Eventually, a distance from the electrode is reached where the sphere resistance becomes zero. Therefore, in any ground resistance measurements, only the part of earth resistance is considered that contributes a major part of the resistance. Theoretically, the earth resistance of the ground system should be measured up to infinite distance from the ground rod.

EARTH RESISTANCE MEASUREMENTS

To maintain sufficiently low resistance values of grounding systems, their periodic testing is required. The testing involves measurement to ensure that they do not exceed design limits. The commonly used methods of measuring and testing the ground resistance are as follows:

- Two-point method
- Three-point method
- Fall of potential method
- Ratio method

Two-Point Method

This method may be used to measure the resistance of a single driven ground rod. It uses an auxiliary ground rod whose resistance is either known or can be measured. The resistance value of the auxiliary ground rod also must be very small compared to the resistance of the driven ground rod so that the measured value can be assumed to be wholly contributed by the driven ground rod. An example of where this test might be applicable is the measurement of resistance of the single driven ground rod for a residence. In this case the municipal metallic water supply line can be assumed as the auxiliary ground rod whose resistance value is approximately 1 Ω. This value is quite small compared to the value of a single driven ground rod, whose value is on the order of 25 Ω. This method is usually adequate where a go, no-go type of test is required.

Three-Point Method

This method is similar to the two-point method except it uses two auxiliary rods. To obtain accurate values of resistance measurements, the resistance of the auxiliary electrodes should be approximately equal to or less than that of the electrode under test. The connections for the three-point method are shown in Figure 8–8.

Either alternating current of 60 Hz or direct current may be used for making this test. The advantage of using alternating current is that it minimizes th effects of stray currents on measurement readings. However, if stray currents happen to be of the same frequency, error will be introduced in the readings. The use of direct current for making this test will totally eliminate the ac stray currents. However, stray direct current and formation of gas around the electrodes will introduce error in the readings when using direct current for this test. The effect of stray direct currents can be minimized by taking readings in one direction and then reversing the polarity and taking the reading with current in the opposite direction. The average of the two readings will give an accurate test value. Apply currents only long enough to take readings.

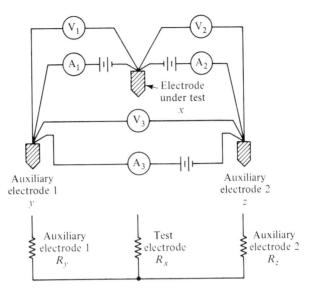

FIGURE 8–8.
Three-point test method and its equivalent circuit.

The resistance value of the test electrode can be calculated as follows:
Let

$$R_1 = R_x + R_y = \frac{V_1}{A_1}$$

$$R_2 = R_x + R_z = \frac{V_2}{A_2}$$

$$R_3 = R_y + R_z = \frac{V_3}{A_3}$$

Solving these three equations, we have

$$R_y = R_3 - R_z$$

$$R_x = R_1 - R_y = R_1 - R_3 + R_z$$

also

$$R_x = R_2 - R_z$$

from which

$$2R_x = R_1 + R_2 - R_3$$

or

$$R_x = \frac{R_1 + R_2 - R_3}{2}$$

Fall of Potential Method

This method measures grounding electrode resistance based upon the principle of potential drop across the resistance. It also uses two auxiliary electrodes that are placed at a sufficient distance from the test electrodes; a current of known magnitude is passed through the electrode under test and one of the auxiliary electrodes. The drop in potential between the electrode under test and the second auxiliary electrode is measured. The ratio of voltage drop (V) to the known current (I) will indicate the resistance of the grounding circuit. Either a dc or ac voltage source may be used for conducting this test. The circuit connection for this test method is shown in Figure 8–9.

The following problems and errors may be encountered with this method.

- Stray currents in earth may cause voltmeter readings to be either high or low.
- The resistance of auxiliary electrode and electrical leads may introduce errors in the voltmeter reading. This error can be minimized by using a voltmeter of high impedance value.

This method can be used with either a separate voltmeter and ammeter or a single instrument which provides a reading directly in ohms. To measure the resistance of a grounding electrode, the current electrode is placed at a

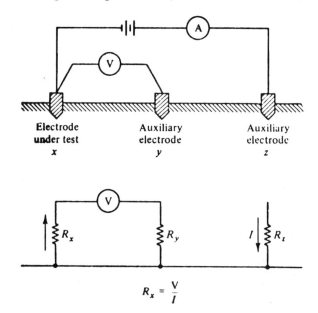

FIGURE 8–9.
Fall of potential method for measurement of ground resistance.

suitable distance from the grounding electrode under test. The potential electrode is placed at approximately 62 percent of the current electrode distance. The 62 percent figure has been determined by empirical data or calculated by various authorities on ground resistance measurement. The current electrode (R_z) distance from the test electrode can be definitely forecast because it varies as a function of earth resistivity, electrode diameter, and the depth of the grounding electrode.

It is recommended that test should be made for ground electrode resistance for each season of the year. The data should be retained for each season for comparison and analysis. Serious deviation of the test data from previous years, other than seasonal variations, could mean electrode corrosion.

Ratio Method

This method uses a Wheatstone bridge or an ohmmeter to measure the series resistance of grounding electrode and the auxiliary electrode. The test connections are shown in Figure 8–10. A slide wire potentiometer is used with a

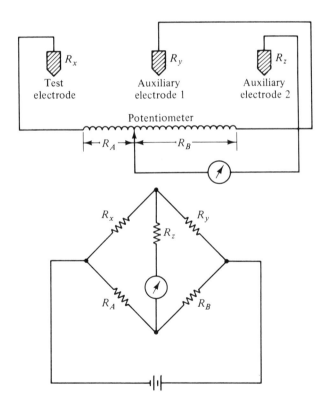

FIGURE 8–10.
Ratio method of measuring ground resistance.

Wheatstone bridge for this test. The potentiometer is connected across the grounding electrode under test and the first auxiliary electrode. The sliding contact of the potentiometer is connected to the second auxiliary electrode through a detector for determining the null point. The resistance of the test electrode and first auxiliary electrode is measured first by the Wheatstone bridge or ohmmeter. Then using the potentiometer and Wheatstone bridge, a new null point is determined with the second electrode in the test circuit. The resistance of the grounding electrode is the ratio of the test electrode resistance to the total resistance of the two in series. The procedure and equations are as follows:

- Measure $R_x + R_y$ by means of a Wheatstone bridge or ohmmeter.
- Determine from the potentiometer the ratio of $R_A / R_A + R_B$.
- Insert second auxiliary electrode (R_z) in test circuit and obtain null point.
- $\dfrac{R_x}{R_A} = \dfrac{R_x + R_y}{R_A + R_B}$ or $R_x = (R_x + R_y) \left(\dfrac{R_A}{R_A + R_B} \right)$.

CHAPTER 9

ELECTRICAL SAFETY, SWITCHING PRACTICES, AND PRECAUTIONS

9-1 INTRODUCTION

Safety in electrical systems concerns three different areas: protection of life, protection of property, and protection of uninterrupted productive output. The required investment to accomplish improved safety often consists merely of additional planning effort without any extra equipment investment. The protection of human life is paramount. Electrical plant property can be replaced and lost production can be made up, but human life can never be recovered nor human suffering compensated for. To achieve improved safety to personnel, special attention should be directed to energized equipment, adequate short-circuit protective devices, a good maintenance program, simplicity of the electrical system design, and proper training of personnel who work around electricity. Many of the items necessary to give improved protection to life will also secure improved protection to plant property and minimize breakdown of electrical system equipment. This chapter deals with electrical safety, switching practices, precautions, and accident prevention.

The following rules are basic to electrical accident prevention:

- Know the work to be done and *how* to do it.
- Review working area for hazards of environment or facility design that may exist in addition to those directly associated with the assigned work objective.
- Wear flame-retardant coveralls and safety glasses plus other recommended protective devices/equipment.
- Isolate (de-energize) the circuits and/or equipment to be worked.
- Lock out and tag open all power sources and circuits to and from the equipment/circuit to be worked on.
- Test with two pre-tested testing devices for the presence of electrical energy on circuits and/or equipment (both primary and secondary) while wearing electrical protective gloves.

- Ground all sides of the work area with protective grounds applied with "Hot Sticks." All grounds must be visible at all times to those in the work area.
- Enclose the work area with tape barrier.

9-2 "ON-SITE" ELECTRICAL SAFETY

Prior to going on an "on-site" electrical assignment, each worker should receive the following rules and should review and abide by them while on the assignment.

A foreman or qualified employee should be designated for each on-site assignment to provide on-site work direction and safety coordination. All personnel assigned to on-site electrical work should comply with the following directions:

- Know the work content and work sequence, especially all safety measures.
- Know the proper tools and instruments required for the work, that they have the full capability of safely performing the work, and that they are in good repair and/or are calibrated.
- Check to determine that all de-energized circuits/equipment are locked out and that grounds are placed on all sides of the work area prior to beginning work.
- Segregate all work areas with barriers or tapes, confine all your activities to these areas, and prevent unauthorized access to the area.
- Insure that all energized circuits/equipment adjacent to the work area are isolated, protected, or marked by at least two methods (e.g., rubber mats, tapes, signs, etc.) for personnel protection.
- Do not perform work on energized circuits/equipment without the direct authorization of your unit manager. When work on energized circuits/equipment has been authorized, use complete, safety-tested equipment (i.e. rubber gloves, sleeves, mats, insulated tools, etc.).
- Your foreman/qualified employee must inform you of all changes in work conditions. You then must repeat this information to your foreman/qualified employee to insure your recognition and understanding of the condition.
- Do *not* work alone; work with another worker or employee at all times.
- Do *not* enter an energized area without direct permission from your foreman/qualified employee.
- Discuss each step of your work with your foreman/qualified employee before it is begun.

- Do *not* directly touch an unconscious fellow worker since he or she may be in contact with an energized circuit/equipment. Use an insulated device to remove him or her from the suspect area.

- Do *not* perform, or continue to perform, any work when you are in doubt about the safety procedure to be followed, the condition of the equipment, or any potential hazards. Perform this work only after you have obtained directions from your foreman/qualified employee.

- Do *not* work on, or adjacent to, any energized circuits/equipment unless you feel alert and are in good health.

9-3 "ON-SITE" SAFETY KIT

The following are recommended protective tools to be used in preparation for and in the performance of on-site electrical work:

- Red safety tape (300 ft.)
- Red flashing hazard lights (6)
- Safety cones (6)
- Red "Do Not Operate" tags (15)
- Padlocks, keys and lock shackle (6)
- Ground fault circuit interrupter—15 ampere, 125 volt (1)
- Fire extinguishers (2)
- Personal protective equipment
  Flame-retardant coveralls
  Safety glasses
  Face shields
  Hard hats
  Other items required for protection on the job
- Combustible gas/oxygen detectors
- Portable ventilation blower
- Ground loop impedance tester, ohmmeter (1)
- Voltage detectors
  Statiscope
    (1) Station type (1)
    (2) Overhead extension type (1)
  Audio
    (1) Tic Tracer
    (2) ESP

- Voltage/ampere meter (1)

  Amprobe

  Simpson

- Rubber gloves and protectors of appropriate class

- Grounding clamps, cables

- "Hot sticks"

9-4   WORK AREA CONTROL

When workers are setting up the control area, it should be standard procedure that the safety coordinator be present and provide the required information.

TAPE—SOLID RED

A red tape barrier (with safety cones and red flashing lights) must be used to enclose an area in which personnel will be working. Other persons may not enter the isolated area unless they are actively working in conjunction with the personnel on the assigned work.

The purpose of the solid red tape barrier is to enclose and isolate an area in which a hazard might exist for individuals unfamiliar with the equipment enclosed. The only persons permitted within the solid red barrier are individuals knowledgeable in the use and operation of the enclosed equipment.

For their safety, workers shall not interest themselves in nor enter any area not enclosed by the red tape barrier except for a defined route to enter and leave the site.

It is important that the tape barrier is strictly controlled and the restrictions regarding its use are enforced.

When any workers are using solid red tape to enclose an area, the following requirements must be satisfied:

- Place the tape so that it completely encloses the area or equipment where the hazard exists.

- Place the tape so that it is readily visible from all avenues of approach and at such a level that it forms an effective barrier.

- Be certain that the area enclosed by the tape is large enough to give adequate clearance between the hazard and any personnel working in the tape enclosed area.

- Arrange the tape so any test equipment for the setup can be operated safely from outside the enclosed area.

- Use the tape to prevent the area from being entered by persons unfamiliar with the work and associated hazards. Do not use the tape for any other purpose.
- Remove the tape when the hazard no longer exists and the work is completed.

It shall be standard procedure that the workers should consider all areas outside the red barrier work area as energized and undertake no investigation unless accompanied by a knowledgeable plant employee.

TAPE—WHITE WITH RED STRIPE

White tape with a red stripe is used to enclose and isolate a temporary hazard (mechanical or electrical). No one is to enter this enclosed area. Obviously, if the enclosing of a hazardous area with tape is to be protective, the use of the tape barrier should be controlled and the restrictions on entering the area strictly enforced.

When any personnel are using white tape with a red stripe, the following requirements must be satisfied:

- Place the tape so that it completely encloses the area or equipment where the hazard exists.
- Place the tape so that it is readily visible from all avenues of approach and at such a level that it forms an effective barrier.
- Be certain that the area enclosed is large enough to give adequate clearance between the hazard and any personnel outside the enclosed area.
- Arrange the tape so that the test equipment for the setup can be operated outside the enclosed area.
- Use the tape only to isolate a temporary mechanical or electrical hazard; do *not* use the tape for any other purpose.
- Consider a striped tape area similar to an interlocked enclosure and treat as such.
- Remove the tape when the hazard no longer exists.

9-5   LOCK-OUT AND/OR TAGGING

For the protection of personnel working on electrical conductor and/or equipment, locks must be placed on all open isolation devices designed to receive them. "DANGER" tags signed by the foreman or qualified employee must *also* be placed on the open isolation device.

DANGER TAGS

Danger tags may be applied only by authorized personnel and the tags must be dated and signed by the person applying the tag. The following requirements must be satisfied when danger tags are used:

- Danger tags are to be used only for personnel protection when the personnel are required to work on or near equipment that, if operated, might cause injury.

- Danger tags are attached to primary disconnecting devices as a means of "locking out" equipment. Tag each source of power to the equipment and associated feeds (instrumentation circuits, PT's, CT's, etc.) to the equipment which is to be locked out.

- Danger tags should be left on the equipment only while the personnel are working on the equipment or when a hazard to the personnel exists.

- A device bearing a danger tag must not be operated at any time (see Figure 9-1).

OUT OF ORDER TAGS

Out of order tags are used to restrict the operation of equipment which has a mechanical defect or for other reasons that are not related to the safety of personnel. Complete information concerning the reasons for the tag and a list of all persons authorized to operate the tagged device must be written on the tag (see Figure 9-2).

OUT OF SERVICE TAGS

Out of service tags are used to indicate equipment that has been taken out of service. It is a white tag with white letters on a black background.

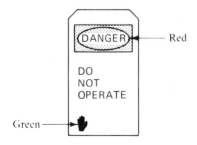

FIGURE 9–1.

FIGURE 9–2.

CAUTION TAGS

Caution tags are used to indicate potential hazard or unsafe conditions. These are yellow tags with yellow letters on a black background.

USE OF DANGER TAGS

Danger tags are authorized for use on any isolation device as a method of "locking out" equipment. These tags must be hung so there is no doubt as to which device they control. The tags may be used and signed only by authorized personnel, who are designated by the plant manager.

When more than one crew or trade are working on the same equipment, each crew must attach its own tag and place its own lock on the device. Gang lock clips can be used as shown in Figure 9-3 to provide maximum protection to a number of crews working on the same equipment or conductors.

Danger tags may be removed only by the person who originally placed and signed the tag. If that person is absolutely unable to remove the tag, a committee selected by the plant manager will fully investigate the situation. This committee will remove the tag only when they are satisfied that they have full knowledge of the intention of the original "tagger" and that the tag may be removed without endangering anyone.

9-6 PROTECTIVE APPAREL—OPERATING ELECTRICAL EQUIPMENT

All personnel must wear the following protective apparel when working on electrical equipment which is, or might be considered, energized, or become energized as a result of the work:

- Fire-resistant coveralls buttoned fully at the throat and wrists.
- Electrical lineman's safety gloves with protectors.

FIGURE 9-3.

- A face shield which also provides forehead and hair protection, or a face shield which can be attached to a hard hat.
- All personnel shall wear protective apparel when withdrawing and inserting circuit breakers, connecting and disconnecting ground connections, and testing for energized circuits and/or equipment.
- Only qualified personnel shall be allowed to operate switching equipment.

9-7   TESTING OF ELECTRICAL CIRCUITS AND/OR EQUIPMENT

GENERAL

- *All circuits and equipment are to be considered as energized* until proven de-energized by testing with voltage detectors, and grounding cables are connected. The voltage detectors selected should be for the class of voltage supplied to the circuits and equipment to be serviced.
- *Personnel* assigned to on-site electrical service work should be *supplied* with at least two (2) electrical *voltage detectors*. The *voltage detectors* provided shall be capable of *safely detecting* the *voltage* present in the circuits and/or equipment to be serviced. The assigned *personnel* shall be instructed in the correct operation of each detector *before each* on-site electrical *job*.
- Each electrical circuit and/or piece of equipment to be serviced should be tested by an assigned craftsman with two detectors and then tested by one other person who has been trained in the correct operation of the voltage detectors. This testing shall be performed in the assigned craftsman's presence to insure that the electrical circuit and/or equipment is de-energized.
- The voltage detectors *should be checked* for proper operation immediately *prior to* and *immediately after* testing the electrical circuits and/or equipment to be serviced. These checks should be made on a known source of energized voltage, such as on the spark plug of a running automobile engine if a "glow stick," or with a specifically designed tester supplied by the detector vendor.
- While testing circuits and/or equipment, the craftsman performing the tests shall wear lineman's safety rubber gloves designed for the class of voltage in the circuits and/or equipment to be serviced and other protective equipment for this work.

CAPACITORS

A capacitor to be serviced must be removed from operation in the following sequence:

- Isolate the capacitors by opening the breakers or isolation devices connecting them to the electrical system.
- Permit the capacitors to drain off the accumulated charge for five to ten minutes. (There is generally a built-in device which accomplishes this drain.)
- Short circuit and ground the capacitors in the manner and with the protective equipment noted in "Grounds—Personnel Protection." While performing these procedures, be very careful that sufficient distance is maintained from the capacitors with a "Hot Stick" in the event the drain-off device is not properly functioning.

VACUUM CIRCUIT BREAKER HIPOTTING—CAUTIONS

Although the procedure for hipotting a vacuum circuit breaker is similar to that used for any other electrical device, there are two areas that require the exercise of extra caution.

During any hipotting operation, the main shield inside the interrupter can acquire an electrical charge that usually will be retained even after the hipot voltage is removed. This shield is attached to the midband ring of the insulating envelope. *A grounding stick should always be used* to discharge the ring as well as the other metal parts of the assembly before touching the interrupter, connections, or breaker studs.

High voltage applied across open gaps in a vacuum can produce hazardous X-radiation if the voltage across the contacts exceeds a certain level for a given contact gap. Therefore, *do not make hipot tests on an open breaker at voltages higher than the recommended 36 kV a-c* across each interrupter. During the hipot test, the steel front panel and partial side panels should be assembled to the breaker. Personnel should stand in front of the breaker to take advantage of the shielding afforded by the panels. If this position is not practical, equivalent protection can be provided by limiting personnel exposure to testing four 3-phase breakers per hour with the personnel not closer than three meters (9 ft. 10 inches) to the interrupters. During equipment operation in the normal current carrying mode, there is no X-radiation because there are no open contacts.

ELECTROSTATIC COUPLING

When personnel are working on a de-energized circuit that is adjacent to an energized circuit, it is important to be certain that solid grounds are attached to the de-energized circuit at all times. *A substantial voltage charge can be generated* in a de-energized circuit by electromagnetic coupling with the energized circuit. The solid grounds will drain off this voltage charge.

9-8   RUBBER GLOVES FOR ELECTRICAL WORK—USE AND CARE

Rubber gloves with leather protectors that have been tested to at least 10,000 volts must be worn when work is performed on or within reach of energized conductors and/or equipment. The rubber gloves and protectors of the appropriate class should be available to all trained personnel as part of the safety kit for on-site electrical work.

The rubber gloves and protectors are of two types:

- *Low-voltage* rubber gloves and protectors (Class 0). These gloves are tested and approved for work on equipment *energized at 750 volts or less*. (Permission should be given by the foreman for the use of low-voltage gloves when working on conductors and/or equipment *energized below 750 volts*.)
- *High-voltage* rubber gloves and protectors. The gloves are tested at 10,000 volts (Class 1) for use on 5 kV or less, tested for 15,000 volts for use on 10 kV or less (Class 2), and at 20,000 volts (Class 3) for use on 15 kV or less voltage ratings.

Both high- and low-voltage rubber gloves are of the gauntlet type and are available in various sizes. To get the best possible protection from rubber gloves, and to keep them in a serviceable condition as long as possible, here are a few general rules that apply whenever they are used in electrical work:

- Always wear leather protectors over your gloves. Any direct contact of a rubber glove with sharp or pointed objects may cut, snag, or puncture the glove and rob you of the protection you are depending on.
- Always wear rubber gloves right side out (serial number and size to the outside). Turning gloves inside out places a stress on the preformed rubber.
- Always keep the gauntlets up. Rolling them down sacrifices a valuable area of protection.
- Always inspect and give a field air test (described later) to your gloves before using them. Check the inside of the protectors for any bit of metal or short pieces of wire that may have fallen in them.
- Always store gloves where they cannot come into contact with sharp or pointed tools that may cut or puncture them.
- All gloves are to be inspected before use.

HIGH-VOLTAGE RUBBER GLOVES

- These gloves must be tested before they are issued. All gloves should be issued in matched pairs in a sealed carton. If received with the seal broken, return them for testing.

- When high-voltage gloves are issued to individuals for use over a three-month period, they shall be inspected and tested at least every three months by a certified testing laboratory. All gloves, must be tested when returned to the tool crib after the job is completed.

LOW-VOLTAGE RUBBER GLOVES

- Low-voltage rubber gloves must be inspected (see Inspection of Rubber Gloves) before each use.

- Defective gloves, or gloves in a questionable condition, must be immediately replaced.

LEATHER PROTECTOR GLOVES

- Approved leather protectors must be worn over rubber gloves to protect them from mechanical injury.

- Protectors that have been soaked with oil should never be used over rubber gloves.

- Protectors that are serviceable for use over rubber gloves are not to be used as work gloves.

- Protectors should be replaced if they have faulty or worn stitching, holes, cuts, abrasions, or if for any other reason, they no longer protect the rubber gloves.

INSPECTION OF RUBBER GLOVES (ALL CLASSES)

Before rubber gloves are used, a visual inspection and an air test should be made at least once every day and at any other time deemed necessary during the progress of the job.

Visual Inspection

When inspecting rubber gloves in the field, stretch a small area at a time (see Figure 9-4), checking to be sure that no defects exist, such as (a) embedded foreign material, (b) deep scratches, (c) pin holes or punctures, (d) snags, or (e) cuts. In addition, look for signs of deterioration caused by oil, tar, grease, insulating compounds, or any other substance which may be injurious to rubber. Inspect the entire glove thoroughly, including the gauntlet.

Gloves that are found to be defective should not be mutilated in the field but should be tagged with a yellow tag and turned in for proper disposal.

Air Test

After visually inspecting the glove, other defects may be observed by applying the air test as follows:

- Hold the glove with thumbs and forefingers as illustrated in Figure 9-5.
- Twirl the glove around quickly to fill with air (Figure 9-6).
- Trap the air by squeezing the gauntlet with one hand. Use the other hand to squeeze the palm, fingers, and thumb in looking for weaknesses and defects (Figure 9-7).
- Hold the glove to the face to detect air leakage or hold it to the ear and listen for escaping air.

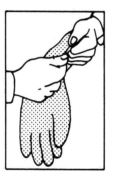

FIGURE 9-4.

FIGURE 9-5.

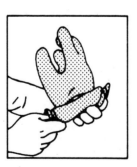

FIGURE 9-6.

FIGURE 9-7.

9-9 LOW VOLTAGE TESTER

This tester may be used for measuring ac or dc voltage from 110 to 600 volts when accuracy is not required. It can be used to test for continuity, blown fuses, grounded side of a circuit or a motor, and polarity. This tester operates on the principle that the current passed through the solenoid of the instrument is proportional to the voltage under test and will cause the tester solenoid plunger to move in the same proportion. A pointer attached to the plunger indicates the voltage on the tester scale. This instrument has no internal protection; therefore, extreme caution must be used at all times.

Some models have a two-part neon bulb. Both parts glow when energized by alternating current. Only the part that is connected to the negative side of a circuit will glow when energized by direct current.

Use of Low-Voltage Tester

When the low-voltage tester is used,

- Wear rubber gloves with protectors.
- Check the operation of the tester by testing a known energized circuit.
- Assure good contact with the tester probes across the circuit being tested.
- Read the voltage on the tester.
- Because the low-voltage tester is designed for intermittent use only, continuous operation might burn out the solenoid, especially on the higher voltage.

TIC TRACER (AN AUDIO VOLTAGE DETECTOR)

The Tic Tracer is an audio voltage detector, which detects the electrostatic field surrounding an energized alternating current circuit and/or equipment.

Use of the Tic Tracer

This detector will operate only on unshielded ac circuits and/or equipment. It will detect the presence of voltages ranging from approximately 40 volts up to 600 volts when hand held; higher voltages when used with approved hot sticks.

- Wear high-voltage rubber gloves and leather protectors when you are using the Tic Tracer to test circuits and/or equipment to be serviced.
- Turn on the actuating switch on the side of the Tic Tracer.
- Check the tracer by bringing it close to a conductor known to be energized. Check for proper tracer operation by placing it near a

lighted fluorescent bulb or at any known energized conductor of ac voltage.

9-10 MEDIUM AND HIGH-VOLTAGE DETECTORS

PROXIMITY TYPE

The *proximity type* high-voltage tester is an instrument intended for use in detecting the electrostatic field surrounding an electrical conductor that is energized with alternating current at high potential. *It is used only on alternating current circuits and/or equipment.* The lowest voltage that can be reliably detected by this device is about 2000 volts. Most detectors of this type have hard rubber or plastic tubular cases with one end for testing and a handle at the other end. A neon tube is used for voltage detection. There are several designs in various lengths for use in different situations. When the test end is brought near an uninsulated conductor that has been energized with alternating current at high potential, the neon tube will light with a red glow. A conductor that is surrounded by grounded metal has its electrostatic field effectively limited by the grounded metal; therefore, care should be taken that a conductor under test is not shielded in such a way as to interfere with the operation of the detector.

Use of a Proximity H.V. Detector

- Wear high-voltage rubber gloves of the appropriate class with protectors.
- Wipe detector clean and dry.
- Check detector by bringing the test end close to an uninsulated conductor known to be energized at high voltage. Or you can use portable tester (Figure 9-8) by placing the lamp-end metal terminal of the detector against the testing point of the tester and pulling the trigger. If neon bulb of the detector glows, it is in good condition.
- To test an uninsulated conductor to determine whether or not it is energized, bring the test end of the detector close to the conductor. A

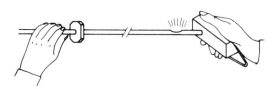

FIGURE 9–8.

red glow from the neon tube indicates that the conductor is energized. If there is no red glow from the neon tube, recheck the detector as explained above to make certain that the instrument is properly functioning.

- In using the detector, turn the neon tube away from the direct rays of strong light in order to make the red glow from the tube more visible.

- Wear rubber gloves and leather protectors when making tests with H.V. detectors and keep hands in back of guards on handles.

- The proper type of detector, having sufficient length or extension, should be used to maintain proper body clearances for the particular voltage being tested. Some detectors are equipped with a periscope (Figure 9-9) so that the glow from the neon tubes will be visible from a greater distance. Care must be exercised in the use of the periscope type so the guard or hand does not block the line of sight.

DIRECT CONTACT TYPE

The *direct contact type* high voltage detector is an instrument intended for use in detecting the presence of an ac voltage with respect to ground by direct contact between the detector and the energized conductor. *It is used only on alternating current circuits and/or equipment*. The lowest voltage that can be reliably detected by this instrument is about 2400 volts to ground. The actual detection is normally done by a neon tube connected to one side of a forked contact terminal. The bulb is illuminated by a very small current flow due to the capacitance between an internal electrode and ground. *This type detector should not be used on ungrounded systems*.

A special type phasing detector with two high voltage wands should be used if the system is ungrounded. These two wands are each touched to a different phase and the neon indicator detects phase-to-phase voltage. This device can also be used on grounded systems. The lowest voltage that can be reliably detected by this device is about 2000 volts.

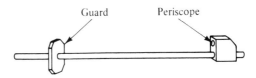

Guard   Periscope

FIGURE 9–9.

IMPORTANT POINTS TO REMEMBER

- Assume all circuits to be energized until proven otherwise.
- All protective equipment is to be proof tested for the voltage being worked.
- Maintain all leads, probes, clips and terminals in good condition. Repair or replace defective leads.
- Wear high voltage rubber gloves of the appropriate class with protectors.

9-11   GROUNDS—PERSONNEL PROTECTION

Grounding is installed to provide a metallic connection from ground to de-energized circuit and/or equipment to be serviced. This is for the purpose of draining off static and induced electricity but, most importantly, to *protect the worker*, in the event that the equipment becomes accidentally energized. Before grounds are attached, the cable, bus or equipment must be de-energized, isolated, locked out, and tagged. It must then be definitely established that the equipment to be grounded is de-energized by testing the circuits and/or eqiupment with voltage detectors.

The selection of the ground clamps is based on both the configuration and the electrical capacity according to the type of equipment to be grounded. The ground cable is to be a flexible insulated copper conductor. The rules for sizing the ground cables to be used as protective grounds are:

- The minimum size of cable to be used is a No. 1/0 conductor.
- The size of ground cables to be used must be at least equal to the size of the conductors feeding the circuit and/or equipment to be serviced. When the size of the ground cables or clusters is too large due to the system capacity, then bus sections, or similar conducting materials must be used.
- The cross-sectional area of the shorting paths and to ground must be sufficient to carry the short-circuit current. One or several conductors in a cluster may function as the grounding cable to carry the current. (A 4/0 Geoprene insulated welding cable will pass 30,000 amperes for 1/2 second without melting the insulation.)

When installing ground clamps on electrical circuits and/or equipment, all workers shall use "hot sticks" rated for the voltage being worked. Several types of "hot sticks," six feet to eight feet in length, are listed as follows:

- Rotary blade—universal end
- 2-prong—universal end
- Fixed blade—universal end
- Rotary prong—universal end

While grounds are applied, the following protective equipment must be worn:

- Flame retardant coveralls
- Safety glasses
- Electrical lineman's gloves with leather protectors
- Hard hat
- Face shield

In applying grounds, perform the following steps in sequence:

- Attach the protective ground cable to the station or building ground grid. If a ground system is not available, drive ground rods of sufficient cross section and number to carry the fault current. Be positive that a "solid" ground connection is made.
- Test the value of the impedance of the ground cable and clamps with an impedance meter. The value should be much less than one (1) ohm. Unless this value is extremely low, the ground connection is *not* adequate for personnel protection.
- Connect one ground cable to the closest phase of the system and connect each succeeding phase in order of closeness. When removing the grounds, reverse the order so the application or removal of a ground will not require the crossing of an ungrounded system phase. The grounds are applied to phases A, B and C, in that order and removed in the reverse order.
- Connect grounds to each phase of the circuit and/or equipment.
- Check to determine that all connected ground cables are visible at all times when work is being performed.
- Install grounds on all *sides of the work area*.

SWITCHGEAR GROUND AND TEST (G & T) DEVICE

A ground and test device is an auxiliary device, used with metal clad switchgear to ground equpment, or to permit various tests, when equipment is out of service. *The G & T device resembles a circuit breaker but is not designed to interrupt a circuit.*

SWITCHGEAR "DUMMY" ELEMENT

A dummy element is a device to provide a current path through a breaker compartment. The element frame resembles a breaker. *The element is not designed to interrupt a circuit.*

9-12 ON-SITE CIRCUIT BREAKER MAINTENANCE SAFETY CHECKLISTS

LOW VOLTAGE (600V AND BELOW) CHECKLIST

Preparation

- Telephone channels must be made available to summon emergency personnel when needed. The telephone must be close to the work site and functional throughout the period during which the work is to be done.
- The light level in the work area must be sufficient to perform the work safely. (M-G Sets, high-powered self-contained lighting systems, and/or emergency feeders will be used/supplied if the electrical shutdown is complete.)
- No employee should work on-site for more than twelve (12) continuous hours, and the work period should be preceded and followed by a minimum of eight (8) hours off (rest).
- The qualified craftsman should provide technical direction on-site.
- *No one shall work alone.*
- General workers shall not energize equipment or systems. These activities are to be performed by an assigned qualified person.
- Damp or recently flooded areas shall be worked completely de-energized. Control power also shall be de-energized.
- *All* stationary (bolted-in) and plug-in type circuit breakers (non-drawout) shall only be worked on when both the line and load sources are de-energized.
- When primary power circuits are energized, no conducting materials, including hardware or tools, shall be inserted in the cubicle.

Examination of Equipment/Breakers

- Prior to working on equipment/breakers, the following precautions must be observed:
- On solenoid operating mechanisms, trip the breaker "open."

■ On stored energy mechanisms, trip the breaker "open" and completely discharge "stored energy springs." (See the appropriate breaker instruction book and determine the exact procedure.)

■ Check for proper operation of mechanical or electrical interlocks. (All low-voltage drawout power circuit breakers have either mechanical or electrical interlocks to protect both personnel and equipment while the breaker is being inserted or withdrawn from its cubicle.) Always check these devices to confirm their proper operation. *In all cases*, consult the manufacturer's instruction to obtain interlock adjustment data (dimensions and tolerances).

■ Check for defeated or bypassed interlocks. (This condition enables the circuit breaker to be withdrawn or inserted in a closed position. *This is an extremely hazardous condition*.) If defeated interlocks are found, the following steps are to be performed:

Reactivate the interlock (or remove the bypass) and test to verify proper performance.

If equipment or materials are not available to make the repair, notify the appropriate person and do *not* re-insert the circuit breaker. The responsible person informed of the risk should decide whether to have his men re-insert a breaker with defective interlocks.

To minimize personnel and equipment exposure, de-energize the equipment (including control power). If this is not possible and the responsible person plans to re-insert the breaker, all other personnel should remove themselves from the immediate area.

■ Place the keys to interlocks on the equipment being worked in the possession of the qualified craftsman or foreman, providing technical and safety direction for the on-site job.

■ Check carefully that the spring-loaded contacts of the primary disconnect assemblies on the low-voltage drawout breakers are mounted properly, that the hardware is tight, and none are missing. Also check to determine that springs are in good condition and exert the proper pressure to insure good contact.

■ Check the hinge pins and spring clips on the primary disconnect assemblies. (The primary disconnect assemblies on competitive breakers may employ hinge pins mounted horizontally and passing through each disconnect cluster. The pins are retained on both ends by spring (or cee) clips. There is one pin per cluster and a total of six (6) clusters—3 line and 3 load. The length of these pins is sufficient to bridge the spacing between the phases, and the pin will still be retained in its original primary cluster. If not properly clipped, these pins will travel with vibration or other external forces. If the pin movement is extreme, a phase-to-phase fault can result.)

- Check each low-voltage breaker with a 1000V megger phase-to-phase-to-ground to assure adequate dielectric resistance between phases and to ground. These tests will prevent reapplying a breaker which could cause a serious "flashover" due to the effects of aging and environment.

- Prior to operation of circuit breaker mechanisms, remove all tools, parts, and equipment from the breaker proper. All personnel are to stand clear of the breaker while it is being energized by a qualified person.

Racking in Precautions

- First insure that the breaker is open.

- Inspect the cubicle for foreign objects (such as tools, rags, hi pot wire or loose hardware, etc.). Adequate lighting is necessary to thoroughly inspect the cubicle.

- Exercise care when cleaning and inspecting cubicles. Use only insulated nonconducting tools (brushes, vacuum hoses, screwdrivers, etc.) to clean or adjust elements within the cubicle. Handles or grips are to be sufficiently long to avoid the necessity of major extensions of the arm into the cubicle. Long sleeves and rubber gloves/gauntlets are mandatory for all interior cubicle adjustments when the system is energized. Technicians are to wear long sleeved shirts and remove all jewelry such as watches and rings. If the stationary line side or load side stabs or bars require maintenance which involves other than vacuuming, the system is to be de-energized.

- Check to determine that the control circuits (24V to 250V dc, 120V to 550V ac) are de-energized. Pulling the fuses on control circuits will ensure that these circuits are de-energized because they are not necessarily de-energized by opening the circuit breaker.

- Inspect the circuit breaker on the lift table or overhead crane just prior to insertion. This is to insure that all parts are tight and in their proper positions. It is also intended to insure that all foreign materials (such as rags, tools, hi pot wire or loose hardware) are removed.

- Perform a 1000V megger test with the circuit breaker in the open position (the last step prior to racking in). Megger phase-to-phase and phase-to-ground on all the circuit breaker primary disconnects.

- The steps above shall be verified by the qualified craftsman. On those competitive units using cee clip retainers, a count is to be made to insure that all clips required are in position and all hardware is properly mounted.

- Before racking in (or racking out) the circuit breaker, communicate audibly your intention to the other members of the work crew.
- Be certain to wear the required protective equipment and position yourself to either side of the cubicle.

MEDIUM VOLTAGE (601V THROUGH 15,000V) CHECKLIST

Preparation

- Telephone channels must be made available to summon emergency personnel when needed. The telephone must be close to the work site and functional throughout the period during which the work is to be done.
- The light level in the work area must be sufficient to perform the work safely. (M-G Sets, high-powered self-contained lighting systems and/or emergency feeders will be used/supplied if the electrical shut-down is complete.)
- No employee should work on-site for more than twelve (12) continuous hours, and the work period should be preceded and followed by a minimum of eight (8) hours off (rest).
- The qualified craftsman should provide technical direction on-site.
- *No one shall work alone.*
- General workers shall not de-energize and/or energize equipment or systems. These activities are to be performed by an assigned qualified person.
- Damp or recently flooded areas shall be worked completely de-energized. Control power also shall be de-energized.
- *All* stationary (bolted-in) and plug-in type circuit breakers (non-draw-out) shall only be worked on when both the primary and secondary (control power) sources are de-energized.
- When primary power circuits are energized, no conducting materials, including hardware and tools shall be inserted into the cubicle.

Examination of Equipment Breakers

- Prior to working on equipment breakers, the following precautions must be observed:

   On solenoid operating mechanisms, trip the breaker "open".

On stored energy mechanisms, trip the breaker "open" and completely discharge "stored energy springs." (See the appropriate breaker instruction book and determine the exact procedure.)

- Check for proper operation of mechanical or electrical interlocks. (All medium-voltage drawout power circuit breakers have either mechanical or electrical interlocks to protect both personnel and equipment while the breaker is being inserted or withdrawn from its cubicle.) *Always* check these devices to confirm their proper operation. *In all cases*, consult the manufacturer's instruction to obtain interlock adjustment data (dimensions and tolerances).

- Check for defeated or bypassed interlocks. (This condition enables the circuit breaker to be withdrawn or inserted in a closed position. *This is an extremely hazardous condition.*) When defeated interlocks are found, the following steps are to be performed:

Reactivate the interlock (or remove the bypass) and test to verify proper performance.

If equipment or materials are not available to make the repair, notify the appropriate person and do *not* re-insert the circuit breaker. The responsible person informed of the risk should decide whether to have his men re-insert a breaker with defective interlocks.

To minimize personnel and equipment exposure, the equipment (including control power) should be de-energized. If this is not possible and the responsible person plans to re-insert the breaker, all other personnel shall remove themselves from the immediate area.

- Place the keys to interlocks on the equipment being worked on in the possession of the qualified craftsman or foreman, providing technical and safety direction for the on-site job.

- Examine the condition of the ball-type contacts on the medium drawout breakers. This examination is to be performed with the breaker removed from the cubicle. Spring-loaded clusters from the mating contact to the primary bus. These clusters are protected by a sliding safety shutter that moves (open or closed) with the breaker elevating mechanism, which is part of the cubicle construction. The clusters must not be exposed by sliding open the shutter when the breaker is not in the cubicle or until the cubicle is *completely* de-energized, tested, and grounded.

- Check the hinge pins and spring clips on the primary disconnect assemblies. (Competitive breakers may employ hinge pins mounted horizontally and passing through each primary disconnect cluster. The pins are retained on both ends by spring (or cee) clips. If not properly clipped, these pins will travel with vibration or other external forces. If the pin movement is extreme, a *phase-to-phase fault* can result.)

- Check each medium-voltage breaker with a 2500V megger phase-to-phase-to-ground to assure adequate dielectric resistance between phases and to ground. These tests will prevent reapplying a breaker which could cause a serious "flashover" due to the effects of aging and environment.
- Prior to operation of circuit breaker mechanisms, remove all tools, parts and equipment from the breaker proper. All personnel are to be away from the breaker and *to keep hands off the breaker*.

Racking in Precautions

- First insure that the breaker is open.
- Inspect the cubicle for foreign objects (such as tools, rags, hi-pot wire or loose haredware, etc.). Adequate lighting is necessary to thoroughly inspect the cubicle.
- Exercise care when cleaning and inspecting cubicles. Cubicle heaters, powered from a CPT source, are an example type of this potential problem. The stationary secondary coupler (control power connections) are mounted vertically and are recessed. Care must be exercised when working close to the bottom of the coupler since potentially dangerous voltages could exist on several of the contact points.
- Check that the control circuits are de-energized (24V to 250V a-c; 120V to 550V ac). Pulling the fuses on control circuits will ensure that these circuits are de-energized because they are not necessarily de-energized by opening the circuit breaker.
- Inspect the circuit breaker just prior to inspection. This is to insure that all parts are tight and in their proper positions. It is also intended to insure that all foreign materials (such as rags, tools, hi-pot wire, or loose hardware) are removed.
- Perform a 2500V megger test with the circuit breaker in the open position (the last step prior to racking in). Megger phase-to-phase and phase-to-ground on all the circuit breaker primary disconnects.
- The steps above shall be verified by the qualified craftsman. On competitive units using cee clip retainers, a count is to be made to insure that all clips required are in position and all hardware is properly mounted.
- Before racking in or racking out the circuit breaker, communicate audibly your intention to the other members of the work crew.
- Close the cubicle door PRIOR to closing the circuit breaker.

9-13 CONFINED SPACES—PROCEDURE FOR ENTERING

General

A confined space is an enclosed structure or space with restricted means of entry (such as a manhole, transformer vault, transformer tank, elevator pits, motor basements, etc.). The confined space is so enclosed and of such volume that natural ventilation through openings provided does *not* prevent the accumulation of dangerous air contaminants nor supply sufficient oxygen to protect the life, health, and safety of any person occupying such structure or space.

General workers are *not* to enter confined spaces (see definition above) where dangerous air contaminants have been present, are present, or could be introduced from potential sources. Workers may enter these confined spaces *only* after the atmosphere has been tested and found free of dangerous air contaminants.

Any such confined space shall be continuously maintained free of dangerous air contaminants by mechanical ventilation or equivalent means during any period of occupancy. If, however, due to emergency conditions, any such confined space cannot be cleared of dangerous air contaminants by mechanical ventilation or equivalent means, any person entering such confined space shall be provided with and shall use an approved air line respirator, or approved self-contained breathing apparatus.

Dangerous contaminants that may be found in confined spaces may be grouped as follows:

- Fuel gases (e.g. manufactured gas, natural gas, or liquefied petroleum gases).
- Vapors of liquid fuels and solvents (e.g. gasoline, kerosene, naphtha, benzene, and other hydrocarbons).
- Products of combustion (e.g., carbon monoxide—engine exhaust or carbon dioxide).
- Nitrogen and/or carbon dioxide used for testing or burning gases and volatile substances within industrial drainage.
- Gases from fermentation of organic matter (e.g., hydrogen, hydrogen sulfide, methane, carbon dioxide, and mixtures deficient in oxygen).
- Gases generated by the customers' processes.

The hazards of explosion, fire, and asphyxiation may all be encountered in the preceding contaminants because mixtures of these classes of contaminants are not uncommon.

Preparing to Enter a Confined Space

All confined spaces shall be considered hazardous until proven safe by tests.

General workers shall not enter a confined space, even momentarily, until it has been tested for oxygen and combustible gas content and then power ventilated for a minimum of five minutes or four complete air volume changes, whichever is the greater.

Smoking, or any device which produces a spark, shall not be allowed in a confined space. In addition, smoking is not permitted within ten feet of an open confined space.

Every employee that is to enter a confined work area should be properly trained in the procedures for detecting hazardous conditions and must be provided with the proper equipment to make this determination. Before a confined space is entered, the foreman/qualified employee must also review with the general workers the work to be performed and the hazards that may be encountered.

Testing a Confined Space

Every confined space that has been closed for any period of time should be tested to determine if sufficient life-supporting oxygen is present and if combustible gases are present. In addition, any instruments that are used to sample a confined space environment must first be tested for proper working operation before they are used. Periodic calibration of the test instrumentation as recommended by the manufacturer of the instrument is a mandatory requirement, and such calibrations must utilize the type of equipment suitable for the air contaminants involved.

- If doors or covers contain vents, the pre-entry test is made with the doors or covers in place in order to test conditions of confined space before it has been disturbed. If the cover or door is unvented, it is opened enough only to admit the test hose or the instrument to be inserted.

- When a test indicates hazardous gases, the cover or door must be very carefully opened or removed in order not to create sparks. If the test indicates that air contaminants are in excess of safe concentrations or that explosive hazards are present in the confined space, the space must be purged by forced ventilation until another test indicates that the air contaminant concentration is safe (see Ventilation).

- If initial tests indicate that the atmosphere is safe, the confined space must be force ventilated for a minimum of five minutes, using a blower of 500 CFM (cubic feet per minute) or more, or four complete air volume changes before it is entered. The blower must be operated during the entire time period when an employee is occupying the confined space.

- After the confined space is entered and the blower hose is positioned, initial testing for gas is accomplished by sampling in the areas of possible gas entrance and then generally throughout the confined space. If the test results are satisfactory, the work may be performed.

- If an unsatisfactory atmosphere is found as the result of the preceding test, employees must immediately leave the confined space. The blower must be operated for 10 additional minutes and then a second test is performed. The second test must be performed away from the direct output of the blower.

- If the second test indicates that the atmosphere is safe, the confined space may be entered. The blower shall be operated during the entire time period that personnel are occupying the confined space. Again, a test is made for gas by sampling or testing in the area of possible gas entrance and then generally throughout the confined space.

- If the confined space is still contaminated and cannot be cleared, after venting and retesting, the cause must be determined. If the area where the contaminant is entering can be plugged, sealed or capped to render it safe, these procedures shall be performed by personnel wearing an approved air line respirator or approved self-contained breathing apparatus. The area is then to be retested, continuously vented, and monitored.

Ventilation Procedures

Confined spaces containing air contaminants and/or explosion hazards must be purged by mechanical ventilation until tests indicate that the concentration of air contaminants in the confined space is not more than 10 percent of the lower explosive level of such air contaminants, and that there is sufficient oxygen to support life available in the confined space.

Personnel performing the ventilation procedure must be familiar with the operating instructions for the particular equipment being used, and must also perform the following general procedures:

- Place the blower so it will not be subject to damage, obstruct traffic, or present a hazard to pedestrians.

- On sloping surfaces, avoid placing the blower on the upgrade side of the confined space opening. If it is necessary to place the blower on the upgrade side of a manhole or vault, block the unit so that vibration will not cause it to move toward the manhole opening.

- Do *not* operate or store blower in a confined space.

- Always remove the blower hose from a confined space before the blower is turned off.

- Place blower on a firm level base at least ten feet from a manhole or vault opening and in accordance with above.

- Attach the blower hose to the air outlet of the blower by slipping the end of the hose, which is equipped with a strap type clamp, over the air outlet and then pull the strap tight to hold the hose in place.
- Connect the power cord to the power source to start the blower. (Only grounded electrical equipment shall be used.)
- Let the blower run for one minute with the hose out of the confined space. Check the end of the hose to see that the hose is securely attached to the air outlet.
- Place the blower hose in the confined space and adjust the position of the blower so the hose will run directly into the confined space without unnecessary bends. The optimum position of the output end of the blower hose is with the hose opening directed toward an end wall.
- If the ventilating blower stops, leave the confined space immediately. Remove the hose from the confined space. Do not replace the hose in the confined space until the blower is operating. When the blower is again operating, purge the hose and test the atmosphere before replacing the hose in confined space.

Equipment Necessary for Entering a Confined Space

Any person entering a confined space should be provided with and should use the following additional safety equipment:

- Either an approved life belt, approved safety harness, approved wrist straps or approved noose-type wristlets should be worn.
- A lifeline should be attached to such life belt, approved safety harness, approved wrist straps or approved noose-type wristlets with the other end securely anchored outside the confined space.
- A safe means of entering and leaving the confined space (such as a portable ladder) should be provided. Such means must not obstruct the access opening.
- An explosion-proof battery-operated portable light in good working order.
- Non-sparking striking, chipping, hammering or cut tools and equipment where the confined space may contain explosive or flammable air contaminants.

Safety Monitors

If the confined space is found to be contaminanted, a person designated as a safety monitor should be stationed at the access opening of any confined space while such space is occupied for any reason. The safety monitor is responsible for performing the following:

- Maintaining visual contact with every person in the confined space where the construction of the space permits.
- Having continuous knowledge of the activities and well-being of every person in the confined space either through verbal communication or other positive means at all times.
- Assisting a person in a confined space with such tasks as handling tools or supplies or removing containers of refuse or debris, provided that these tasks do not interfere with his primary duty as a safety monitor.

The safety monitor selected should have the following characteristics:

- Be an alert, competent person, and fully capable of quickly summoning assistance for the administration of emergency first aid when required.
- Be physically able to assist in the removal of a person from a confined space under emergency conditions.

The following should be available to the safety monitor or rescue personnel for use if required.

- Approved air line respirator, approved hose mask, or approved self-contained breathing apparatus.
- Explosion-proof battery-operated portable light in good working order.

The emergency equipment should be located at the access opening of the confined space or not more than 15 feet from such opening. In the case of a manhole or in-the-ground enclosure, a universal tripod should be set up before the confined space is entered.

Emergency Conditions

The safety monitor should not enter a confined space until he is relieved at his post. An additional employee or another person should be available to summon aid immediately. The monitor will attempt to remove the victim by the use of the lifeline and to perform all other necessary rescue functions from the outside. Upon arrival of help, the monitor may enter the confined space for rescue work only when he is assured that his outside assistance is adequate. Rescuers entering confined space should be protected with the approved safety equipment required by the situation such as lifeline and harness and proper personal protection equipment.

9-14 ELECTRICAL SWITCHING PRACTICES

There are many types and designs of disconnecting switches, commonly known as disconnects, which are used to sectionalize a line or feeder, make connections, and isolate equipment on electrical systems. The type used depends upon the kind of service, voltage, current-carrying capacity, and the equipment design. This section discusses only the most common types, which use air as an insulating medium, and the hazards involved and what measures should be taken to avoid them.

GENERAL PRECAUTIONS

- Management should thoroughly define who has the authority to disconnect switches or operate electrical controls or apparatus that will in any manner affect the safety of personnel or interrupt electrical service. Switching should be done by persons who are fully qualified and authorized to do this work and by other individuals only when they are under the direct supervision of such qualified and authorized persons.

- All apparatus should be legibly marked for every identification. This marking should not be placed on a removable part.

- Switching orders should be in written form, with every step in the switching sequence spelled out in detail. Telephone or radio orders should be written down and then repeated. These procedures are particularly important for long or complicated operations.

- Every manual switching operation exposes the operator to some degree of hazard. Therefore, for his own safety he must understand the switching job to be done and be completely familiar with every detail of his part of the operation. An operator should not start a switching sequence until he has carefully checked the written order and is satisfied that it is correct in every respect. Once he has begun the operation, he must keep his mind on what he is doing, ignoring distractions, until the job is completed. If his attention is diverted to another task while he is executing a switching operation, he should not continue the operation before carefully checking what has already been done.

LOADS AND CURRENTS

- Ordinary disconnects should not be used to interrupt loads and magnetizing currents or to energize lines, cables, or equipment unless all the following conditions are met:

  The amount of current should be small.

The kVA (kilovolt-ampere) capacity of the equipment being interrupted should be relatively low.

The location and design of the disconnect assure that it can be operated without danger of flashover.

Experience has shown that the disconnect can be used successfully for the particular purpose. Therefore, disconnects should be properly connected and installed before proceeding with an operation.

- Disconnecting switches are frequently used to break parallel circuits. As the blade leaves the clip, a relatively light or weak arc is drawn, which is quickly broken as the arc resistance increases. This operation is safe provided that the impedance of the circuit is low enough to permit the arc to break. Here again, experience is the best guide as to which parallels can be broken. Energizing or magnetizing current is the most difficult to break because of its low power factor.

- Disconnects should never be used to de-energize lines, cables, capacitors, transformers, and other equipment unless specific approval is given and then with full knowledge that the disconnects will interrupt the current.

- Underhung disconnects are mounted horizontally, and careful consideration must be given before they are used to break a parallel or to interrupt load current. The heat and ionized gas of even a small arc may be enough to cause a flashover.

SWITCH STICKS

- Switch sticks or hook sticks are insulated tools designed for the manual operation of disconnecting switches and should be used for no other purpose. A switch stick is made up of several parts. The head or hook is either metal or plastic. The insulating section may be wood, plastic, laminated wood, or other effective insulating material, or a combination of several such materials. Glass fiber and epoxy resin materials are being used instead of wood by some manufacturers, and although they may cost somewhat more than switch sticks made of wood, the extra expense can be justified by longer life and reduced maintenance. Some manufacturers make a switch stick with a thin extruded plastic coating. This type of stick requires less maintenance than other types because the coating is tough and can be easily repaired.

- A stick of the correct type and size for the application should be selected. Standard switch sticks are made in lengths up to 24 feet with proportional diameters. Special or telescoping sticks are available in longer lengths.

- Switch sticks with insulated heads should be used to operate disconnects mounted indoors or on structures where the metal head of the stick might be shorted out when inserted into the eye of the switch.
- The parts of a switch stick are pinned together and are therefore subject to wear. Consequently, they should be examined frequently. Varnish or a similar non-conductive coating used to seal the wooden parts and prevent their absorbing moisture, should be in good condition at all times.
- It is recommended that personnel do not approach electrical conductors any closer than indicated below unless you are certain that the conductors are de-energized.

Voltage range (phase to phase) kilovolt	Minimum working and clear hot stick distance
.3 to .75	1 ft. 0 in.
2.1 to 15	2 ft. 0 in.
15.1 to 35	2 ft. 4 in.
35.1 to 46	2 ft. 6 in.
46.1 to 72.5	3 ft. 0 in.
72.6 to 121	3 ft. 4 in.
138 to 145	3 ft. 6 in.
161 to 169	3 ft. 8 in.
230 to 242	5 ft. 0 in.
345 to 362	7 ft. 0 in.
500 to 552	11 ft. 0 in.
700 to 765	15 ft. 0 in.

- Storage of switch sticks is important. When stored indoors, a stick should be hung vertically on a wall to minimize the accumulation of dust. (It should be located in a convenient place but not where it might be subject to damage.)
- If a switch stick must be stored outdoors, it should be protected from sun and moisture. The varnish or insulating coating on a stick exposed to direct sunlight or excessive heat may soften and run. A long pipe capped at both ends, ventilated, and shielded or insulated from direct sun rays makes a good storage place.

OPENING DISCONNECTS BY USING THE "INCHING" METHOD

The "inching" method of opening manually operated disconnects should be used wherever the opening operation can be controlled. The inching method should *never* be used for loadbreak disconnects, airbreak switches, or other switching devices designed to break load or magnetizing currents.

In the inching method, the operator opens the disconnect gradually until he is sure that there is no load current. He then opens the disconnect fully. If a small static arc develops, but no more than is expected, the disconnect may be opened further, with caution, until the arc breaks. The opening can then be completed. If an arc develops that is greater than the normal charging current warrants or, in the case of breaking a parallel, greater than expected, the disconnect should be quickly closed.

Using these techniques, an operator can open disconnects by the inching method nearly as fast as he can by other methods and with maximum safety.

SELECTOR DISCONNECTS

- A selector disconnect has three phases with a double blade in each phase. The blade may be placed in either of two positions. Each blade is operated separately. The three operations—to open, to open and close, and to transfer from one position to the other under load conditions—must be done in the right sequence for proper functioning.

  To open a set of selector disconnects, first one blade of each phase is fully opened. Then the second blade of each phase is fully opened.

  To open a set of selector disconnects from one position *and close* them to the other position, first one blade of each phase is fully opened, and then the second blade of each phase is fully opened. All six blades are then open. One blade of each phase is then closed to its selected position; and to complete the operation, the second blade of each phase is closed to this position.

  To transfer selector disconnects *from one position to the other under load conditions*, first one blade of each phase is fully opened. After these blades have been opened, they are then closed one at a time to the selected position. The two sources of power for the circuit are thus paralleled. In a like manner, the second blade of each phase is opened from the original position, breaking the parallel, and then closed to the selected position. Now all six blades are closed to the selected position, and the transfer is completed without interruption to load.

- When operating selector disconnecting switches, the operator should never open a blade of one phase from one position and swing it closed to the selected position in one operation. The corresponding blades in each of the phases should be opened successively, and only one step should be taken at a time.

CIRCUIT BREAKER DISCONNECTS

- The bus and line side disconnects of a circuit breaker must not be operated until the operator has made certain by observation of the circuit breaker indicating target or mechanism that the breaker is in the open position. (The exception to this rule is that the line side disconnects may be operated to make or break a parallel, for example, to shunt out feeder voltage regulators.)

- Checking the position of the breaker is a routine part of operation that must never be neglected. Sometimes a breaker operated by remote control may not open because the control contact has failed or the operator has not held the opening control long enough.

- Even if a mechanical failure has occurred or a control fuse has blown, it is still possible for a breaker to operate partially, reaching a semi-closed position. Wherever possible, all three phases of a breaker should be checked for failure of a lift rod or other mechanical failure that could cause a phase to remain closed. (An operator should always be on the alert for such conditions.)

- Before the circuit breaker is restored to service after maintenance work has been completed, the operator must check to make sure that it has been left in the open position.

INTERRUPTER SWITCHES

- The need to interrupt load currents and to deenergize regulators and similar equipment has led to the development of the interrupter switch. There are many different designs, and the type used depends upon the voltage and the current interrupting capacity required.

- Generally, there is an auxiliary blade or contact in addition to the regular load contacts. Before the switch is opened, it is important to check this auxiliary contact, where possible, to make sure that it is fully engaged. When the switch is opened, the load contact breaks first and then the auxiliary contact is opened. The arc is extinguished by an arc chamber, arcing horns, or other means. *No attempt should ever be made to inch an interrupter switch.*

CLOSING DISCONNECTS UNDER LOAD CONDITIONS

- While disconnects are not designed to be used as load-pickup devices or to energize lines, cables, or apparatus, they may be used for these purposes where all the following conditions are met:

    The length of line or cable should be limited;

    The load and the capacity of the apparatus should be small; and

    The voltage should be low.

    Approval for these operations should be obtained from the person in charge only after all conditions have been studied.

- In all cases, the procedure to be followed is the same. An operator must be aware that he is closing a disconnect under load conditions; he should select a switch stick of the correct length and then take a comfortable stance in direct line with the disconnect; and he should first move the disconnect to about the three-fourths closed position. After checking to see that the blade is in line with the clip, he should then use a firm direct stroke to seat the disconnect completely.

- An operator should never re-open the disconnect to make a second attempt at closing it. If it is not seated completely, he should use added pressure to finish the closing. If the alignment is wrong, the lines or apparatus should be deenergized before the disconnect is opened.

AIRBREAK SWITCHES

- An airbreak switch is a gang-operated disconnect designed with arcing horns and with sufficient clearance to energize and deenergize load currents, magnetizing current of power transformers, charging current of transmission lines, and to make and break transmission line parallels.

- Airbreaks, like other types of gang-operated disconnects, are connected so that operation of all three phases is controlled by means of a hand lever. Some of the procedures governing stick-operated disconnects apply also to airbreaks. The inching procedure should not be applied to airbreaks designed to interrupt load or magnetizing currents.

- When airbreak switches are installed, their use should be specifically stated and any limitation must be made known to all operating personnel concerned.

- Weather conditions can affect the successful breaking of current by an airbreak—a strong wind can blow the arc across phases or a heavy rain can change the normal insulating air clearances.

- Airbreaks should be firmly opened and closed. When closing an airbreak to pick up a load, an operator should be careful not to open it after the load circuit has been completed by either the arcing horns or the main contacts, regardless of whether or not the airbreak has been closed properly.

- Before airbreaks are used to break transmission line parallels, the load current should be checked to assure that it is within the capacity of the airbreak to interrupt.

- The operator should never depend upon the position of the operating lever to determine whether the airbreak is open or closed. He should check the airbreak visually before and after operation and make sure that each operating blade is in the selected position. One blade may fail to operate and remain either closed or open.

- To prevent inadvertent operation when maintenance, repair, or other work is to be done, all airbreaks should be locked in an open position and tagged.

PROTECTION AGAINST AIRBREAK FLASHOVER

- During the operation of airbreaks, a flashover causing a flow of fault current may occur. Several measures have been commonly used to protect the operator against electric shock. They include using an insulating section in the handle of the operating rod, grounding the handle of the rod, and providing ground mats or insulating stools at the operating position. (Opinions vary concerning the effectiveness of these measures and there are no widely accepted standards.) Rubber gloves should always be worn by the operator.

- The handle of the operating rod may be insulated against possible contact with energized parts of the airbreak by a section of nonconductive wood or porcelain, in order to effectively protect an operator against the hazards of an airbreak failure. However, this does not protect against the shunting effect of the pole mounting and attachments. The ground voltage gradient is reduced but not eliminated by an insulating section.

- Whether or not an insulating section is provided, the handle of the operating rod should be grounded with the lowest possible resistance. (A large majority of airbreak installations have a continuous metal operating rod that is grounded.)

- Ground mats should be provided for operators to stand on; they will give him maximum protection against touch voltage and ground gradient voltage and prevent any potential differences from occurring across the body in case of an insulation failure or flashover. Some companies provide portable ground mats of small iron mesh. Other companies install fixed ground mats, and specifications for installation vary widely. (Whether a ground mat is portable or fixed, however, it must be electrically connected to the operating rod and to ground to equalize the ground gradient in the area where an operator stands.)

- Operators should keep both feet on ground mats. Regardless of the type of installation or the protection provided, they should always stand with their feet as close together as is comfortable.

MOTOR-CONTROLLED DISCONNECTS AND AIRBREAKS

- Many of the routine procedures and practices previously discussed for manually operated disconnects and airbreaks also apply to motor-controlled disconnects and airbreaks. In addition, the practices and precautions outlined in the following paragraphs should be observed.

- The operators should hold the remote control contact long enough for the operating relay to seal in and ensure opperation of the disconnect.

- To determine whether the switch is open or closed, operators must never rely upon the indicating lights or upon the position of the operating handle. Instead, they must always visually check the position of the blades at the switch, making sure that each blade is in the selected position. (This check is particularly important for switches with high pressure contacts.)

- When a motor-operated switch is used as a tagging point for work clearance, the motor drive should be uncoupled from the operating rod. If this precaution cannot be taken, a heavy pin, lock, or blocking device must be used on the switch to prevent inadvertent operation. In addition, the switch for the motor control circuit should be tagged and locked in an open position to prevent operation of the motor in case of an accidental ground.

9-15   ELECTRICAL FIRE EMERGENCIES

This section is written as a guide for fire fighting personnel for handing electrical fire emergencies. Electrical personnel are not usually fire fighting experts but, because of their knowledge of electricity, they can provide vital and helpful information to others who are involved in fighting fires. Therefore, a cooperative effort is needed among the various groups when dealing with electrical emergencies. The various safety considerations dealing with such emergencies are listed as follows:

NEVER MAKE DIRECT CONTACT WITH ANY ENERGIZED OBJECT

Electricity, whether from a powerline or from a thundercloud, is always trying to get to the earth, which is at ground voltage—also called zero voltage. Voltage is a measure of the "pressure" that pushes electric charge through a conductor. An object with *any* voltage above zero is called "energized". Any energized object will produce a flow of electric charge through a conductor placed between it and the earth or any other object at ground voltage, such as a grounded wire. Since nearly all common materials—including the human body—are conductors to some extent, the only way to keep the electricity where it belongs is to place some sort of insulator (non-conductor) between the energized object and the earth.

One can get just as "shocked" from 120-volt house current as one can from a 500,000-volt powerline! In fact, a high voltage shock, because of the clamping action it has on the heart (cardiac arrest), may prevent the deadly irregular beating of the heart (fibrillation) often associated with lower-voltage shocks. Cardiac-arrest victims often respond readily to artificial respiration and external heart massage; whereas a fibrillation victim may only respond to an electrical defibrillator device. Also with the lower-voltage shock, instead of enough current to knock you out, you may get just enough to set your muscles so you can't let go.

STAY CLEAR OF VICINITY OF ANY FAULTY ENERGIZED OBJECT

One can be injured *without* touching an energized object. When an energized object is sparking, it emits excessive heat and ultraviolet rays. Such sparking occurs while trying to interrupt the flow of electric charge, such as when an energized wire is cut or when a fallen energized wire is lifted away from the earth. The electric charge tries to maintain its flow through the air—this results in a flash, an electric arc. The excessive heat from such a flash can burn human flesh several feet away.

The heat of an electric arc has been known to fuse contact lenses to the cornea of a man's eyes. Ultraviolet rays emitted from an electric flash may also damage unprotected eyes. Eye injuries may not be immediately apparent— there may be no noticeable eye irritation for several hours after exposure. If your eyes are exposed to an electric arc, consult a doctor for proper treatment without delay. Electrical employees should wear specially treated goggles to prevent ultraviolet-ray damage whenever an electric arc may occur.

BE ALERT IN VICINITY OF ANY ENERGIZED OBJECT

We have already emphasized the danger from contacting an energized object, or even getting in the vicinity of a faulty energized object, such as a fallen wire. It is just as important to be cautious in the vicinity of energized facilities that are operating properly. Most electrical emergency work is performed without deenergizing all electric facilities in the vicinity. In many cases, it is even advantageous to leave power on as long as possible. However, all personnel must continuously be alert. Don't let the quiet, "harmless" appearance lull you into a false sense of security.

Beware Covered Wires!

Many overhead wires are covered. *But*, that covering is often designed to protect the wire from the weather or tree contact, not to protect you from the wire. Never consider a covered wire any safer than a bare wire. And remember, most wires on utility poles are bare, even though they may appear to be covered when viewed from the ground.

Beware "Telephone" Cables!

Telephone cables are rarely dangerous when accidentally contacted. *But*, are you so sure you can tell the difference between telephone cable and electric power cable, that you'd stake your life on it—and the lives of others? Although higher voltage facilities are generally installed higher up on utility poles, this is *not* true always—electric power cables operating at 34,000 volts may be attached *below* telephone cables on the same pole. And a fallen telephone cable may be contacting a powerline!

- Never rest ladders on wires or on any other electric equipment.
- Never drag hose over wires.
- Never even come too close to wires—brushing against one can be fatal.

You may have had some experience where you were able to contact energized facilities without incident. *But*, just because you "got away with it" before doesn't guarantee you will get away with it again. And remember, higher-voltage facilities have much greater "pressure" behind the electricity—something you "got away with" on 120-volt facilities can bring disaster if attempted on 34,000-volt facilities. And since normal water is a conductor of electricity, even slightly damp objects become much more hazardous.

ASSUME EVERY FALLEN WIRE IS ENERGIZED AND DANGEROUS

Wire on Ground

Some fallen wires snap and twist—bursting warning sparks. Others lie quietly—no sparks, no warning rattles like a snake. Both types are equally deadly. It is impossible to determine from the appearance of a wire whether or not it is energized. Also, automatic switching equipment may re-energize fallen wires. Always stay clear and keep everyone else clear until an electric company employee arrives and clears the wire or de-energizes it.

Wire on Object

If a wire is in contact with any object—fence, tree, car, or person—that object in turn may be energized and deadly. Keep yourself and others away from metal highway dividers and metal fences that may be in contact with fallen wires. A fallen wire draped over such dividers and fences can energize them for their entire length.

Wire on Vehicle

If anyone is in a vehicle which is in contact with a wire, the safest thing he can do is stay inside. If possible, he should drive the vehicle away from the contact. If the vehicle is on fire, tell him to jump free with both hands and feet clear of the vehicle when he hits the ground. At no time can the person simultaneously touch both the vehicle and the ground or any other object that is touching the ground, such as yourself. If he does, he will become a path for the electricity to flow to ground. Never board a vehicle that may be energized. A spray or fog nozzle should be used to direct water onto a burning vehicle—even then, stay back as far as practicable (at least 6 feet) whenever the wire on a vehicle may be energized.

NEVER CUT WIRES EXCEPT TO PROTECT LIFE

And even then, only thoroughly trained persons, such as electric company employees, using approved procedures and equipment can cut wires. Otherwise cutting wires can create more hazards than leaving them alone. When taut wires are cut, the change in tension may cause utility poles to fall or wires to slack off and sag to the ground some distance from where the wires are cut. Wire which retains some of its original "reel-curl" may coil up when cut and get out of control with resultant hazards.

Take Care After Cutting

Cutting a wire at one place does not necessarily ensure that the wire on *either* side of the cut is de-energized because:

- Wires are frequently energized from both directions;
- Wires may be in accidental contact with other energized wires;
- Wires may be energized from a privately owned generator within a building.

Cutting Service Wires

When protection of life requires de-energizing a building, cutting service wires should be considered *only* when it is not practicable to remove fuses, open circuit breakers, open the main switch, or wait for an electric company representative. *Specialized equipment* must be used to cut each wire individually and then bend each one back, to prevent short-circuiting the wires together. *All* wires must be cut. Never assume that one wire is a ground wire and is therefore safe. Even a "ground" wire may be contacting an energized wire at some unseen location. If the service wires can be cut on the supply side of where they connect to the building's wires, it will be possible to restore the service more quickly when required. However, far more important, service wires should always be cut on the building side of where they are first attached to the building—this avoids having wires fall on the ground.

USE APPROVED PROCEDURES AND EQUIPMENT IF YOU MUST WORK NEAR ENERGIZED FACILITIES

This rule certainly applies whether or not there is any victim to be rescued. However, the presence of a victim requires you to be even more conscientious.

Notify Electric Company

If you see no safe way of separating a victim from an energized object, request electric company assistance. Your first consideration must be your own protection—you cannot help by becoming a victim yourself.

Moving the Victim

Electric company employees have *specialized equipment* that they can use to drag a victim clear of electric equipment. They can use other specialized equipment to keep the wire in contact with the ground while the victim is being dragged clear—this reduces the amount of electricity flowing through the victim and minimizes further injury from additional burns.

Moving the Wire

Electric company employees have *specialized equipment* that they can use to remove a wire from a victim. They can control the wire to prevent it from recontacting the victim. Electric company employees will put the wire toward themselves while walking away—rather than pushing and walking toward it—to reduce the danger to themselves in case the wire gets out of control. And, again, they can use other *specialized equipment* to keep the wire in contact with the ground while moving it—this reduces the amount of electricity flowing through the victim and minimizes further injury from additional burns.

Cutting the Wire

If a victim is entangled with an electric wire, the wire on *both* sides of the victim must be cut to be certain that no source of electricity remains. Wires should only be cut by an individual who is thoroughly trained to cut wires safely and who uses *specialized equipment*.

First Aid

A victim who has been separated from energized electric facilities *does not* retain an electric charge—so there is no danger in handling the victim, administering first aid, or applying artificial respiration. Electric burns, even if insignificant on the surface, may involve serious destruction of tissues and must receive expert medical treatment as soon as possible.

AVOID USING HOSE STREAMS ON ENERGIZED FACILITIES

The application of water on electric facilities by hand-held hoses may carry the electricity back to the nozzle. This electricity might be sufficient to cause serious injury. Tabularized "safe distances" can be misleading, since water conductivity and nozzle design vary widely. The National Board of Fire Underwriters' Special Interest Bulletin No. 91 advises that for 120-volt facilities there is no danger unless the nozzle is brought within a few inches. However, fire fighters should consider all electric facilities to be high voltage, because even low-voltage wires may inadvertently be crossed with high-voltage wires.

Spray or Fog Preferred

For maximum safety to the fire fighter, when either intentional or unintentional application of water on energized facilities may occur, a spray or fog nozzle should be used.

Beware Run-off Water!

A dangerously energized puddle of water may be formed by water running off energized electric facilities.

Beware Adjacent Equipment!

Take care not to damage uninvolved electric facilities nearby. A porcelain insulator supporting energized facilities may flashover (arc), and even explode, if hit by a straight stream (even spray or fog) directed onto it. Wires may swing together, short-circuit, and burn down if hit by the force of a straight stream.

Other Extinguishing Agents

Dry chemical and carbon dioxide are non-conductive and may be used around energized facilities. These may be used to extinguish a surface-type utility pole fire. Foam, soda acid, and the loaded-stream type are conductive and should not be used on fires around energized facilities.

BE EQUALLY ALERT INDOORS AND OUTDOORS

Medium-Voltage Installations

Medium voltage services do exist in many larger buildings—commercial, institutional, and industrial. Do not enter any transformer room or open any electric switch without advice of an authorized individual. Besides the obvious electric hazard, privately owned transformers may be filled with flammable oil or with non-flammable liquids. Such equipment is not required to be isolated outdoors or in a fire resistant room and therefore may be located anywhere on the premises. The non-flammable liquid, while safe from a fire standpoint, may be caustic and may generate poisonous fumes. Call the plant electrician to identify specific hazards and to de-energize facilities as needed.

Low-Voltage Installations

Low-voltage services exist in practically every building and can be as danger-ous as medium-voltage facilities.

Leave Power on as Long as Possible

The power may be needed to operate pumps or other equipment which, if stopped, would cause additional damage to the building or to any materials being produced in it.

REMOVE FUSES OR OPEN CIRCUIT BREAKERS
To shut off an affected section, remove fuses or open circuit breakers.

OPEN MAIN SWITCH
Open the main switch to shut off entire building when electric service is no longer useful. If you must stand in water or if the switch is wet, do not grasp the switch handle in the palm of your hand. Use dry equipment such as a piece of rope, pike pole, or handle of fire axe to open the switch. Then attach a warning tag indicating that the power has been intentionally shut off.

CUT WIRES ONLY TO PROTECT LIFE
Cut wires only when life would be endangered by leaving a building energized, or when a victim must be rescued. However, cutting electric wires should only be considered when it is not practicable to remove fuses, open circuit breakers, open the main switch, or wait for an electric company representative.

PULL ELECTRIC METER
Pull the electric meter only to protect life when no other method is practicable. Wear gloves and face shield or goggles to protect against electric arcing. Meters at most large buildings, as well as many house meters, can produce extensive arcing when removed—especially if the interior wiring is faulty. In addition, removing some meters does *not* interrupt the power. Such meters should be identified by a small label reading "CAUTION: Apply Jumpers Before Remov-ing Meter". If a meter is removed, cover panel to protect public, and notify electric company.

FLAMMABLE FUMES

Whenever flammable fumes may be present, avoid operating any electric switch within the area—even a simple light switch—because even a small spark can cause an explosion.

PALMS INWARD

When walking through a building or any enclosure where visibility is poor, proceed with arms outstretched and the palms of the hands turned toward the face. In this way, if contact is made with an energized object the tendency of the muscles to contract may assist in getting free from the contact.

PROTECT PEOPLE AND PROPERTY IN SURROUNDING AREA AND DON'T FIGHT FIRES ON ELECTRIC EQUIPMENT UNTIL AN ELECTRIC COMPANY REPRESENTATIVE ARRIVES

Where electric power equipment is involved, wait for the electric company representative and coordinate the fire-fighting operation with him to ensure maximum effectiveness and safety. Cooperate with his requests because he knows what is necessary to fight fires on his equipment.

Danger From Switches

Never operate electric company switches that are mounted on utility poles or located in manholes or within substation properties. Many of these switches are not intended to open and drop the electric load, and attempting such an operation could damage the switch and even cause it to explode.

Danger From Oil

Oil may be present in any pole-mounted, underground, or surface equipment, such as transformers. This oil will burn. Under the intense heat of a fire, the equipment may even rupture and spray its burning oil. This may be followed by subsequent explosions caused by ignition of the mixture of air with hot oil vapor or with burning insulation vapor.

Danger From Water

Water greatly increases the danger of electrocution from energized facilities. Until it is confirmed that electric facilities are de-energized, use only dry chemical, carbon dioxide, water spray or fog—and even then, take extreme care to avoid physical contact with energized facilities. Also, take care not to direct a straight stream onto uninvolved electric facilities nearby.

Contain Liquids Leaked From Equipment

Any liquid leaked from electrical equipment may be flammable oil or a non-flammable liquid such as askarel. Avoid contact with these liquids—they may be caustic and fumes may be irritating. Both types of liquids must be thoroughly cleaned up by the utility company to prevent environmental damage. After extinguishing any fire, try to contain any leaked liquid—use absorbent granules, dry sand, ashes, or sawdust. *Do not wash it away with a hose stream.*

HOSE STREAMS MAY BE MORE HAZARDOUS THAN HELPFUL UNTIL ANY UNDERGROUND FAULT IS DE-ENERGIZED

Electric facilities are installed underground in many urban areas and new residential developments. Switching equipment and transformers are installed in manholes or in metal cabinets on the surface, and they supply electricity through an interconnected network of electric cables. The cables may be directly buried beneath only two or three feet of earth—or they may be installed in duct. Voltages are both low and high. The two major causes of fires are:

- Cable faults that ignite the cable insulation, or the fiber duct, or both:
- Oil-filled manhole equipment which overheats and spills oil that ignites.

Notify Electric Company

Specify location of all manholes involved. A cable fault usually clears itself, or it can be cleared manually by opening appropriate switches. Until the fault which caused the fire is de-energized, no attempt should be made to extinguish the fire. An electric arc cannot be extinguished by fire-fighting techniques, and the arc is sustaining the fire.

Clear the Area

Under normal conditions, the insulation and jacketing of underground cables provide adequate protection. However, an explosion or fire can remove these protective coverings and expose the energized conductors. Such a condition is a major hazard, and fire fighting personnel are cautioned to stay clear.

Beware of Toxic or Explosive Gases!

Flammable vapors, which are not always detectable by sense of smell, may be coming from (a) nearby sewers, (b) gas mains, or (c) buried gasoline or oil storage tanks, as well as from (d) smoldering insulation and fiber duct. Inside a duct, the vapor-air mixture may be too rich to ignite. Upon reaching a source of fresh air, such as a manhole, the vapor-air mixture may fall within the explosive limits. The resulting explosions may be intermittent, with their frequency depending on how fast the vapors are coming out and mixing with the air. They may vary in intensity from a slight "puff" to an explosion of sufficient violence to blow a manhole cover high in the air. If the mixture becomes too rich to ignite within the confined space of a manhole, an explosion may occur when the manhole cover is removed.

Prepare to Assist Electric Company Employees

The electric company may discharge water into a duct line to cool it after the circuit has been de-energized. If a hose line is supplied by the local fire company, let the electric company employees handle the nozzle, using their approved rubber gloves for protection.

Leave Manhole Covers as Found

Only electric company employees should remove manhole covers using hooks or long-handled tools and standing safely to one side. And everyone must be kept a reasonable distance back to avoid injury. Removing manhole covers may help to ventilate the conduit system and pin down the location of the fault. However, removing a manhole cover may re-ignite flammable vapors—or even cause low-order explosions, if the atmosphere was too rich to burn before removing it.

Never Direct Water into a Manhole

Until requested by the electric company representative, never direct water into a manhole. The source of the fire and any other facilities that might be damaged must be de-energized before water can be used safely and effectively.

9-16   EFFECTS OF ELECTRICAL SHOCK

Current is the killing factor in electrical shock. Voltage is important only in that it determines how much current will flow through a given body resistance. The current necessary to operate a 10-watt lightbulb has eight to ten times more current than the amount that would kill a lineman, that is, if it actually breaks through skin and body resistance and flows at this amperage. A voltage of 120 volts is enough to cause a current to flow which is many times greater than that necessary to kill. Currents of 100 to 200 milliamperes cause a fatal heart condition known as ventricular fibrillation for which there is no known remedy.

The following figures are given for human resistance to electrical current:

Type of Resistance	Resistance Values
Dry skin	100,000 to 600,000 Ohms
Wet skin	1,000 Ohms
Internal Body	
Hand-to-Foot	400 to 600 Ohms
Ear-to-Ear	About 100 Ohms

With 120 volts and a skin resistance plus internal resistance totaling 1200 Ohms, we would have 1/10 ampere electric current, that is 100 milliamperes. If skin contact in the circuit is maintained while the current flows through the skin, the skin resistance gradually decreases. The following is a brief summary of the effects of current values as shown in Table 9-1.

9-17   FIRST AID

First aid kits for the treatment of minor injuries should be available. Except for minor injuries, the services of a physician should be obtained. A person qualified to administer first aid should be present on each shift on "on-site" jobs.

Prior to starting "on-site" jobs, telephone communications should be available and tested to summon medical assistance if required. Each "on-site" job should have the telephone number of the closest hospital and medical personnel available.

SHOCK

Shock occurs when there is a severe injury to any part of the body from any cause. Every injured person is potentially a patient of shock and should be regarded and treated as such, whether symptoms of shock are present or not.

Proper Treatment for Shock Is As Follows

- Keep the patient warm and comfortable, but not hot. In many cases, the only first aid measure necessary and possible is to wrap the patient underneath as well as on top to prevent loss of body heat.
- Keep the patient's body horizontal or, if possible, position him so that his feet are 12 to 18 inches higher than his head. In any case, always keep the patient's head low. The single exception to this positioning is the case of a patient who obviously has an injury to his chest, and who

has difficulty breathing. This patient should be kept horizontal with head slightly raised to make his breathing easier.

- Do not let the patient sit up, except as indicated in chest injury or where there is a nose bleed. If there is a head injury and perhaps a fracture of the skull, keep the patient level and do not elevate his feet.

- If the patient is conscious, you may give him hot tea, coffee or broth in small quantities since the warmth is valuable in combating shock.

- Proper transportation practice is never more *imperative* than in the case of a person who may develop shock. It is the most important single measure in the prevention and treatment of shock. Use an ambulance, if possible. If other means must be used, follow the above points as closely as possible.

TABLE 9-1.

EFFECTS OF 60-HZ CURRENT ON AN AVERAGE HUMAN

Current Values through Body Trunk		Effect
SAFE CURRENT VALUES	1 Milliampere, or less	CAUSES NO SENSATION—NOT FELT. Is at threshold of perception.
	1 to 8 Milliamperes	Sensation of shock. Not painful. Individual can let go at will, as muscular control is not lost. (5mA is accepted as maximum harmless current intensity.)
UNSAFE CURRENT VALUES	8 to 15 Milliamperes	Painful shock. Individual can let go at will, as muscular control is not lost.
	15 to 20 Milliamperes	Painful shock. Muscular control of adjacent muscles lost. Cannot let go.
	20 to 50 Milliamperes	Painful. Severe muscular contractions. Breathing is difficult.
	100 to 200 Milliamperes . . .	VENTRICULAR FIBRILLATION (A heart condition that results in death—no known remedy.)
	200 and over Milliamperes .	Severe burns. Severe muscular contractions, so severe that chest muscles clamp heart and stop it during duration of shock. (This prevents Ventricular Fibrillation.)

RESUSCITATION

- Seconds count. Begin artificial respiration as soon as possible. *In electric shock cases, do not rush and become a casualty yourself.* Safely remove victim from electrical contacts before starting artificial respiration. Do not move victim unless necessary to remove him from danger or to place him in the proper position for artificial respiration.
- Attempt to stop any hazardous flow of blood.
- Clear victim's mouth of false teeth or any foreign objects or fluids with your fingers or a cloth wrapped around your finger. Watch victim closely to see that mucus or stomach contents do not clog air passages.
- If help is available, have the following taken care of while applying artificial respiration:

  Call a doctor and ambulance.

  Loosen victim's clothing about neck, chest, and waist.

  Keep victim warm during and after resuscitation. Use ammonia inhalants. Do not give liquids while victim is unconscious.
- Continue uninterrupted rescue breathing until victim is breathing without help or until pronounced dead.
- The change of operators, when necessary, shall be done as smoothly as possible without breaking the rhythm. If necessary to move victim, continue resuscitation without interruption.
- Watch victim carefully after he revives. Do not permit him to exert himself.

RESUSCITATION-MOUTH-TO-MOUTH (NOSE) METHOD

- Place victim on his back. Place his head slightly downhill, if possible. A folded coat, blanket or similar object under the victim's shoulders will help maintain proper position. Tilt the head back so chin points straight upward.
- Grasp the victim's jaw and raise it upward until the lower teeth are higher than the upper teeth; or place fingers on both sides of the jaw near the earlobes and pull upward. Maintain jaw position throughout resuscitation period to prevent tongue from blocking air passage.
- Pinch victim's nose shut with thumb and forefinger, take a deep breath and place your mouth over victim's mouth making air-tight contact; or close victim's mouth, take a deep breath and place your mouth over victim's nose making air-tight contact. If you hesitate at direct contact, place a porous cloth between you and victim.

■ Blow into the victim's mouth (nose) until his chest rises. Remove your mouth to let him exhale, turning your head to hear outrush of air. The first 8 to 10 breaths should be as rapid as the victim will respond; thereafter, the rate should be slowed to about 12 times a minute.

IMPORTANT POINTS TO REMEMBER

■ If air cannot be blown in, check position of victim's head and jaw and re-check mouth for obstructions; then try again more forcefully. If chest still does not rise, turn victim face down and strike his back sharply to dislodge obstruction. Then repeat rescue breathing procedure.

■ Sometimes air enters victim's stomach, evidenced by swelling of stomach. Expel air by gently pressing down on stomach during exhalation period.

TWO-VICTIM METHOD OF RESUSCITATION—MOUTH-TO-MOUTH (NOSE)

In those rare instances where two men working together are in shock, both require resuscitation, and only one worker is available to rescue them, the following method may be used:

■ Place two victims on their backs, with their heads almost touching and their feet extended in a straight line away from each other.

■ Perform the mouth-to-mouth resuscitation method previously described. Apply alternately to each victim. The cycle of inflation and exhalation does not change so it will be necessary for rescuer to work quickly in order to apply rescue breathing to both victims.

EXTERNAL HEART COMPRESSION

PERFORM HEART COMPRESSION ONLY WHEN INDICATED. After rescue breathing has been performed for about half a minute, if bluish or gray skin color remains and *no pulse can be felt,* or if *pupils of the eyes are dilated,* heart compression should be started. Heart compression is always accompanied by rescue breathing. If only one rescuer is present, interrupt compression about every 10 to 15 compression cycles and give victim 3 or 4 breaths.

■ Place victim on his back on a firm surface.

■ Put hands on breastbone. Place heel of one hand on lower third of breastbone with other hand on top of first.

■ Press downward. Apply pressure until breastbone moves 1-1/2 to 2 inches.

- Lift hands and permit chest to return to normal.
- Repeat compression 60 times per minute.

Heart compression should not be performed in the following instances:

- When victim has a pulse.
- When his pupils do not remain widely dilated.
- When his ribs are broken.

APPENDIX A

INSPECTION AND TEST FORMS

A key factor in an efficient maintenance and testing program is the preparation and filing of all inspection and test records. This enables mathematical trends to be established, and to a great extent future performance and maintenance measures can be predicted.

Forms permit the orderly recording of data and are a reminder to record all pertinent factors, for example, temperature and relative humidity. A variety of forms are available in the industry. On the other hand, one may wish to prepare one's own. They can be tailored to fit requirements as needed.

One method of filing is by apparatus with the original inspection or test, and all successive tests for that apparatus would be filed in chronological order with the latest test on top. The important fact is that records should be maintained (in whatever order or format that may be suitable) for comparison and evaluation.

Following are sample test data forms that the reader may wish to adopt for recording test data.

- *Substation inspection report:* It can be used daily or weekly to monitor pertinent operating conditions
- *Power transformer test record:* A summary of all tests performed at installation, scheduled maintenance, or special occasions (trouble or suspected trouble).
- *Bushing current transformer test record:* Same as for power transformer.
- *Power circuit breaker test record:* Same as for power transformer.
- *Insulation resistance—dielectric absorption test sheet:* Available in pads from the James G. Biddle Company; very useful for motors and generators.
- *Microohm tests:* Used in switchgear to detect imperfect connections.
- *High-potential and megger tests:* This is useful when one or several circuit components are subjected to insulation resistance and go, no-go

447

high-potential tests. This form should be modified to include equipment ambient temperature, relative humidity, and to state "megohms."

- *Insulate megger and live line tests:* This form is for switchyards where insulators are mounted in sections, and confirms that each layer is doing its share in a series string.

- *Cable test graph paper:* Prepared by Associated Research, Inc., and is useful in dc hi-pot tests of generators or other apparatus, as well as cables.

- *Transducer test sheet:* A calibration record of transducers when used in instrumentation schemes in connection with supervisory control. This application is increasing in municipal and other customer installations, for example, large pumping stations.

- *Instrument test:* A calibration form for switchboard voltmeters, ammeters, wattmeters, and other indicating and recording instruments. Additional columns can be added by user as required for polyphase connections or other multipliers.

FORM A—1.
SUBSTATION INSPECTION REPORT

DATE: _____   SUBSTATION: _____

TIME: _____   INSPECTOR: _____

TRANSFORMERS						
RATING						
K.W.						
K.V.A.R.						
A PH. AMPS.						
B PH. AMPS.						
C PH. AMPS.						
A PH. VOLTS						
B PH. VOLTS						
C PH. VOLTS						
TAP RANGE						
TAP POSITION						
MAX. TAP. POS.						
TAP OPERATIONS						
GAS GAUGE						
OIL TEMP.						
MAX. OIL TEMP.						
HOT SPOT TEMP.						
COOLERS - FANS						

PEAK OF THE WEEK	DAY:		TIME:		DATE:	
K.W.						
K.V.A.R.						
PH. AMPS.						
PH. VOLTS						

BUS	4 K.V.	13 K.V.	33 K.V.	69 K.V.	115 K.V.	138 K.V.	230 K.V.
VOLTS							
BATTERY	SPEC. GR.	VOLTS	WATER	BATTERY	SPEC. GR.	VOLTS	WATER
NO. 1				NO. 2			
PROPANE	NO. 1	NO. 2	EMERGENCY	HOURS RUN	CAPACITOR		
TANK	%	%	GENERATOR		OPERATIONS		

BREAKER OR FUSE OPERATIONS

_____

_____

_____

FORM A —1 (continued).

AMPERES

Fdr. No.						
A ¢						
B ¢						
C ¢						

Fdr. No.						
A ¢						
B ¢						
C ¢						

Fdr. No.						
A ¢						
B ¢						
C ¢						

REMARKS

FORM A–2.
POWER TRANSFORMER TEST RECORD

Installation ( )   Station _____

Special ( )   Designation _____

Scheduled ( )   Date _____

Thermal Devices:

	Top Oil				Winding Temperatures		
Contact	Operates	Resets	Function	Contact	Operates	Resets	Function
#1	°C	°C	___	#1	°C	°C	___
#2	°C	°C	___	#2	°C	°C	___
#3	°C	°C	___	#3	°C	°C	___

Ten ohm RTD Connected to indicate _____ and is _____ connected to indicator.

Gas Test: AS Found O_2 _____ %   AS Left O_2 _____ %

Doble Test: Date _____   Sheet Number _____

Oil Tests:

	IFT	Neutralization	Power Factor	Breakdown	H_2O PPM
Main Tank					
Dial Head					
TC - OCB					

Insulation Tests:

	Transformer Only		Transformer & Leads or Leads Only	
	Megger	Hi Pot Volt	Megger	Hi Pot Volt
PRI TO SEC & GRD (& TER)				
SEC TO PRI & GRD (& TER)				
PRI TO SEC				
TER TO PRI & SEC & GRD				
PRI TO TER				
SEC TO TER				
CORE TO FRAME (500 V)				

UST TAPS (Megger)   H1 H2 H3 H0 X1 X2 X3 X0 Y1 Y2 Y3 Y0

To Flange (V) ___ ___ ___ ___ ___ ___ ___ ___ ___ ___ ___ ___

To Cond. (V) ___ ___ ___ ___ ___ ___ ___ ___ ___ ___ ___ ___

(Do not exceed voltage rating of UST Tap)

Lightning Arresters - Rated _____ KV   A Phase   B Phase   C Phase

Hi Pot _____ Volts   Megger _____   _____   _____

Sketch   Bushing Diagram   Vector Diagram

Tap ___ ___ ___ Calc Volts   Tap ___ ___ ___ Calc Volts

___ ___ ___ ___ ___   ___ ___ ___ ___ ___
___ ___ ___ ___ ___   ___ ___ ___ ___ ___
___ ___ ___ ___ ___   ___ ___ ___ ___ ___
___ ___ ___ ___ ___   ___ ___ ___ ___ ___

FORM A—2 (continued).

Radio Tests - Under load tap changer (No load tap on full winding)

Tap				Calc	Volts	Tap					

DATA: MFG _____ KVA _____ CLASS _____

SERIAL NO. _____ PEPCO NO. B - _____

WINDING	VOLTAGE	AMPS	IMPULSE	MISC.
E	_____	_____	_____	_____
X	_____	_____	_____	_____
Y	_____	_____	_____	_____

Instruction Book _____ Control Drawing _____

Impedance _____ % Tester _____

FORM A –2 (continued).

Primary Current _____Amperes

DESIGNATION ——— ——— ——— ——— ———

_____CALC ——— ——— ——— — — — ———
ACTUAL ——— ——— ——— ——— ———

_____CALC ——— ——— ——— ——— ———
ACTUAL ——— ——— ——— ——— ———

_____CALC ——— ——— ——— ——— ———
ACTUAL ——— ——— ——— ——— ———

_____CALC ——— ——— ——— ——— ———
ACTUAL ——— ——— ——— ——— ———

_____CALC ——— ——— ——— ——— ———
ACTUAL ——— ——— ——— ——— ———

_____CALC ——— ——— ——— ——— ———
ACTUAL ——— ——— ——— ——— ———

_____CALC ——— ——— ——— ——— ———
ACTUAL ——— ——— ——— ——— ———

_____CALC ——— ——— ——— ——— ———
ACTUAL ——— ——— ——— ——— ———

_____CALC ——— ——— ——— ——— ———
ACTUAL ——— ——— ——— ——— ———

_____CALC ——— ——— ——— ——— ———
ACTUAL ——— ——— ——— ——— ———

_____CALC ——— ——— ——— ——— ———
ACTUAL ——— ——— ——— ——— ———

_____CALC ——— ——— ——— ——— ———
ACTUAL ——— ——— ——— ——— ———

_____CALC ——— ——— ——— ——— ———
ACTUAL ——— ——— ——— ——— ———

_____CALC ——— ——— ——— ——— ———
ACTUAL ——— ——— ——— ——— ———

_____CALC ——— ——— ——— ——— ———
ACTUAL ——— ——— ——— ——— ———

_____CALC ——— ——— ——— ——— ———
ACTUAL ——— ——— ——— ——— ———

_____CALC ——— ——— ——— ——— ———
ACTUAL ——— ——— ——— ——— ———

_____CALC ——— ——— ——— ——— ———
ACTUAL ——— ——— ——— ——— ———

TESTER

FORM A-3.
BUSHING CURRENT TRANSFORMER TEST RECORD

Installation ( )

Special ( )

Station _____

Designation _____

Date _____

DATA:

Designation	Bushing	Max. Ratio	Conn Ratio	Mfg.	Type	Use

Bushings Installed On:

Misc. Notes:

FORM A−4.
POWER CIRCUIT BREAKER TEST RECORD

Installation ( )   Station _____

Special ( )   Designation_____

Scheduled ( )   Date _____

Contact Resistance: (Micro-ohms)   Tank No. 1_____ No.2 _____ No. 3 _____

Pressure Switch: Type _____

Contacts	Operates	Resets	Total Breaker Operations to
No. 1	_____psi	_____psi	Compressor Motor Start _____
No. 2	_____psi	_____psi	Alarm Contact Operation _____
No. 3	_____psi	_____psi	Breaker Lockout _____

Travel Analyzer	Tank No. 1	Tank No. 2	Tank No. 3	Mfg. Rec.
Breaker Contact Opening Time (Cycles)	_____	_____	_____	_____
Lift Rod Travel (Feet/Sec)	_____	_____	_____	_____
"a" Switch Opening Time (Cycles)	_____	_____	_____	_____
Total Lift Road Travel (Inches)	_____	_____	_____	_____
Breaker Trip Free Time (Cycles)	_____	_____	_____	_____

Doble Test: Date _____ Sheet Number _____

Oil Tests:	IFT	Neutralization	Power Factor	Breakdown
Tank No. 1	_____	_____	_____	_____
Tank No. 2	_____	_____	_____	_____
Tank No. 3	_____	_____	_____	_____

Rectox Tests: Normal Operating Conditions

	% Age R	Sta. Ser. V	A C - Volts	D C - Volts	A C - Amps	D C - Amps
A F	_____	_____	_____	_____	_____	_____
A L	_____	_____	_____	_____	_____	_____

C B Min Close Volts A F _____ A L _____   Closing Relay Min Close Volts A F _____ A L _____

Cubicle Heaters: Number _____ Thermostat Set _____ Feed _____
                 Protection _____

Insulation Tests:

	PCB Only		PCB & Leads or Leads Only	
Closed Breaker	Megger	Hi Pot Volt	Megger	Hi Pot Volt
A to Ground	_____	_____	_____	_____
B to Ground	_____	_____	_____	_____
C to Ground	_____	_____	_____	_____
A TO B	_____	_____	_____	_____
A TO C	_____	_____	_____	_____
B TO C	_____	_____	_____	_____

Open Breaker Megger

1 to Grd. _____	4 TO Grd. _____	1 to 2 _____	3 to 4 _____
2 to Grd. _____	5 to Grd. _____	1 to 3 * _____	3 to 5 * _____
3 to Grd. _____	6 to Grd. _____	2 to 4 * _____	5 to 6 _____

Omit on three tank breakers

Open Breaker Hi Pot, each pole _____ K V, other poles and tank grounded.

UST Taps:	(Megger)	Pole No. 1	Pole No. 2	Pole No. 3	Pole No. 4	Pole No. 5	Pole No. 6
To Flange		_____	_____	_____	_____	_____	_____
To Conductor		_____	_____	_____	_____	_____	_____

(Do not exceed voltage rating of UST Tap)

FORM A—4 (continued).

DATA:

Pole 5 | 0   0 | Pole 6 _____ Phase
       | Tank 3

Pole 3 | 0   0 |
       | Tank 2 | Pole 4 _____ Phase

Pole 1 | 0   0 |
       | Tank 1 | Pole 2 _____ Phase

Operating Mech.

Top View
(Indicate Bus & Line)

Pole   1   3   5

0   0   0

Rear - GE
0   0   0   Top - Other

Pole   2   4   6

Phase _____ _____ _____

Top View - GE
Stud Side View - Others
(Indicate Bus & Line)

MFG _____ VOLTS ___ __ _ _____ AMPS _____

INT CAP _____ TYPE _____

SERIAL _____ PEPCO NO. _____

CLOSE VOLTS _____ AMPS _____ CYCLES _____

OPEN VOLTS _____ AMPS _____ CYCLES _____

COMP MOTOR VOLTS _____ AMPS _____ CYCLES _____

_____
TESTER

FORM A–5.
INSULATION RESISTANCE—DIELECTRIC ABSORPTION TEST SHEET

ROTATING EQUIPMENT

TEST NO _____

_____ COMPANY   DATE_____

_____ LOCATION   TIME_____

EQUIPMENT		RATING		VOLTAGE	
TYPE		MFR		SERIAL #	

RECENT OPERATING HISTORY

WINDING CONDITION AS TO CLEANLINESS AND REPAIR

ARMATURE INSULATION AGE		CLASS	FIELD INSULATION AGE		CLASS

DESCRIBE END TURN CORONA SHIELDING

LIST ASSOCIATED EQUIPMENT INCLUDED IN TEST

LINE CABLE LENGTH	CONDUCTOR SIZE	INSULATION MATERIAL	INSULATION THICKNESS

A C ARMATURE PHASES CONNECTED   DELTA ☐   STAR ☐   NEUTRAL CABLE

JAMES G. BIDDLE CO. · PLYMOUTH MEETING PENNSYLVANIA 19462 · MADE IN U.S.A. CAT 951-1

FOR USE WITH "MEGGER" INSULATION TESTERS. SEE INSTRUCTION MANUAL 21-J

S-1692

108 10 74 WN

TEST DATA - MEGOHMS

PART TESTED					TEST MADE	HOURS DAYS	AFTER SHUTDOWN
GROUNDING TIME					DRY-BULB TEMP		°F
Test Voltage					WET-BULB TEMP		°F
TEST CONNECTIONS	TO LINE	TO LINE	TO LINE	TO LINE	DEW POINT		°F
	TO EARTH	TO EARTH	TO EARTH	TO EARTH	RELATIVE HUMIDITY		%
	TO GUARD	TO GUARD	TO GUARD	TO GUARD	ABSOLUTE HUMIDITY		GR / #
½ MIN					EQUIPMENT TEMP		°F(C)
¾ "					HOW OBTAINED		
½ "							
1 "							
2 "					"MEGGER" INST –		
3 "					SERIAL #		
4 "					RANGE		
5 "					VOLTAGE		
6 "							
7 "							
8 "							
9 "							
10 "							
10/1 MIN RATIO							

REMARKS

TESTED BY

FORM A −6.
MICROOHM TESTS

INSTALLATION TESTS
METAL CLAD SWITCHGEAR

<u>MICRO-OHM TESTS</u>

LOCATION:_____   SWITCHGEAR:_____KV

BUS SECTION NO._____   BUS MEASUREMENTS
FROM   TO   A Ø   B Ø   C Ø
CUB_____CUB_____   _____   _____   _____
CUB_____CUB_____   _____   _____   _____
CUB_____CUB_____   _____   _____   _____
CUB_____CUB_____   _____   _____   _____
CUB_____CUB_____   _____   _____   _____
CUB_____CUB_____   _____   _____   _____   A Ø   B Ø   C Ø
CUB_____CUB_____   _____   _____   _____   TOTAL _____   _____   _____

BUS SECTION NO._____
CUB_____CUB_____   _____   _____   _____
CUB_____CUB_____   _____   _____   _____
CUB_____CUB_____   _____   _____   _____
CUB_____CUB_____   _____   _____   _____
CUB_____CUB_____   _____   _____   _____
CUB_____CUB_____   _____   _____   _____   A Ø   B Ø   C Ø
CUB_____CUB_____   _____   _____   _____   TOTAL _____   _____   _____

BUS SECTION NO._____
CUB_____CUB_____   _____   _____   _____
CUB_____CUB_____   _____   _____   _____
CUB_____CUB_____   _____   _____   _____
CUB_____CUB_____   _____   _____   _____
CUB_____CUB_____   _____   _____   _____
CUB_____CUB_____   _____   _____   _____   A Ø   B Ø   C Ø
CUB_____CUB_____   _____   _____   _____   TOTAL _____   _____   _____

OUTGOING LINE MEASUREMENTS   DESIGNATION
CUB_____   _____ _____ _____   _____
CUB_____   _____ _____ _____   _____
CUB_____   _____ _____ _____   _____
CUB_____   _____ _____ _____   _____
CUB_____   _____ _____ _____   _____
CUB_____   _____ _____ _____   _____
CUB_____   _____ _____ _____   _____
CUB_____   _____ _____ _____   _____
CUB_____   _____ _____ _____   _____
CUB_____   _____ _____ _____   _____
CUB_____   _____ _____ _____   _____
CUB_____   _____ _____ _____   _____
CUB_____   _____ _____ _____   _____
CUB_____   _____ _____ _____   _____
CUB_____   _____ _____ _____   _____
CUB_____   _____ _____ _____   _____
CUB_____   _____ _____ _____   NO._____ TRANS SEC
CUB_____   _____ _____ _____   NO._____ TRANS SEC
CUB_____   _____ _____ _____   NO._____ TRANS SEC

FORM A−7.
HIGH POTENTIAL AND MEGGER TESTS

Installation ( )
Special ( )
Scheduled ( )

Location _____
Date _____

Temp. _____   R.H. _____

Circuit Designation	HIGH Potential Test K V	MEGGER TESTS						
		Voltage	A Phase To Grd	B Phase To Grd	C Phase To Grd	A to B Phase	B to C Phase	C to A Phase

FORM A—8.
INSULATOR MEGGER AND LIVE LINE TESTS

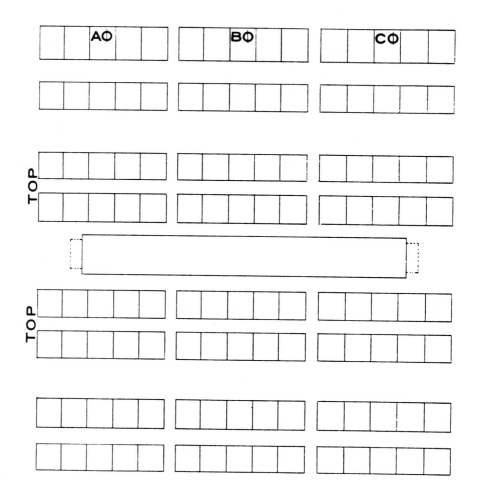

FORM A-9.
CABLE TEST GRAPH PAPER

JOB LOCATION

DATE

CABLE MFR

CABLE RATING

TEMPERATURE

HUMIDITY

INSULATION TYPE

CONDUCTOR SIZE

LEAKAGE CURRENT AT FULL TEST

DISCHARGE TIME

VOLTAGE INCREMENTS

STABILIZATION TIME

VOLTAGE AFTER   MINUTES

DOWN TO   KV

VOLTAGE AFTER

TYPE OF TEST

PHASE   A   μA   SEC.

MIN. DISCHARGE   KV   OPERATOR

B   μA   SEC.   KV

C   μA   SEC.   KV   WITNESS

MINUTES   (I vs. TIME)

MICROAMPS

DC TEST VOLTAGE, KV

Test

Tech.

FORM A-10.
TRANSDUCER TEST SHEET

CODES:

E.A. = Esterline-Angus
T.D. = Trans Data
W   = Westinghouse

PAGE _____ OF _____

DESIG. # _____

LOCATION _____

TESTER _____

DATE	CIRCUIT	WATTS		VARS		VOLTS		AMPS		REMARKS
		% ERROR	MFR.	% ERROR	MFR.	% ERROR	MFR.	% ERROR	MFR.	

FORM A—11.
INSTRUMENT TEST

CIRCUIT NO. ------------------------------

DATE OF TEST ------------------------------   STATION NO. ------------------------------

Instrument Under Test: ------------------------------

Location ------------------------------

Serial No. ---------------- Type ---------------- Amp. Cap. ---------------- Volts ----------------

Scale ---------------- C. T. Ratio ---------------- P. T. Ratio ---------------- Freq. ----------------

Cap. C. T. Used ---------------- Amps. Ratio ---------------- Make ---------------- Type ----------------

Cap. P. T. Used ---------------- Volts.-Amps. Ratio ---------------- Make ---------------- Type ----------------

AS FOUND TEST DATA

Standard	Meter Under Test	% Error	Standard	Meter Under Test	% Error

AS LEFT

Standard	Meter Under Test	% Error	Standard	Meter Under Test	% Error

Remarks: ------------------------------

Tester ------------------------------   Assistant ------------------------------

APPENDIX B

AMERICAN STANDARD DEVICE FUNCTION NUMBERS

1. Master Element
2. Time-delay Starting or Closing Relay
3. Checking or Interlocking Relay
4. Master Contactor
5. Stopping Device
6. Starting Circuit Breaker
7. Anode Circuit Breaker
8. Control Power Disconnecting Device
9. Reversing Device
10. Unit Sequence Switch
11. Reserved for future application
12. Overspeed Device
13. Synchronous-Speed Device
14. Underspeed Device
15. Speed or Frequency-Matching Device
16. Reserved for future application
17. Shunting or Discharge Switch
18. Accelerating or Decelerating Device
19. Starting-to-Running Transition Contactor
20. Valve
21. Distance Relay
22. Equalizer Circuit Breaker
23. Temperature-Control Device
24. Reserved for future application
25. Synchronizing or Synchronous-Check Device
26. Apparatus Thermal Device
27. Undervoltage Relay
28. Flame Detector
29. Isolating Contactor
30. Annunciator Relay
31. Separate Excitation Device
32. Directional Power Relay
33. Position Switch
34. Master Sequence Device
35. Brush-Operating or Slip-Ring Short-Circuiting Device
36. Polarity or Polarizing Voltage Device
37. Undercurrent or Underpower Relay
38. Bearing Protective Device
39. Mechanical Condition Monitor
40. Field Relay
41. Field Circuit Breaker
42. Running Circuit Breaker
43. Manual Transfer or Selector Device
44. Unit Sequence Starting Relay
45. Atmospheric Condition Monitor
46. Reverse-Phase or Phase-Balance Current Relay

Note: Suffix letters are used with device function numbers for various purposes; for instance, suffix N is generally used if the device is connected in the secondary neutral of current transformers, and suffixes X, Y, and Z are used to denote separate auxiliary devices. Where more than one device is used for similar functions, a numerical suffix is used to differentiate (e.g., 52-1, 52-2).

47. Phase-Sequence Voltage Relay
48. Incomplete Sequence Relay
49. Machine or Transformer Thermal Relay
50. Instantaneous Overcurrent or Rate-of-Rise Relay
51. AC Time Overcurrent Relay
52. AC Circuit Breaker
53. Exciter on DC Generator Relay
54. Reserved for future application
55. Power Factor Relay
56. Field Application Relay
57. Short-Circuiting or Grounding Device
58. Rectification Failure Relay
59. Overvoltage Relay
60. Voltage or Current Balance Relay (use 60°C when 60 V is also present)
61. Reserved for future application
62. Time-Delay Stopping, or Opening, Relay
63. Liquid or Gas Pressure or Vacuum Relay
64. Ground Protective Relay
65. Governor
66. Notching or Jogging Device
67. AC Directional Overcurrent Relay
68. Blocking Relay
69. Permissive Control Device
70. Rheostat
71. Liquid or Gas-Level Relay
72. DC Circuit Breaker
73. Load-Resistor Contactor
74. Alarm Relay
75. Position-Changing Mechanism
76. DC Overcurrent Relay
77. Pulse Transmitter
78. Phase Angle Measuring or Out-of-Step Protective Relay
79. AC Reclosing Relay
80. Liquid or Gas Flow Relay
81. Frequency Relay
82. DC Reclosing Relay
83. Automatic Selective Control or Transfer Relay
84. Operating Mechanism
85. Carrier or Pilot-Wire Receiver Relay
86. Locking-Out Relay
87. Differential Protective Relay
88. Auxiliary Motor or Motor Generator
89. Line Switch
90. Regulating Device
91. Voltage Directional Relay
92. Voltage and Power Directional Relay
93. Field-Changing Contactor
94. Tripping or Trip-Free Relay
95.
96.
97.   Used only for specific applications on individual installation where none of the assigned numbered functions from 1 to 94 is suitable.
98.
99.

BIBLIOGRAPHY

American Society for Testing and Materials. *ASTM Standard D877-67, Dielectric Breakdown Voltage of Insulating Liquids Using Disk Electrodes.* Philadelphia: The Society, 1978.

——. *ASTM Standard D-1816, Dielectric Breakdown Voltage of Insulating Oils of Petroleum Origin Using VDE Electrodes.* Philadelphia: The Society, 1978.

——. *ASTM Standard D924, Power Factor and Dielectric Constant of Electrical Insulating Liquids.* Philadelphia: The Society, 1978.

Beeman, D. *Industrial Power System Handbook.* New York: McGraw-Hill Book Company, 1955.

Croft, T., C. C. Carr, and J. H. Watt. *American Electrician Handbook.* New York: McGraw-Hill Book Company, 1970.

DaGrosa, V. *Underground Fault Locating Techniques.* Missouri Valley Electric Association Annual Engineering Conference, 1979.

Dawalibi, F., and D. Mukhedkar. *Resistance Measurement of Large Grounding Systems.* IEEE Summer Power Meeting, 1979.

Doble Engineering Company, *Use of Doble Power Factor Insulation Tests for Maintenance Testing of Electrical Apparatus.* Doble Engineering Co., Watertown, Mass., 1968.

Downey, A. M. *A Review of Testing Methods as Applied to Insulating Oils.* Watertown, Mass.: Doble Engineering Company, 1973.

General Electric Co. *Fundamentals Relay Testing.* General Electric GET-1891, Schenectady, N.Y. 1950.

——. On Site Electrical Safety and Precautions, 1979.

467

Institute of Electrical and Electronic Engineers. *Guide for Insulation Testing of Large AC Rotating Machinery with High Direct Voltage.* IEEE Standard No. 95. New York: The Institute, 1971.

McGrath, R. J., and E. J. Marottoli. *Power Factors and Power-Factor Tip-Up Test Data for Motor-Starter Insulation.* Doble Engineering Company, 47th Annual International Conference of Doble Clients, 1980.

Meliopoulis, A. P., R. P. Webb, and E. B. Joy. *Analysis of Grounding Systems.* Georgia Institute of Technology, IEEE Winter Power Meeting, 1980.

Miller, Harold N. *DC Hypot Testing of Cables, Transformers, and Rotating Machinery,* Manual P.-16086, Skokie, IL. 1965. Associated Research, Skokie, IL. 1965.

National Electrical Manufacturers Association. *Maintenance of Motor and Generator.* NEMA Publication RP-1968, Washington, D.C., 1968.

——. *NEMA Motor and Generator Standards.* Publication MGI-1967, Washington, D.C., 1967.

National Electrical Testing Association, Inc. *Acceptance Testing Specifications for Electrical Power Distribution Equipment and Systems*, Meriden, Conn., 1977.

National Fire Protection Association. *Electric Equipment Maintenance.* NFPA 70B, Boston, Mass. 1977.

National Safety Council, *Industrial Data Sheets:*

——. *Methods of Locking Out Electric Switches,* No. 237.

——. *Flexible Insulated Protective Equipment,* No. 598.

Rickley, A. L. *Maintenance Testing of Transformers.* Doble Engineering Company, Watertown, Mass.

Stagliano, E. L. *Periodic Relay Testing.* General Electric Co. GET-3473, Philadelphia, PA. (Note: no date available)

Terase, H., and others. *New AC Current Testing Method for Non-Destructive Insulation Tests.* IEEE Summer Power Meeting, 1979.

U.S. Department of the Interior. *Power O and M,* Bulletin No. 11, September 1974, Bureau of Reclamation, Denver, Colorado.

U.S. Government. Polychlorinated Biphenyls (PCB's) Disposal and Marking. *Federal Register,* Part V, February 17, 1978.

Vitols, A. P., and R. A. Fernandes. *Incipient Fault Detection for EHV Transformers.* IEEE Summer Power Meeting, 1979.

Westinghouse Electric Corp., *Applied Protective Relaying,* Newark, N.J., 1976.

——. *Distribution System,* Volume 3, Westinghouse Electric Corp., East Pittsburgh, PA. 1965.

——. *Electric Maintenance Hints,* Westinghouse Electric Corp., Trafford, PA. 1976.

——. *Transmission and Distribution Reference Data Book,* Westinghouse Electric Corp., East Pittsburgh, PA. 1964.

Wilkes, R. B. *Insulation Tests for Power Generating Systems.* Brewster, N.Y.: Hipotronics, Inc., 1976.

Zimmerman, C. S. *Automatic Fault Location for Transmission Lines.* Missouri Valley Electric Association Annual Engineering Conference, 1979.

INDEX